Dornier

Do 217–317–417

An operational history

Manfred Griehl

Airlife

England

Copyright © Motorbuch Verlag 1987, 1991.
English translation © Airlife Publishing Ltd.

First published in the UK in 1991 by
Airlife Publishing Ltd

British Library Cataloguing-in-Publication Data
A catalogue record for this book is available from
the British Library.

ISBN 1 85310 072 2

Printed by Livesey Ltd, Shrewsbury.

Airlife Publishing Ltd

101 Longden Road, Shrewsbury, England

CONTENTS

FOREWORD

It is a sad fact that, although almost two thousand Dornier Do 217 aircraft were produced, there is not a single example in existence. That could be one of the reasons why the aircraft has never received the recognition it deserves. Another reason could be the fact that existing documentation concerning the Do 217 is scattered among a number of private collections. This book has been completed with the help of innumerable aircraft enthusiasts, and by more than eight years of intensive research.

Most of the documentation contained in this book concerns the historical development of the Do 217 V-1, through the standard versions of the Do 317 and 417, to the first production, missile-carrying aircraft. The Do 217 was not only one of the Luftwaffe's standard aircraft (for which it flew as a bomber, a night fighter, and a reconnaissance aircraft), it was used extensively as a test bed also.

I would like to extend my special thanks to Messrs Appel, Arena, Balke, Bekker, Chapman, Charles, Creek, Cuny, Dabrowski, Dressel, Ferenc-Antal, Francella, Gentilli, Heck, Hefner, Jayne, Klöckner, Koos, Kössler, Kruse, Lange, Lutz Jr, Martinez, Menke, Mohr, Müller-Romminger, van Mol, Nowarra, Parry, Petrick, Radinger, Regel, Selinger, Schliephake, Sheflin, Smith, Stapfer, Stipdonk, H. Thiele, O. Thiele, and Zucker.

I would like to thank also the Militärarchiv of the Bundesarchive, Daimler-Benz AG, the Deutsche Museum Munich, the Forschungsgruppe Luftfahrtgeschichte eV, the Henschel Aircraft Co, Messerschmitt-Bölkow-Blohm, Mr Spencer of the National Air and Space Museum, Herr Bernhard of the Schweizer Fliegertruppe, Frau Knebel of the Wehrbereichsbibliothek IV, and the staff of the Zentralbibliothek der Bundeswehr, who have all provided invaluable help towards the production of this book.

I would like to express my special thanks to Dornier GmbH, to their director of Public Relations, H. Pratt, and his staff for their encouragement.

I would like to thank the late Herr Zucker of the Deutsche Museum, Munich, for the valuable information which came to light as a result of the conversations I had with him and the material he gave to me. Together with Herr Ramala, he gave me valuable support in my work.

For the section concerning engine development, I would like to thank Herr von Pein and Herr Karnowski of Daimler-Benz AG for their kind assistance.

For evaluating and supplying archive material, and supplying photographs of the Do 217, I would like to thank Herr Albinus and Herr Nilges of the Bundesarchiv.

My thanks are extended also to Frau Neumann-Siry for reading the manuscript; and to Dr Scholten-Pietsch for making the decision for Motorobuch Publishers to be the first company to publish the history of the Do 217.

Finally, this book relates a small part only of the Do 217's history because of the small amount of material which I found. If anybody can supply me with additional material, or advise me of any corrections to material contained in this book, I would be extremely grateful.

Manfred Griehl, Mainz

CHAPTER ONE

From the 'Flying Pencil' to the Do 215

The concealed rearmament of the German Air Force during the 1930s has always been an interesting chapter in German aviation history. In 1932, when it was overseeing the formation of the Friedensfliegerwaffe (Peace-time Air Force), the Heeres-Waffen-Amt (HWA) issued the first specifications for the development and production of a twin-engined combat aircraft, having a retractable undercarriage.

With as much secrecy as was possible, all of the notable aircraft manufacturers went to work on the specifications. In Friedrichshafen, Dornier produced two designs: one for a cargo-carrying aircraft for the German State Railway; the other for a high-speed postal aircraft for Deutsche Lufthansa. Dornier submitted its postal aircraft design, designated, provisionally, Do 15, on 1 August 1932. On 17 March 1933 it was followed by the design of the first 'flying pencil'. Two months later, on 24 May, the future Secretary of State, Erhard Milch, gave the go-ahead for two prototype aircraft to be produced.

With the establishment of the Ministry of Technology on 1 October 1933, aviation bureaucracy got the future Do 17 in its grasp. At the end of 1933, the German Ministry of Aviation (RLM) issued a development and supply contract for a high-speed aircraft having a twin fin-and-rudder assembly, and for a cargo aircraft which could carry special equipment (in other words: a bomber aircraft!).

Three months later, the first project meeting was called, on 13 April 1934, at Dornier in Manzell, to consider the cargo-carrying aircraft design and its flexible defensive armament. On the agenda also, under the heading 'special equipment', were the first proposals for bomb-jettisoning equipment.

In accordance with Air Ministry instructions, a dummy military version of the aircraft was completed by 20 May 1934. The next step was the manufacture of three prototype aircraft: the Do 17 V1 (Model C, serial number 256); the Do 17 V2 (Model A, serial number 257); and the Do 17 V3 (Model 3, serial number 258). The first prototype was handed over to the Bauaufsicht Luft (Aircraft Construction Inspectorate) on 20 November 1934, and made its maiden flight successfully three days later. The Dornier Do 17 V2 (D-AHAK) first flew on 18 May 1935; both aircraft having flown without problems, piloted by Dornier's chief test pilot, Flugkapitän Egon Fath.

On the basis of these thoroughly positive experiences and the test reports submitted to the RLM, a further eleven prototypes were ordered with type designations up to Do 17 V14.

The first flight of the Do 17 V3 took place as early as 19 September 1935. As had the second Do 17 V2, it was delivered to Rechlin for testing. As the V2 had made a good impression, not least due to the efforts of Flugkapitän Fath, tests were carried out with a 20 mm cannon installation. The fourth prototype aircraft was used for weapons testing also, when two semi-fixed mounted MG 15s were tested under simulated operational conditions. Meanwhile, the Luftwaffe had started to expand its flying units, under the cover of such names as Verkehrsinspektion der Deutschen Lufthansa (German Lufthansa Traffic Inspectorate), equipping them with auxiliary combat aircraft.

An order to manufacture aircraft to equip the squadrons of KG 154 followed shortly after. In addition to the Ju 52, the squadrons' aircraft were to include Do 11s and 23s. The build-up of KG 152 to operational standard started on 15 March 1936.

The Do 17 VI was the first of a long line of development aircraft. Pictured is D-AJUN (serial No 256).
The second Do 17 (D-AHAK; serial No 257) was demonstrated at Rechlin on 20 August 1939.

Effective from 1 May 1939 the Kampfgeschwader 'Hindenburg' was designated No 1.

KG 253 was then formed and equipped with the Do 23 and the Ju 86. In the spring of 1937 KG 155 was formed. It had been expected that it would be equipped with Do 17E bombers, but it had to make do with Ju 52s.

In August and September 1938 I/KG 252 underwent training at Cottbus, where it was joined by II/KG 252 of IV/KG 153. This was the start of the history of what was to become known later as the Holzhammer — Geschadwers. In 1939, KG 2, whose III Gruppe would not be formed for another two years, was allocated the much improved Do 17E and Z.

In the meantime, trials with the bomber and reconnaissance variants of the 'flying pencil' had made good progress. The Do 17 V6 and V9 prototypes served the RLM as rapid transport aircraft, while the eighth variant became the forerunner to the F-1 reconnaissance aircraft. Fitted with a reconnaissance camera, the Do 17 V11 became the F-2 prototype. Dornier equipped the Do 17E-2 with two DB 600 aero-engines and started an extensive test programme.

In 1937 the experimental prototypes Do 17 V15 to V17 were produced and became the forerunners to the E-1 series, which were powered by two Bramo 323 engines. The Do 17 V18 to V21 aircraft were fitted with BMW 132F aero-engines.

Dornier conducted trials with three experimental prototypes which resulted in the M-series of aircraft. The Do 17M V1 (serial No 691) created astonishment at the 'Züricher Flugmeeting' (Zurich Air Show) in 1937 when it emerged as the victor in its class of aircraft. It was faster and more powerful than all contemporary foreign aircraft. It was still flying as D-AELE for the DFS in Ainring in the spring of 1945.

Unlike the first prototype, the Do 17M V2 (D-AUQO) was fitted with two Bramo 323 engines; the Do 17M V3 was the prototype for later series production aircraft.

In 1937 the Do 17P prototype was produced and, together with the Do 17F, was later to become the mainstay of Aufklärungsgruppen (Reconnaissance Groups) 10, 11, 14, 22 and 31.

The Dornier construction team's next prototype was the `Do 17Z, which was considerably more powerful. The first V-series, D-ABVD, bore a

The second Do 17M prototype (D-AUQO; serial No 692).

The prototype
Do 17Z-1.

strong resemblance to the planned Do 17Z-1 which was to be the first of ten prototypes.

A bomber variant of the aircraft was equipped with a defensive armament of three MG 15s and powered by two Bramo 323A-1 engines followed the Z-2 version, the main difference between the aircraft being the use of updated Bramo 323P Fafnir engines. By 2 December 1939 a total number of 346 Z-1 and Z-2 series aircraft were in service with the Luftwaffe. By 11 May 1940 the number of Do 17Zs in operation with Kampfgeschwader (Combat Wings) 2, 3, 76 and 77 had increased to 422.

Of the Do 17 Z-2 aircraft produced, a few 'reconnaissance' variants were built for the role of pathfinder aircraft for larger aerial formations. The variant was designated Z-3 and it differed from the Z-2 variant by being equipped with five MG 15s, a reconnaissance camera and long-range radio equipment. Occasionally, the Z-3 was equipped with a

mounted MG 151. The next prototype series to be produced by Dornier was the Do 17Z-4, which was a blind-flying trainer, equipped with dual controls.

Another variant, structurally similar to the Do 17 Z-2 but carrying the same equipment as that of the Z-3, was the Do 17Z-5 which, because it was fitted with additional maritime distress equipment, was predestined for maritime warfare operations mainly.

A lesser number of Do 17 Z-6s were built for weather reconnaissance operations, but whether or not more than one prototype was ever produced remains uncertain. A combat variant of the Do 17, code-named 'Vulture', never got beyond the planning stage. Production of this aircraft failed as the result of the high costs involved, and because the heavy armour plating which was required would have reduced its performance severely. Therefore, the Z-8 disappeared quickly into the drawers of the Reichsluftfahrtministerium-RLM (German Air Ministry).

However, the Z-9 prototype (a bomber variant, fitted experimentally with an EIVe-Mag unit) was test-flown. A special feature of this variant was the specially-designed bomb-bay, which had a modified, staggered bombing arrangement.

The first fighter variant was the Do 17Z-7, code-named 'Kauz I', which was an experimental night-fighter equipped with the same armament as that of the Ju 88C: three MG 17s and one MG 151 cannon.

This provisional variant was followed by the Do 17 Z-10, code-named 'Kauz II', a three-seated night fighter which had a newly-designed nose cone, and was armed with a 20 mm cannon and a maximum of four MG 17s. The few Do 17 Z-10s that were produced were allocated to 2 Staffel of NJG 1 which was formed on 28 June 1940, and whose 1 and 3 Staffeln were equipped with Ju 88 C-1s and C-2s. Later, the early version of the Dornier night fighter was flown by NJG 1, and by 4 and 5 Staffeln of NJG 2.

The Do 215 was a derivative of the Do 17, differing mainly in the respect that it had a liquid-cooled, twelve-cylinder, V-engines. Production of that type of aero-engine began in the spring of 1936 in Stuttgart. V-series production, which began in 1937, later pushed the Bramo 323 engine into the background.

In contrast with the A-1 and P-'Fafnir' engines the Daimler-Benz DB 601A-1 and DB 601Aa engines produced 1100 and 1175 hp respectively, giving a ten per cent increase, approximately, in aircraft performance on long-range operations. The first Do 215 prototype was a modified Do 17Z, as was the Do 215 V-1 (D-AFFY), which was first flown on 29 October 1938 but it was written off following a flying accident, soon after that date.

Flight tests continued with a Do 215 V-2 (D-AIIB), which was fitted experimentally with French Gnome & Rhône 14 VN engines. Finally, the Do 215 V-3 was built. It was the forerunner to the planned Do 215A-1 series of aircraft which were to be powered by DB 601 A-1 engines.

Sweden and Yugoslavia had both expressed an interest to purchase the Do 215A combat aircraft, however the German Air Ministry neither would, nor could, bring itself to issue the necessary export permits.

B-series production began with the Do 215B-1, a four-seat, long-range reconnaissance aircraft, which had an all-up weight of 9,055 kg. A subsequent variant, the 'Kampfmehrsitzer' Do 215B-2, was equipped with an increased defensive armament of up to five MG 15s, and was powered by DB 601A-1 engines. Some of these aircraft, together with a few Do 215B-4s, were handed over later to the Hungarian Air Force. Prior to this, the Soviet Air Force had taken delivery of two Do 217B-3s. The B-3 was a bomber variant, powered by DB

One of the twelve pre-series Do 215B aircraft with DB 601A engines.

12

A Do 215B long-range reconnaissance aircraft on an airfield in northern France, 1940.

601A-1 engines, and, like the B-4, it was a long-range reconnaissance aircraft, having been equipped with cameras to fulfil that role. The B-4's specifications had stated that it should be able to achieve 480 km/h at an altitude of 5500 m.

On 10 May 1940, the Luftwaffe began intensive reconnaissance operations over the French highlands, using Do 17Ps mostly, which equipped those long-range reconnaissance units based in the west. Between them, the units had nine Ju 88s, three re-equipped Bf 110s and twenty-two Do 215B-4s. Of the twenty-two long-range reconnaissance aircraft available on 11 May 1940, nine were serving with 1(F)/124, and three were operated by 2 Aufklärungsgruppe ObdL (Luftwaffe C-in-C Reconnaissance Group), which had seven He 111s also on its inventory. The remainder were stationed with a third reconnaissance squadron.

During reconnaissance operations over the Netherlands, between 10 and 19 May 1940, two of 1(F)/124s nine Do 215s were lost as the result of either enemy action, or other causes.

The Luftwaffe's subsequent long-range reconnaissance target was the British Isles. In July 1940, it deployed twenty crews on these operations, of which four failed to return across the Channel. A further three aircraft were lost in August, one aircraft was lost on 18 September, and one on 21 September. Shortly before the end of the air battle, another aircraft failed to return from an operation. Later, 1/ObdL took delivery of one Do 217A-O at least, while the two other reconnaissance squadrons operated Do 215B-4s mostly.

Do 215 long-range reconnaissance aircraft operated over the Eastern Front, during the German invasion of the Soviet Union. Kommando Rowehl received orders to undertake photo-reconnaissance sorties deep into the hostile Russian hinterland. Following the delivery of Ju 88 D-1s, the Do 215 B-4 was withdrawn gradually from combat units and assigned to training, or other units of the Luftwaffe. Nevertheless, the story of the B-4 variant of the Do 215 did not end there.

13

Dornier produced a night fighter variant (code-named 'Kauz III') which had Spanner IR equipment and an FuG 202 Lichtenstein radar. Given the limited number of B-4 aircraft that were produced, the changes concerned Do 17Z-10 aircraft mainly, which had DB 601 engines. Against this background, production of the high-altitude, long-range reconnaissance Do 215 B-6 variant was terminated. A single prototype, equipped with DB 601T engines, designed for a critical altitude of 9000 m and fitted with two TK 9A turbo-compressors (to improve the aircraft's high-altitude performance) was tested for a short period. At a maximum weight of 9605 kg, the aircraft should have attained a maximum operating ceiling of 11,000 m, but difficulties with the complicated and under-developed powerplant prevented this and any further trials in that direction.

Following the manufacture of 506 Do 17s and a further 101 Do 215s, a total number of 1730 Do 217s approximately, of all variants, was produced.

In common with contemporary intermediate bomber aircraft manufactured in Germany, the Do 217 was the product of a then relatively young Luftwaffe which was equipping itself feverishly.

The estimated period of eight years for establishing of a modern fighting air arm was not long enough. Technical difficulties, among them the slow pace of aero-engine development, proved to be crucial when the Luftwaffe was trying to build up its strength of aircraft. The difficulties were compounded further by inevitable teething troubles, involved with introducing new aircraft designs, which could not be resolved according to a timetable but were governed by other factors. Finally, tactical operations' requirements had to be considered also, when developing the new generation of combat aircraft. The Luftwaffe Operations Manual LDv 16, *Aerial Warfare*, dated May 1936, emphasised that, for tactical operations, 'The aerial combat units shall, from the beginning, take the war to enemy territory. Their attacks will strike at the fighting strength of the opposition' (eg. immediate support to one's own military) 'and

the resistance strength of the population' (a double-edged sword). The Blitzkrieg idea triumphed. Strategic aerial warfare was reduced, largely because of the Luftwaffe's lack of aircraft. As to who had been responsible for scrapping both the Do 19 and the Ju 89 strategic bombers — Göring, Milch, Deichmann, or Udet — this book does not warrant its discussion.

In 1937, the International Air Fair at Dübendorf, near Zürich, exerted a strong German aeronautical influence which was to prevail for many years to come. The 'flying pencil' arose, in the true sense of the word, above all of the overseas competition. Surprisingly, the Bf 109 made an impression on the European participants, also.

Nevertheless, in Germany, the Luftwaffe General Staff were committed totally to the idea of a Blitzkrieg from the air. To enable the idea to be put into practice, the Luftwaffe required higher-performance, intermediate bomber aircraft.

The conduct of later Luftwaffe operations on the Western Front were compatible with a secret plan, drawn up in August 1938. This was concerned as much with the war on land as it was with the war against maritime targets on the Atlantic and the North Sea, to strike directly at Britain by cutting her off from vital supplies, at least.

Additionally, on 23 August 1938, at a meeting attended by Göring, Milch, Felmy and other leading Luftwaffe officers, the subject of 'reprisal attacks' was raised, together with the possibility of annihilating vital industrial plants in the British Isles. However, given that the He 111 was the current backbone of the Luftwaffe's bomber force, and that it did not have any long-range fighter aircraft, its leaders had to have reached the conclusions that the pin-point and area target attacks, necessary to achieve the aims discussed at the meeting, could not be undertaken.

By 17 September 1938, following much internal deliberation concerning the types of aircraft at its disposal (including a fighter strength which consisted of Bf 109s) the Luftwaffe concluded, beyond all doubt, that it was not in a position to attack

Britain, a strong naval power, and achieve thereby a speedy and successful conclusion to the war.

Ten days later, at Karinhall, Göring's favourite residence, the subject of the possibility of an offensive air war was raised again. On that occasion, the leaders agreed, although with some reservations, that the only solution to the situation (which was precarious enough before the outbreak of war) would be to put the Ju 88A into mass production, as soon as it was possible. Of paramount importance was the development of a modernised Do 17 which would have a better performance and carry a heavier offensive payload. At that time, the late 1930s, aircraft production was devoted almost entirely to the enormous He 177 programme. The new plan was to equip four long-range bomber Geschwader (wings) with a total of five hundred, at least, Heinkel He 177 heavy bombers.

At a meeting, held on 26 October 1938, consideration was given to the idea of phasing out the production of both the He 111 and the Do 17 by 1942.

Heedless of the general situation within the German aircraft industry, particularly with regard to the economic aspect, and the shortage of steel, aluminium and other high-grade materials, the aircraft production commenced. However, a gross underestimation of the timescale involved, together with the belief that high-quality aircraft could be produced within a very short space of time both presented the very real possibility that the entire plan would end in disaster. The Luftwaffe's leaders had hoped that, by supplying different aircraft companies with similar design specifications, they could stimulate the inventiveness of the respective companies' drawing office staffs, the result being that alternative solutions would be available when the time came to review the designs. Nevertheless, in doing so, the Luftwaffe's leaders had neglected to account for the risks involved. In particular, they overestimated the pace of aero-engine development, and they overlooked the fact that engines could not be improved as quickly as armaments and airframes were. More time was needed; but time was something that the Luftwaffe did not have.

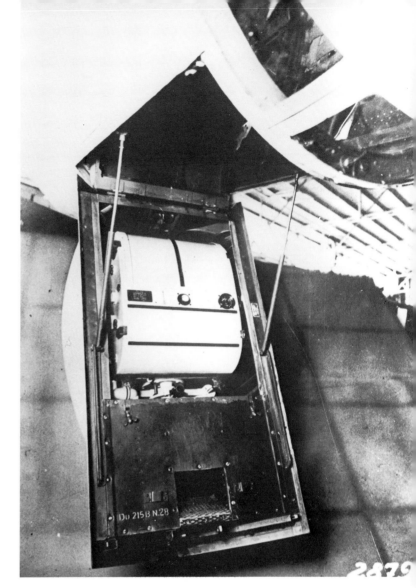

Camera mounting in the crew access hatch on aircraft serial No 0028.

At the beginning of 1938 Specification 1323 for a twin-engined bomber, a long-range reconnaissance and a screening aircraft, powered by two DB 601 B engines, was drawn up and submitted to the German Air Ministry for evaluation in February of that year.

Dornier's proposal, the Do 217, was an adaptation of the Do 17M, and was based on the

15

A Do 217B (NO+TB) during factory testing at Oberschwaben.

performance specifications for high-speed bombers, issued on 26 May 1936, and those for glider bombers, issued on 22 January 1938. The proposed design included a wide-view cockpit, and the fuselage had a larger bomb bay than that of the Do 17Z, capable of holding a maximum of two 500-kg and ten 50-kg bombs. For long-range reconnaissance, an Rb 50/30 camera was to be mounted forward of the leading wing spar, and an Rb 20/30 camera pod was to be mounted in the aft bomb bay. For long-range operations, auxiliary drop-tanks could be installed in the forward bomb bay. Finally, a maximum of two S 200 fog generators could be installed in those aircraft operating in a screening role only.

On all three versions the wing span was increased by one metre, compared with the Do 17M's wing span of nineteen metres. Under the wings, the installation of a retractable diving air brake was planned. To power the aircraft, Dornier's drawing office staff at Manzell had decided in favour of two

DB 601 B engines which could generate 1175 hp for take off. However, the Jumo 211, the Bramo 329, and the BMW 139 (the forerunner to the BMW 801) were considered to be candidates also. Whichever of the powerplants was used, eventually, the new combat aircraft were expected to be capable easily of achieving a maximum speed of 520 km/h, and have an all-up weight of 10.2 tonnes.

An overview of the Do 217, dated 5 June 1938, was produced by Dornier and submitted to the Technische Amt (Technical Bureau). It highlighted the structural differences between itself and the Do 17. In particular, the proposed increase in the bomb load to 1500 kg had to have been a vital factor when the aircraft design was considered for acceptance. Although the planned fuselage was to be not only larger than that of Do 17 series aircraft but, above all, stronger also, there was still a long way to go before the Do 217 went into production.

The German Air Ministry had been posed with a problem: with what would they equip the naval air arm? In January 1938, the Naval Air Arm Inspectorate of the Luftwaffe presented its requirements for an all-metal monoplane, for multi-role operations. On 5 February, Luftwaffe Inspectorate 8 agreed with the Luftwaffe's General Staff that practice attacks against maritime targets had proved to be not exactly successful. The experienced crews at the Travemünde Test Centre, together with Greifswald training units and a few naval air units were tasked with the high-altitude bombing of the target ship *Zähringen*, using concrete bombs. Although this former regular service ship was very slow and evasive manoeuvres were not undertaken, the hit ratio peaked at two per cent. The results could not have been worse! Following that exercise, the *Zähringen* was dive-bombed by Ju 87s; their hit rate was forty per cent. The superior effectiveness of dive-bombing maritime targets could not be doubted any longer.

The combat aircraft required by the Naval Air Arm Inspectorate of the Luftwaffe had to have a dive-bombing capability, and be able to operate as a fighter also, in order to combat enemy aircraft. Consequently, the concept of the 'Sea Stuka' began to take shape. The aircraft would have twin floats, an effective range of 1500 km, and a maximum speed of 400 km/h. Four fixed guns would be installed in the nose for attacking air and seaborne targets. For attacking enemy warships, emphasis was placed on the aircraft's ability to carry one 500-kg, or two 250-kg bombs.

Following a meeting on 6 January 1938, Dornier, Heinkel and Junkers were requested to tender their designs for a heavy Sea Stuka type aircraft to the Technische Amt (Technical Bureau). Proposals for a Do 217 and a Ju 88, both fitted with floats, were rejected as early as 18 February because both aircrafts' landing speeds were considered to be too high. Consequently, the Technische Amt invited Blohm & Voss to submit a design, expecting a dive bomber variant of their Ha 140. Between 12 and 18 March consultations were held in Berlin with individual aircraft manufacturers concerning the development of various existing projects, specifically the Ha 140, Do 217, He 115 and Ju 88 prototypes. Together with the plans for a modified Ha 140 and an He 115, Dornier's project P 85 and the studies in progress at Junkers factory in Dessau all attracted special attention.

The fuselage of the Dornier float plane was similar to that of the Do 217, although it could seat three crew members only in the forward section. The aircraft's forward-firing armament consisted of two MG 204s, each using 200 rounds of ammuntion; and two MG 17s, each firing 500 rounds. Instead of the MG 204s, MG 151, or MG FF weapons could

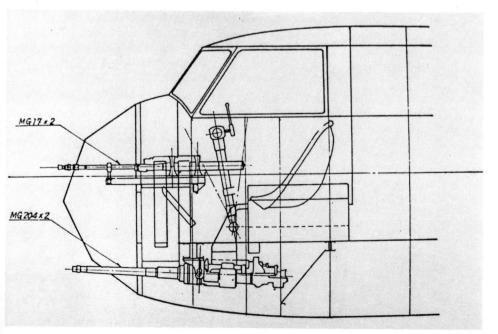

Armament layout of the Dornier P 85 project with two MG 17 and two MG 204 forward-firing machine guns.

be installed. The aircraft's defensive armament would comprise two MG 15s to cover the airspace aft of the aircraft. In addition to one 500-kg bomb, the payload could comprise eight 50-kg, or two SC 250 stores also. The floats had a volume of 8100 l and were compartmented for safety reasons. Each float was to contain a fuel tank, having a capacity of approximately 550 l. The tail unit and wings would be the same as those for the Do 217. As it was on the Ju 88A, the dive brake was positioned under the outer wings. For its power-plant, the design team envisaged either two DB 601G engines, generating 1300 hp, or two Jumo 211s. The fuel tanks would have a capacity of 2000 l of fuel and 190 l of lubricating oil. At an average all-up weight, and a speed of 360 km/h, the aircraft's maximum effective range was expected to be 1880 km. Its optimum range, at an average cruising speed of 270 km/h at an altitude of 4000 m, was 2800 km. (All of these specifications were given in the project description, dated 8 March 1938.)

The first evaluation did not favour the float-borne Do 217; the Technische Amt preferring the Ha 140, provisionally. However, in May 1938, the Luftwaffe General Staff regarded the land-based version of the Ju 88, general-purpose, combat aircraft to be the type required by the Naval Air Arm. The Junkers aircraft satisifed the performance requirements. All that remained was to investigate its operational potential with various types of torpedo and mine. It was decided also to install emergency float equipment, which would be of value for the survival of the crew, in the event of an emergency landing in the sea.

The war games, held in the spring of 1938, had demonstrated also that aerial attacks against warships could be carried out successfully only by using the dive-bombing technique. Furthermore, the representative of the German Air Ministry was of the firm opinion that neither the He 115, intended for maritime warfare, nor the new BV 138 would be able to combat enemy scouts and long-range reconnaissance aircraft.

For those reasons the specifications for the 'Sea Stuka' were rewritten. The new aircraft was to be a three-seat dive-bomber, heavy fighter and reconnaissance aircraft for maritime operations, designed to be a twin-engined, float aircraft, having a maximum speed of 500 km/h and a crusing speed of 300 km/h. The Technische Amt required the aircraft to have an operating range of 2700 km, and an operating ceiling of 6000 m. The requirements concerning the aircraft's armament and bomb load were largely unchanged. A new requirement, however, was that the aircraft should have the ability to be catapult-launched, the Technische Amt having taken into consideration the poor weather conditions which prevailed over the North Sea. Taking off on floats was prevented sometimes by heavy seas or ice. Nevertheless, by 15 June 1938 the Luftwaffe General Staff were neither for, nor against the planned float-equipped aircraft. They were not happy with the land version of the aircraft either, because they could see the danger of forced landings at sea.

In August 1938, the Technische Amt indicated that the mock-up of the 'Sea Stuka' would not be ready until the spring of 1939. The first prototype of the four-seat, dual-control maritime variant was to be ready for use from spring 1940. It was estimated that series production could start from early 1941.

On 13 August 1939 the Lutfwaffe's Chief of Staff wrote to the Supreme Commander of the Navy, informing him that the production of prototype aircraft was underway, and that the decision as to which one of the aircraft would be chosen to go into Navy service would be made certainly in the summer of 1940. In the meantime, a realistic assessment of the performance of the Stuka was required and would be made from the prototype's trials.

By the end of August 1938, there was a clear move away from the idea of equipping the Naval Air Arm with a heavy seaplane, and the call for a land-based bomber aircraft, capable of filling as many roles as it was possible to fill, could not be ignored.

The ideas of equipping seaplanes with bicycle undercarriages, or of producing amphibious aircraft even were considered; however, a satisfactory conclusion was not reached. At the beginning of October 1938, the Technische Amt stopped the development of the 'Sea Stuka', downgraded the production of the dummy model and the preparation of the prototype.

On 6 January 1939 it was made clear unequivocally that all work in that direction was to cease immediately. Nevertheless, in April and May 1938 the completed dummies of the Do 217W V1 and W V2 were inspected at Friedrichshafen.

A letter from the Luftwaffe General Staff contained an urgent directive from Göring which requested the development of a combat aircraft, which would have a very long operating range, and which would be heavily armed for the defensive role. In addition to the heavy seaplanes, land-based aircraft, equipped with naval warfare systems, were to have the ability to operate in coastal areas also.

The production specifications for the Do 217, dated 8 July 1939, took this into account; the ultimate goal being the glider-bomb equipped Do 217E for all maritime operations powered by BMW 801 engines.

This four-seat combat aircraft was adaptable to both land-based and maritime operations wherein the tactical emphasis was placed on bombing from a fifty-degree dive angle, and it had a maximum speed of 680 km/h. In contrast with the earlier specifications for a modified version of the Do 17M, the proposed Do 217E had a new-design nose section in which the A position was armed with an MG 15. Additional MG 15-type machine guns were to be placed in the B and C positions. A maximum of two SC500 and two SC250 bombs, or four SC250 bombs, could be carried. In addition, an LMB III aerial mine, or an F5 torpedo could be carried also, in the bomb bay. Instead of the dive brakes being situated under the wings, as they were later on the Do 217R, the new specifications

General arrangement drawing, dated 2 February 1940, of a combat floatplane project with a central tail fin.

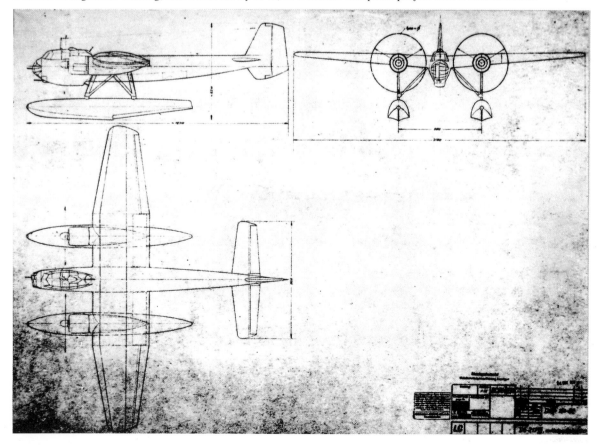

Front view of the maritime Do 17Z with a buoyancy tank on either side of the fuselage.

for the Do 217E required an aft-mounted brake, which was tried and tested first on the Do 217E-1 and so placed on production models. The strengthened wing assembly and tail unit increased the aircraft's weight unavoidably. Nevertheless, carrying a full bomb load and its defensive weaponry this 10.5-tonne aircraft was capable of achieving a maximum speed of approximately 530 km/h.

In spite of this tempting design, Dornier's drawing office staff continued to concern themselves unofficially with the float-variant of the Do 217. In January 1940, a data sheet was produced for the Do 217G, which was powered by two BMW 801 engines, and had a central tailplane and the same airframe as that of the Do 217E-1.

In the meantime, operations over the North Sea and the Baltic were carried out using Do 18s, He 115s and outdated He 59s. (Later, land bombers, such as the Ju 88, He 111 and, to an increasing extent, the Do 217, came to the fore.) In July 1939, the Supreme Commander of the Luftwaffe issued instructions that the He 111 and the Ju 88 were to be discounted as maritime combat aircraft and that the Do 217 was to be introduced as the standard aircraft for the Naval Air Arm. At the same time, plans were drawn up to equip long-range reconnaissance and multi-role units with Dornier aircraft. It is quite possible that the very

detailed data sheet produced for the Do 217G was connected directly with those plans, because one of the specifications for the new float-plane was that it should be able to reach a maximum speed of 460 km/h.

Unlike the 'Sea Stuka', the Do 217G was to carry an MG 151, mounted in the nose, together with three MG 15s for defending the aircraft. The 14.9-tonne, four-seat aircraft was to be equipped with sprung floats, according to the design department at Manzell, which would enable the aircraft to be landed onto water — even on fairly rough seas. Because the entire range of the Do 217E-1's bombs and stores could be carried by the Do 217G, its military payload was double that of the earlier P 85 project aircraft. Nevertheless, when comparing the performance of the production model Do 217E-1, which had a wheeled undercarriage, with the float variant the former aircraft was the more favoured version.

As it had with the Do 217E-4 (which later went into mass production as the 'combat aircraft for the Battle of the Atlantic'; and of which I shall discuss in greater detail later in this book), the Luftwaffe's General Staff became very interested in the idea of a special, maritime bomber aircraft, which could be equipped with systems and carry a weapons payload compatible with maritime operations.

20

CHAPTER TWO
A New Bomber is Born

Three weeks prior to the first flight of the Do 215, Dornier's Friedrichshafen factory made preparations for a no-less-important event — the first flight of the Do 217 V1.

Following numerous project studies, a modified version of the Do 17M appeared on the drawing board. The aircraft was equipped with improved systems, an uprated powerplant, and a more powerful armament.

In July 1938, Dornier's first priority was to decide which powerplant to use in the aircraft. Consequently, several full-scale mock-ups were produced at Dornier's parent factory, incorporating either DB 601 or Jumo 211 engines. The engine specialists at Dornier having been more than satisfied with the cooling equipment, fire bulkhead and fuel system connections on the Daimler-Benz engine, it was decided that the first prototype aircraft would be powered by DB 601A engines, initially. In addition, the types of bomb-aiming equipment, armament, payload and the flight instrumentation, which would all be required for the future operational roles of the new combat aircraft, were considered also.

The moment of truth arrived on 4 October 1938, when the new high-speed bomber made its maiden flight over Upper Swabia. Because the new, intermediate bomber aircraft resembled the Do 17 only superficially, investigating its performance and stability characteristics were given priority in the works test programme.

A week later, on 11 October 1938, the prototype aircraft (serial No 687) stalled and crashed during a test flight of its handling abilities when it had one of its two engines feathered. The aircraft had been piloted by Dipl-Ing Rolf Koeppe, a flight commander at the test station at Rechlin. Eugen Bausenhart, one of Dornier's mechanics, was on board the aircraft also. As a result of the damage caused, a further V1 prototype was considered to be out of the question.

The first of the development aircraft, the Do 217 V2 (serial No. 688, and bearing the letters CN+HJ) soon followed, and was ready to fly by 5 November 1938. In March 1939, the aircraft was used for stability tests at Löwental. The aircraft was equipped with an ejector seat, a jettisonable cockpit canopy, and provision was made for one crew

Side view of the Do 17 V4 (D-AMSD) with MG 15 armament.

A Do 17 V4 during factory testing at Friedrichshafen.

Front view of the Do 217 V4 with mock-up of an enlarged weapons bay.

member only so that, when diving tests were undertaken, there would be as little risk to the aircraft and its pilot as could be made possible. A second Do 217 V2 arrived at Rechlin, in June, where further performance evaluations and stability tests took place.

Following its return to Friedrichshafen, plans were made to equip the aircraft with DB 603E engines, specifically for the high-altitude reconnaissance role. This involved placing the existing powerplant and fitting a pressure chamber. However, because Daimler-Benz was unable to supply the engines specified, work on the V2 came to a standstill. Approximately one year later, on 29 October 1940, the Rechsluftfahrtministerium (German Air Ministry) ordered that the aircraft should be scrapped, or that an alternative use should be made of its components by Dornier.

The production of a subsequent development aircraft was not delayed long. It made its maiden flight on 25 February 1939. In contrast to both of its predecessors, the Do 217 V3 was powered by two Jumo 211A-1 engines. In April 1943, the aircraft underwent airframe fitting trials, and tests were undertaken using a fuel jettison system. On 15 August 1939 and 23 January 1940, the aircraft was flown to Rechlin where it was made available to Luftwaffe pilots for night flying. A number of flight trials were undertaken also, to test the new Siemens navigation system. At the same time, Dornier carried out fuel jettisoning and droptank trials, using 900-1 external tanks. Between June 1941 and the beginning of 1942, the Do 217 V3 flew with triangular, single- and dual-fin tail assemblies, which were fitted later to the Do 217M-3, M-9 and the Do 317.

The fourth Do 217 (VH) was flown at Friedrichshafen-Löwental also. This was preceded by numerous mock-ups until April 1939. D-AMSD (CN+HL), a forerunner to the C series of aircraft, arrived at Rechlin in June 1939. The main priority was to evaluate the aircraft's performance with the Jumo 211 powerplant, and some technical flights were undertaken also. Under the criticial scrutiny of the officers from the Rechlin Test Centre, loading trials were performed, using various calibres of bomb. In July 1940, wind-assisted, catapult take-off tests, which were planned also for the He 111 with overload, were concluded.

Close-up of the Do 217 V4 with Jumo 211 engines and VDM propellers.

The Do 217 V4 returned to southern Germany in February 1941, where development was continuing on the quick-release engine. Following the completion of drop trials, it returned to Rechlin for developmental tests using a braking parachute, which was mounted in the aft of the fuselage and intended to enable landings in areas so small that they would have precluded a landing without the use of this parachute. Also, the idea of using the parachute as a dive brake was very popular.

The fourth prototype (coded CN+HL) seen during factory testing at Löwental.

Do 217 V7 with BMW 139 engines, the precursors of the BMW 801.

The Do 217 V7 (D-ACBF, later CO+JK) during flight trials with Dornier.

Side view of the eighth Do 217 V8 with BMW 801 engines (D-AHJE).

Following refit in the late summer of 1940, the ribbon parachute, which was to replace that of the lattice type, was evaluated.

Do 217 V5 (serial No 703) was handed over at Dornier from the Air Inspectorate on 22 June 1939, and was flown to Rechlin within the following few days. Under the expert supervision of Wittmanns, long-range trials were carried out to evaluate the performance of the Jumo 211B-1 engines. In September 1939, a number of small faults occurred, such as a failure of the cooling system, and of the water pump. From 28 April 1940, the prototype was fitted with two DB 601A-series engines which replaced the Junkers powerplant. From that date, until the spring of 1942, this prototype played an important role in the Do 217's development.

Together with the Do 217A-0 and C-0, several other variants, including the Do 217E, were under construction. The Do 217 VE (serial No 694) was built at this time. At the beginning of 1939, Dornier had produced new cabin and load mock-ups from wood, and had invited the engineers from the Technische Amt to come to assess their proposals. It showed that the people involved had done a good job. When the RLM representative left Dornier, he was in possession of all but a few minor details. From October the aircraft entered the final assembly stage. Its first flights followed, at Löwental, on 29 November and 30 December

1939. Talks between Hansa-Luftbild (later to become Kommando Rowehl), the RLM and Dornier, resulted with the decision that three, rather than six, Do 217 A-1s were to be produced, and they were assigned the temporary designation Do 217A (Rowehl). Their equipment, comprising two oblique-mounted cameras (designed as a jettisonable equipment pack for emergencies), which were located in an extended front fuselage, was discussed in detail on 10 March 1939. The powerplant for the reconnaissance variant was to consist of two DB 601Fs. The Do 217 V4s systems were to include a gyroscopic control, the FuG X radio, and the PeilG V. The three aircraft were to be ready for tests at Rechlin between September and November of that year, a deadline which could not be met, as it turned out.

Aircraft bearing the serial numbers 2704 to 2710, were provisionally projected to be Do 217Bs, which would be powered by Jumo 211B engines. They were to have the same equipment as the Do 217 VE had, including dive brakes and a bomb release system. The planned six B-series aircraft were to be ready by October 1939.

Dornier designated an improved variant of the Do 217B, the C-O, which was to be fitted with bomb aiming equipment. Five aircraft, bearing serial numbers 2711 to 2715, were to be produced and powered by Jumo 211B engines before the end of the year. A further five aircraft, bearing the

25

serial numbers 2716 to 2720, were to be fitted later with BMW 801 engines.

The Do 217A-0 was intended to be a reconnaissance aircraft primarily and was based essentially on the design specifications for a Do 217 powered by DB 601A engines; which were produced initially at the beginning of 1938, and presented subsequently to the RLM, following numerous revisions. Although the specifications had called for a dual-role bomber and reconnaissance aircraft, it was the latter role which came to the fore finally. As the result of a meeting held on 10 March 1939, the aircraft was designated Do 217 (Rowehl). The fuselage had to be extended considerably to accommodate two camera units which could be accessed directly by the crew.

The first statement, which proposed the production of three 0-series aircraft up to Do 217E, was followed by a revised statement, issued on 31 May 1939, in which the need for more reconnaissance aircraft was acknowledged. The small production series would comprise six aircraft, bearing the serial numbers 2701 to 2706. Because the DB 601F engines, planned originally to power these aircraft, could not be manufactured within the time specified, lower performance DB 601B engines were used, as a temporary measure.

By the end of 1938 the details were almost completed, enabling preparations to be made for assembly to commence in 1939. A further meeting, including Rowehl, took place at Dornier on 1 February 1939 to consider the Do 217 reconnaissance aircraft. Six long-range reconnaissance aircraft were to be equipped with camera units of the type used on the Do 17S. Together with an Rb 20/30 camera, mounted in the rear fuselage, two jettisonable Rb 50/30 camera units were to be installed in the cockpit. In addition, accommodation had to be made for four film cassettes. A four-man crew were to be provided with an automatic pilot, oxygen equipment for long-range operations, and heated flying gear. For emergencies, they were to be provided with a fuel transfer unit and an emergency control.

On 9 January 1940 Aufklärungsgruppe ObdL requested that the B- variant be provied with a fairing, behind which a film cassette could be stowed. For the subsequent aircraft, thought was given to

Nose of the Do 217 V8 (D-AHJE, CO+JL) which flew for the first time on 23 March 1940.

providing a Plexiglass cover, to improve the crew's visibility. The first four Do 217A-0 aircraft were powered by DB 601 B engines. The two remaining aircraft of the A-0 series were to be powered by modified P-type DB 601 N engines, for the time being. Dornier had calculated that these engines would be ready for delivery in February 1940.

The Air Inspectorate took delivery of the first 'Rowehl' reconnaissance aircraft at the beginning of 1940. At the same time, in Löwental, works testing was being conducted without any problems. However, Dornier reported that the constrution of the high-altitude, long-range reconnaissance aircraft had had to be delayed provisionally, because the engines required to power the aircraft were not available. The Do 217B project was subsequently axed!

The C-0 series of aircraft, which were equipped with the same systems, generally, as those of the V1E, consisted of nine aircraft, having the serial numbers 2710 to 2718.

Meanwhile, Dornier had completed its work on the Do 217 V6, the fourth A-0 series aircraft (serial No 2704, CO+JJ). On 15 October 1939, this aircraft was first flown successfully, by a Dornier works crew. It had an enlarged bomb bay, and was used later, for quite some time, for mine tests at the Travemünde Test Centre. The aircraft returned subsequently to Friedrichshafen, at the beginning of 1941, to be equipped with DB 601R engines and a temporarily enlarged outer wing. The new engines were similar, in essence, to the DB 601Q, but they had a different transmission system, and were rated to operate at a maximum altitude of 5800 m and would use high-octane C3 aviation fuel. Aircraft serial number 2704 should have been ready to fly by March 1941, but Daimler-Benz experienced problems with the aircraft's powerplant.

Meanwhile, Dornier's drawing office staff were busy with a Do 217A project for an aircraft fitted with a pressurized cabin, powered by DB 601R engines, and having supplementary GM 1 booster units. Also, as part of a high-altitude test-flight programme, a fifth Do 217A-0 (serial No 2705) was to be equipped with more powerful DB 601R engines. The first development aircraft was rolled out on 23 April 1940, and completed its first flight successfully. The RLM had stipulated that the

Do 217 Development Models

Version	Serial No	Markings	Engine	Used on
Do 217 V1	687	—	DB 601 A-1	Versuch Do 217
Do 217 V2	688	CN+HJ (D-ABWC)	DB 601 A-1, DB 601E	Versuch Do 217
Do 217 V3	689	CN+HK (D-ACDE)	Jumo 211 A-1	Versuch Do 217
Do 217 V4	690	CN+HL (D-AMSD)	Jumo 211 A-1, Jumo 211 B-1	Versuch Do 217
Do 217 V1E	694	unbekannt	DB 601 A-1, BMW 801 A-1	Do 217 E-1
Do 217 V5	2703	GM+AF (D-ADBE)	Jumo 211 B-1/DB 601 Aa	Do 217 A-0
Do 217 V6	2704	CO+JJ (D-ADBE)	DB 601 A-1/DB 601 R/DB 801 A-2	Do 217 E-1
Do 217 V7	2707	CO+JK (D-ACBF)	BMW 139/BMW 801 D-1/BMW 801 Ds	Do 217 E-1
Do 217 V8	2708	CO+JL (D-AHJE)	BMW 801 A-1/BMW 801 D-1/BMW 801 Ds	Do 217 E-1
Do 217 V9	2709	CO+JM	BMW 801 A-1/BMW 801 D-1/BMW 801 Ds	Do 217 E-1
Do 217 V10	2719	CO+JN	BMW 801 A-1/BMW 801 B-1	Do 217 E-2
Do 217 V11	2720	CO+JO	BMW 801 A-1	Do 217 E-2
Do 217 V12	1012	DD+LL	BMW 801 A-1	Do 217 E-2
Do 217 V13	0032	DB+BC	BMW 801 A-1/DB 603 mit TK 9	Do 217 M-8
Do 217 V14	0030	Nicht fertiggestellt	BMW 801 A-1/DB 603 mit TK 11	Do 217 M-8

The Do 217 V9 during flight trials with Dornier.

Side view of the Do 217 V9.

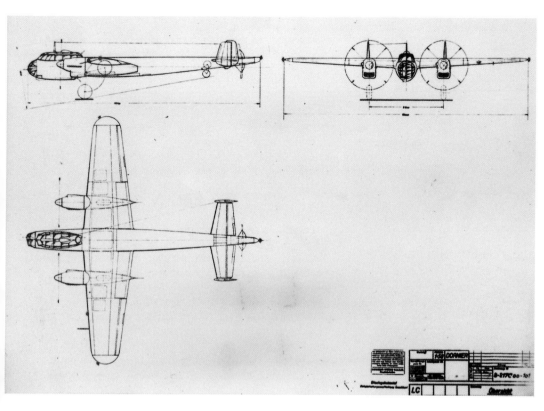

Factory drawing of the Do 217C-0 with split rear fuselage air brakes.

The Do 217C-0 during range trials in Norway.

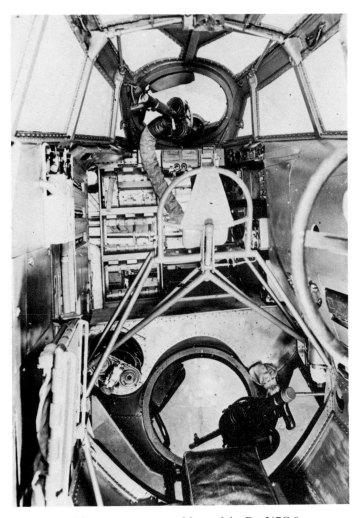

The two rear gun positions of the Do 217C-0.

The conversion was to have been completed by February 1942, but the aircraft were not operationally ready. Finally, a series of flights was undertaken by an aircraft bearing the serial No 2704, powered by DB 601F engines. The first transport aircraft was allocated to Befehlstelle Süd on 30 December 1942. The second transport aircraft (serial No 2705) was last mentioned in C-Amt despatches on 1 October 1941. The sixth, and final, Do 217 A-0 (serial No 2706) flew at Löwental at the end of July 1940, where a number of test flights were made with an automatic pilot. The aircraft was transferred to Aufklärungsgruppe ObdL from 30 July 1940.

From March 1941, month-long trials were undertaken with a BMW 801A-1 powerplant. Later, a BMW 801A-2 powerplant was installed, to ensure the aircraft's operating reliability on long-range sorties, which was a pressing requirement. In the summer of 1942, test flights were made with more powerful BMW 801D-1 engines, which had been installed subsequently. The next stage involved flight trials using the BMW 801D-2 powerplant, supplemented, in January 1943, with a number of trials using the GM-1 power boost unit.

Up to October 1944, the Do 217 V7 formed a part of the aircraft complement at Rechlin-Roggentin. Flight Engineer Huber made numerous flights at an altitude of 9000 metres which were aimed at improving the heating and de-icing systems. The last one of these flights took place at the end of December 1944. Further tests were curtailed because of a lack of aviation fuel.

In 1940, the eighth Do 217 prototype, which was equipped with BMW 801A-1 engines, was first flown by Dornier's test pilot, Schropp, on 21 March, and was flown at Löwental subsequently, prior to its delivery to Rechlin in the summer of 1940. In addition to taking part in the long-term BMW 801A-1 test programme, D-AHJE (later marked CO+JL) took part in the BMW 801D development programme also. Following a programme of flights between Rechlin and almost all of the airfields in south Germany, which served also to procure important spare parts between May and July 1943, arrangements were made to refit the aircraft with BMW 801D engines.

aircraft should be test-flown with its high-altitude engines in May. However, because of unresolved engine problems, the test flight was postponed month after month. Finally, an order was issued, on 1 October 1941, to configure the aircraft to its original condition.

At the beginning of January 1942, a directive was issued that both high-altitude Do 217As should be converted, as quickly as it was possible to do so, for the transport role for front-line support operations.

Dummy loading of a Do 217C-0 with SC 50 HE bombs.

A Do 217A-0 with DB 601 engines pictured in service with II/KG 2 on the Western Front. (BA)

Further long-range development flights were undertaken subsequently, from October.

The eighth prototype was followed by a ninth variant, on 19 July 1940, which, since May 1939, had been planned to be the prototype of the Do 217E-1. In the design studies, special attention had been given to the installation of a fixed MG 151 with a 250-round ammunition magazine. The use of an MG 204, mounted in the nose, was also examined. The provisional dummy configuration incorporated the Lotfe 7 and BZA 1 bombing systems; much consideration was given to the possibility of the aircraft carrying a torpedo and other ordnance, in which respect the SD 1000 and the SC1700 were prime candidates. When the mock-up of the Do 217 E-1 had been approved, and a final loading test had been carried out, construction began in the spring of 1940. During the first test flight in September, engine vibration problems were detected, and these had to be rectified immediately. When that was done, measurements

of speed-loss, caused by the lattice-type air brake, were made; these showed the loss to be 2 m/s. Following lengthy tests by Dornier, Do 217 V9 (serial No 2709) was flown to Rechlin where it underwent tests until October 1943 at least. Flight trials were made with a BMW 801A-1 powerplant, and several flights were made subsequently with BMW 801D and D-1 engines.

The serial numbers assigned to aircraft subsequently to the Do 217 V9, up to and including 2719, were for variants of the Do 217C-0 series. These were three-seat combat aircraft, having a dive-bombing capability, were powered by Jumo 211B engines and had four-bladed, 3.8-m diameter airscrews. The RLM inspected the mock-up at Dornier's factory in June 1939. Apart from one or two minor details (such as the view from the pilot's seat) the RLM did not find any faults with the aircraft. Apart from the same powerplant and the same small belly compartment as those C-series aircraft, the C-0 closely resembled the A-0 exter-

A Do 217A-0, seen here with aircraft of KG 2 in the Netherlands, taxying out for take-off.

A Do 217A-0 seen during factory trials.

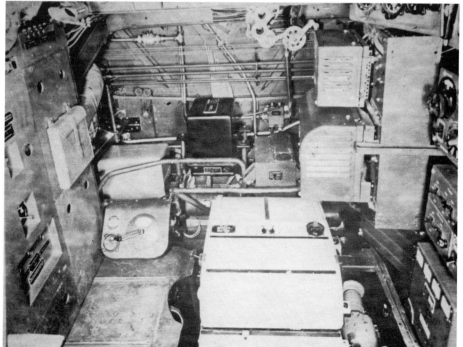

Interior of a Do 217A-0 reconnaissance aircraft, with an automatic aerial camera installation in the lower fuselage.

33

nally. Albeit in a somewhat modified form, the same characteristics could be found on the Do 217 E-1. When the loading plan was drawn up in October 1939, work proceeded with perfecting the safety controls, the practical testing of which was to start in the spring of 1940, hopefully.

With effect from 12 November 1940, Dornier planned to increase the number of crew members from three to four, thereby enabling the three defensive MG 15 weapons to be operated with equal effectiveness in the A, B and C positions. In the meantime, the layout of the bomb bay had been also finalised. Its design permitted the mounting of a maximum of four SC 500s, or three frames, each having four grips for a 50kg bomb, which had been installed already and were adapted for the aircraft's various operational roles. An Rb 21 camera unit could be carried for photographing targets, and could produce 18 x 18 cm pictures. The Do 217 C-0 was equipped with a Lotfe 7A bomb-aiming system and a Revi 12C sight for the pilot. For high altitude operations, the crew were provided with four sets of breathing aparatus and 32 l of oxygen, contained in sixteen bottles. Under normal operational conditions, it was estimated that the Do 217C-0 was capable of achieving a maximum speed of 475 km/h

at an altitude of 5600 m. Carrying a maximum operational load, its maximum speed was reduced by approximately 20 km/h. A dive brake, of the same type as that on the Do 217 V4, was installed under the aft section of the C-0's fuselage. In contrast with the Do 217E-1 and all subsequent variants, the twin-sparred wings of the Do 217C-0 were constructed of metal, and partly of fabric. The undercarriage of this medium bomber could be operated hydraulically, or manually in an emergency.

The first of the Do 217C-0 series of aircraft was assigned the serial number 2710 and underwent tests with Dornier in September 1940. The prototype bore the registration NF+UU and flew to Rechlin on 2 July 1942 where, a few days later, it crashed.

Initially, the second C-0 prototype (serial No 2711) was fitted with a lattice-type dive brake also, but it was removed in January 1941 and replaced by a Fist brake parachute. This work was not completed until March. Following a short test programme at Löwental, the aircraft underwent ordnance carrying development with Rheinmetall-Borsig.

On 6 September 1940, Dornier's test pilot, Schropp, took the third Do 217C-0 prototype

A reconnaissance Do 217A-0 in service with Kommando Rowehl.

(serial No 2712) on its maiden flight. Between September and November 1940, a further four 0-series aircraft (serial Nos 2713 to 2716) were produced. These were flown at Löwental also. The eighth C-0 aircraft completed its maiden flight successfully on 6 November 1940. The final Do 217 C-0 variant took quite a long time to produce, and was flying at Löwental until April 1941 at least. One of the C-0 series of aircraft was used for bombing trials at Rechlin between 10 September 1941 and the end of July 1942.

The conversion was to have been completed by February 1942, but the aircraft were not operationally ready. Finally, a series of flights was undertaken by an aircraft bearing the serial No 2704, powered by DB 601F engines. The first transport aircraft was allocated to Befehlstelle Süd on 30 December 1942. The second transport aircraft (serial No 2705) was last mentioned in C-Amt despatches on 1 October 1941. The sixth, and final, Do 217 A-0 (serial No 2706) flew at Löwental at the end of July 1940, where a number of test flights were made with an automatic pilot. The aircraft was transferred to Aufklärungsgruppe ObdL from 30 July 1940.

From March 1941, month-long trials were undertaken with a BMW 801A-1 powerplant. Later, a BMW 801A-2 powerplant was installed, to ensure the aircraft's operating reliability on long-range sorties, which was a pressing requirement. In the summer of 1942, test flights were made with more powerful BMW 801D-1 engines, which had been installed subsequently. The next stage involved flight trials using the BMW 801D-2 powerplant, supplemented, in January 1943, with a number of trials using the GM-1 power boost unit.

Up to October 1944, the Do 217 V7 formed a part of the aircraft complement at Rechlin-Roggentin. Flight Engineer Huber made numerous flights at an altitude of 9000 metres which were aimed at improving the heating and de-icing systems. The last one of these flights took place at the end of December 1944. Further tests were curtailed because of a lack of aviation fuel.

In 1940, the eighth Do 217 prototype, which was equipped with BMW 801A-1 engines, was first flown by Dornier's test pilot, Schropp, on 21 March, and was flown at Löwental subsequently,

prior to its delivery to Rechlin in the summer of 1940. In addition to taking part in the long-term BMW 801A-1 test programme, D-AHJE (later marked CO+JL) took part in the BMW 801D development programme also. Following a programme of flights between Rechlin and almost all of the airfields in south Germany, which served also to procure important spare parts between May and July 1943, arrangements were made to refit the aircraft with BMW 801D engines. Further long-range development flights were undertaken subsequently, from October.

The eighth prototype was followed by a ninth variant, on 19 July 1940, which, since May 1939, had been planned to be the prototype of the Do 217E-1. In the design studies, special attention had been given to the installation of a fixed MG 151 with a 250-round ammunition magazine. The use of an MG 204, mounted in the nose, was also examined. The provisional dummy configuration incorporated the Lotfe 7 and BZA 1 bombing systems; much consideration was given to the possibility of the aircraft carrying a torpedo and other ordnance, in which respect the SD 1000 and the SC1700 were prime candidates. When the mock-up of the Do 217 E-1 had been approved, and a final loading test had been carried out, construction began in the spring of 1940. During the first test flight in September, engine vibration problems were detected, and these had to be rectified immediately. When that was done, measurements of speed-loss, caused by the lattice-type air brake, were made; these showed the loss to be 2 m/s. Following lengthy tests by Dornier, Do 217 V9 (serial No 2709) was flown to Rechlin where it underwent tests until October 1943 at least. Flight trials were made with a BMW 801A-1 powerplant, and several flights were made subsequently with BMW 801D and D-1 engines.

The serial numbers assigned to aircraft subsequently to the Do 217 V9, up to and including 2719, were for variants of the Do 217C-0 series. These were three-seat combat aircraft, having a dive-bombing capability, were powered by Jumo 211B engines and had four-bladed, 3.8-m diameter airscrews. The RLM inspected the mock-up at Dornier's factory in June 1939. Apart from one or two minor details (such as the view from the pilot's seat) the RLM did not find any faults with the aircraft. Apart from the same powerplant and the same small belly compartment as those C-series aircraft, the C-0 closely resembled the A-0 externally. Albeit in a somewhat modified form, the same characteristics could be found on the Do 217 E-1. When the loading plan was drawn up in October 1939, work proceeded with perfecting the safety controls, the practical testing of which was to start in the spring of 1940, hopefully.

With effect from 12 November 1940, Dornier planned to increase the number of crew members from three to four, thereby enabling the three defensive MG 15 weapons to be operated with equal effectiveness in the A, B and C positions. In the meantime, the layout of the bomb bay had been also finalised. Its design permitted the mounting of a maximum of four SC 500s, or three frames, each having four grips for a 50kg bomb, which had been installed already and were adapted for the aircraft's various operational roles. An Rb 21 camera unit could be carried for photographing targets, and could produce 18 x 18 cm pictures. The Do 217 C-0 was equipped with a Lotfe 7A bomb-aiming system and a Revi 12C sight for the pilot. For high altitude

operations, the crew were provided with four sets of breathing aparatus and 32 l of oxygen, contained in sixteen bottles. Under normal operational conditions, it was estimated that the Do 217C-0 was capable of achieving a maximum speed of 475 km/h at an altitude of 5600 m. Carrying a maximum operational load, its maximum speed was reduced by approximately 20 km/h. A dive brake, of the same type as that on the Do 217 V4, was installed under the aft section of the C-0's fuselage. In contrast with the Do 217E-1 and all subsequent variants, the twin-sparred wings of the Do 217C-0 were constructed of metal, and partly of fabric. The undercarriage of this medium bomber could be operated hydraulically, or manually in an emergency.

The first of the Do 217C-0 series of aircraft was assigned the serial number 2710 and underwent tests with Dornier in September 1940. The prototype bore the registration NF+UU and flew to Rechlin on 2 July 1942 where, a few days later, it crashed.

Initially, the second C-0 prototype (serial No 2711) was fitted with a lattice-type dive brake also, but it was removed in January 1941 and replaced by a Fist brake parachute. This work was not

Front view of the Dornier Do 217A-0 long-range reconnaissance aircraft.

completed until March. Following a short test programme at Löwental, the aircraft underwent ordnance carrying development with Rheinmetall-Borsig.

On 6 September 1940, Dornier's test pilot, Schropp, took the third Do 217C-0 prototype (serial No 2712) on its maiden flight. Between September and November 1940, a further four 0-series aircraft (serial Nos 2713 to 2716) were produced. These were flown at Löwental also. The eighth C-0 aircraft completed its maiden flight successfully on 6 November 1940. The final Do 217 C-0 variant took quite a long time to produce, and was flying at Löwental until April 1941 at least. One of the C-0 series of aircraft was used for bombing trials at Rechlin between 10 September 1941 and the end of July 1942.

The third C-0 variant (registration NF+UW) had been equipped initially with the new Lotfe 7D bomb-aiming system, together with the BZA 1 system for bombing trials in inclined flight. On 27 December 1942, one of the Do 217 C-0s was transferred to Aufklärungsgruppe ObdL. A second aircraft was assigned to the Holzhammer Geschwader. Both aircraft operated together with the new Do 217E-1 and E-2 on the Western Front.

According to the instructions of Dornier's management team, the tenth C-0 variant (serial No 2719) was designated Do 217 V10. This aircraft carried the same equipment and systems as those of the Do 217 V9, and was to undergo the same tests as the first E-series aircraft had undergone. The aircraft was powered by BMW 801A-1 engines initially, but these were replaced by BMW 801B-1s when it underwent engine trials. Subsequently, the V10 was flown to Rechlin. In addition to the up-rated BMW engines, the prototype was fitted with a more powerful de-icing system.

The next development aircraft was the Do 217 V11 (serial No 2720), which was taken on its maiden flight by Karl-Heinz Huber on 24 March 1941. It had been envisaged originally that the aircraft would commence its tests at Dornier as early as October 1940, but a variety of difficulties resulted in these being delayed by six months. When the tests commenced, the aircraft was powered by a standard engine because the engine control unit planned for installation was not available at that time. As far as the aircraft's weapons were concerned, the MK 101 and the MG 131 were both to be tested. Because the development aircraft had been out of action for some time (the result of an accident), the planned series of tests was carried out at the Rechlin Test Centre.

The second Do 217E-2 prototype, the V12, was a modified version of the Do 217E-1 (serial number 2170520012) and bore the registration DD+LL. This aircraft was equipped with a powered gun turret, and a powerful MG 131 B. Testing of the split landing flaps was delayed also. Furthermore, the prototype was damaged on 22 May 1942, resulting in the second E-2 being left to stand in the construction bay until June 1942.

As the result of the very severe test programme (specifically, diving trials and landings having been performed frequently), misgivings arose as to the aircraft's future operational safety. Accordingly, the RLM issued an order, on 29 October 1942, to the effect that the Do 217 V12 should be transferred to Dornier's training workshop for instruction purposes.

Following numerous flights by the first twelve prototypes, together with those made by A-0 and B-0 series aircraft, and having assessed the first two aircraft of the Do 217E series, the Technische Amt gave the green light for the production of the new bomber to commence. Because the BMW 801 engines chosen for the Do 217E series of aircraft had satisfied the RLM's requirements clearly, the Do 217D project was laid aside without any qualms.

CHAPTER THREE

Production Begins

By 1939, the planned large fleet of Ju 88s had not materialized, and was not likely to do so within the next two years, and the Junkers bomber had become gradually heavier and slower, because of the extra equipment it had had to carry. The result was that a feeling of disquiet became noticeable at the RLM.

When, at the same time, problems began to be experienced with the He 177 and the Me 210 heavy fighter, the only course of action, seemingly was to fall back on the already authorised He 111 and the Do 17. There did not appear to be any other solution to all of these problems.

The invasion of Poland on 1 September 1939, and the preceding war in Spain had both cost Germany many casualties. During the air battle over Poland, the Luftwaffe lost a total of 285 aircraft. This number included seventy-eight He 111 and Do 17 medium bombers. On 13 March 1940 (prior to the German invasion of France), the production of both the He 111H-4 and the new Do 217 was given high priority in Germany's re-arming policy. The Ju 88A's initial teething troubles were far from being solved completely, leading to serious doubts concerning the speedy equipping of the Kampffliegergruppen (bomber groups). At the beginning of 1941, the planned production figures for that year were for 240 Ju 88s; at least 160 He 111s; and 65 Do 217s per month.

Before this, and following the production of a few prototypes of the Do 217A-0 and C-0 series of aircraft, the first Do 217E-1 had appeared in October 1940 and, together with the first twelve aircraft, was designated an 0-series aircraft. The Do 217E-1's first flight took place on 1 October 1940 at Friedrichshafen. The flight, together with the test flights of a further four Do 217E aircraft in Löwental, up to the end of the year, proved to be problem-free.

The Do 217E-1 had been built according to its specifications largely, which had been issued on 8 July 1939, with the exception that it was powered by two 1560 hp BMW 801Ma-1 engines, that is, engines which included a quick-release connector. The first E-series aircraft could carry a maximum of 4360 l of fuel in the fuselage and wings, and provision was made to install extra tanks in the bomb-bay, if that should prove to be necessary. Some of the bomber versions had a 20-mm fixed cannon installed in their noses, together with the three MG 15s.

Because the Do 217E-1 was to have a glider-bomb carrying capability, additional dive brakes were needed. Initially, it had been planned to install these under the aircraft's wings, but this proved to be too complicated. Consequently, Dornier decided to install the lattice type of brake in the aircraft's tail, that brake having been tested already on the Do 17.

The stores which could be carried by the Do 217 E-1 and its successor, the E-2, were specified precisely each month:

Weapon	Do 217 E-1	Do 217 E-2
SC 50	16	16
SC 250	4	4
SC/SD 500 and SC 250	2+2	—
SC/SD 500	3	4
PC 1000	1	3
SC 1000	1	3
SC 1000 and SC 500	—	1+2
SC 1400	1	1
SC 1700	1	1
SC 1800	1	1
LMA	2	2
LMB	—	1
F5 Torpedo	1	1

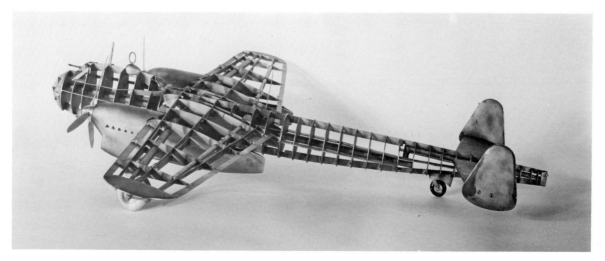

Mock-up version of the Do 217C, for wind tunnel tests, which was undergoing construction in 1938.

Inspecting the mock-up of the Do 217E-2 during wind tunnel tests.

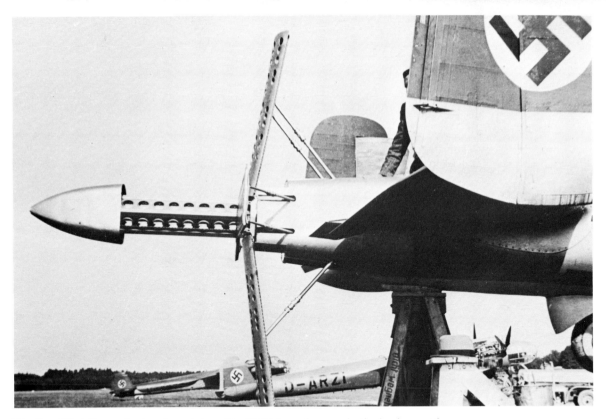

The Do 17's tail cone brake. A prototype Do 217E-2 can be seen in the background.

Drawings of the Do 217E-1 which was planned originally without the lattice-type tail brake.

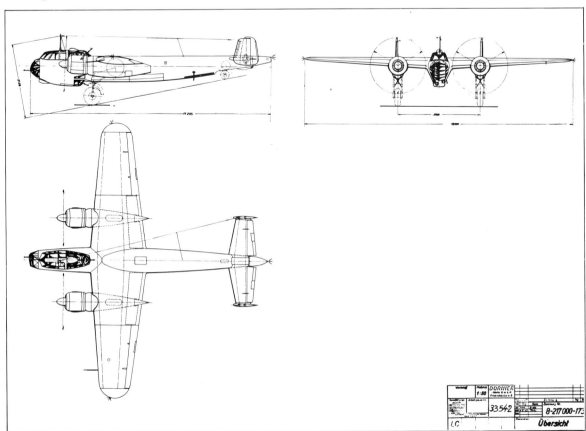

Photographs showing
Do 217E-1 production
at Wismar.

The first twelve Do 217E-1s carried small white markings below the cockpit glazing, giving each aircraft's designation (E1 to E12), which indicated that they belonged to the preliminary series. The third Do 217E-1 prototype (serial No 1003; call sign DD+LC), was flown for the first time on 14 December 1940, but was lost on 22 May 1941, during trials at Rechlin. The sixth E-1 (F8+HP) underwent skid-control tests, before it was delivered to KG 40, with which unit it was damaged severely on 11 April 1941. The first twenty-five Do 217E-1s were allocated the successive call signs of DD+LA to DD+LZ, and the serial numbers 1001 to 1026.

By the end of March 1941, thirty-seven bomber aircraft had been built and test-flown. Three of these aircraft were allocated the call signs TC+ZA to TC+ZC (serial Nos 1027 to 1029). Many of the Dornier 217E-1 bombers had been selected for conversion to the improved fighter variant of the planned Do 217H, Do 217P and R series of aircraft. Subsequently, a large number of the new fighter bombers were tested by Dornier at Löwental in the summer of 1941. Between July and September of that year, six aircraft (serial Nos 1002, 1004, 1007, 1031, 1037 and 1040) underwent tests which enabled Dornier to gain valuable knowledge for the future improvement of the armament and bomb jettisoning systems.

At Rechlin, Luftwaffe tests with the Do 217E-1 and E-2 were not completed until the end of March 1942. A prototype of the Do 217, D-ABWC, had arrived at Rechlin in mid-July 1939 for performance and tactical evaluations.

In all, thirty-four reports were written between July 1939 and March 1942, and these contained every minute detail of all the important aspects of the aircrafts' performances and systems. Subsequently, new design aspects were incorporated in the prototypes Do 217 V2 and V11 primarily. Gradually, several Do 217E-1s (serial Nos 1002–3, 1008, 1016 and 1043) and Do 217E-2s (serial Nos 1107–8, 1132 and 1143) went into operational service.

Following the construction of the Do 217 V2, which was powered by DB 601 engines, and the V4

with its Jumo 211 powerplants, a further study began on 15 August 1939, in which other operational roles for the Do 217 were examined. Various mock-ups were constructed for the improved glider-bomber, dive-bomber and torpedo-carrying roles. Emphasis was placed also on the Do 217's role as a reconnaissance aircraft. These developments were especially significant because none of the trials undertaken by the prototype Do 217E-1 had shown any negative results, up to the end of 1940.

According to Dornier's test pilot, the E variant's flight characteristics in the level bombing configuration left nothing to be desired. Only glide attacks, using interception control, and with the dive brake open, did not quite match quite the stringent specifications.

Dornier Do 217 — Bomber trails

Version	Markings	Date	Comments
V5	D-ADBD	18.4.41	Test flight with six SC 50 bombs
V5	D-ADBD	9.5.41	Test flight with Lotfe 7D
V5	D-ADBD	12.5.41	Test flight with Lotfe 7D
V5	D-ADBD	5.6.41	Test flight with Lotfe 7D
V5	D-ADBD	25.6.41	Test flight with SEZ unit
V6	D-ADBE	25.9.41	Test flight with Lotfe 7D
C	NF+UW	25.9.41	Test flight with Lotfe 7D
C	NF+UW	27.9.41	Test flight with Lotfe 7D
E	RH-FPD	8.10.41	Dive tests
E	RH+EN	16.10.41	Dive tests
E	RH+EO	11.11.41	Dive tests with four SC 250 bombs
E	RH+EO	28.11.41	Dive tests with four SC 250 bombs
E	RH+EN	28.12.41	Dive tests with four SC 250 bombs
C	NF+UW	2.12.41	Attitude flight test with TZA, three SC 50 and six SBE 50 bombs
E	NF+UW	6.1.42	Dive tests (four dives) with BZA1 unit
C	NF+UW	13.1.42	Attitude flight test with TZA, and three SC 50 bombs
C	NF+UW	15.1.42	Attitude flight test with six SC 50 bombs
E	RH+EN	26.2.42	Dive-bombing trials (four dives) with four SC 50 bombs and BZA equipment

Version	Markings	Date	Comments
E	BW+CW	14.4–22.4.42	Dive-bombing trials (eleven dives) with BZA-1 equipment and SC 250 bombs
E	BW+CZ	23–24.4.42	Dive-bombing trials (four dives) with BZA-1 equipment and SC 250 bombs
E	RH+EN	23.6 + 30.6.42	Test flights (two) with BZA-1 equipment and Lotfe 7D
E	RH+EQ	23.6.42	Test flight with BZA equipment
E	RH+EN	1.7.42	Test flight with BZA equipment
E	BW+CU	1.7.42	Dive tests (four dives)
C	NF+UU	2.7.42	Test flight of the automatic pilot
C	NF+UU	2.7.42	Test flight with Lotfe 7D
K	RH+EI	3.7.42	Dive test with BZA
K	RH+EI	4.7.42	Dive test with BZA
E	RH+EN	5.7.42	Test flight with Lotfe 7D (two flights)
E	BW+CU	7.7.42	Test flight with BZA-1
K	RH+EI	8.7.42	Test flight with BZA-1
E	RH+EN	1.8.42	Test flight with Lotfe 7D
E	BW+CU	11.8.42	Dive test with BZA-1
E	RH+EQ	19.8.42	Dive test with BZA-1
E	RH+EN	19.8.42	Test flight with Lotfe 7D and NC 50
K	KE+JA	27.8.42	Dive test
E	RH+EN	29.8.42	Test flight with Lotfe 7D and NC 50
K	RH+EI	29.8.42	Dive test with BZA-1
K	KE+JA	29–31.8.42	Dive test with BZA-1
E	BW+CV	7.9.42	Testing of windvane pylon
K	KE+JA	8.9.42	Test flight with BZA-1
E	RH+EN	10–12.9.42	Test flight with Lotfe 7D at altitudes of 4000 and 6000 m
E	BW+CX	28.10.42	Test flight with Lotfe 7D
E	RH+EN	31.10.42	Test flight with Lotfe 7D
E	RH+EN	9.11.42	Test flight with Lotfe 7D
E	RH+EN	17.11.42	Test flight with Lotfe 7D
E	RH+EN	21–26.11.42	Test flights with Navi 3 and Beute MK1 systems
E	RH+EN	27.11.42	Test flight with Lotfe 7D and SD 1 bombs
E	RH+EN	2.12.42	Test flight with Lotfe 7D
E	BW+CX	2.12.42	Dive tests (five dives)
K	KE+JA	11.12.42	Test flight with automatic pilot

Version	Markings	Date	Comments
E	BW+CX	11.12.42	Test flight with BZA and of the automatic pilot
E	BW+CX	8.02.43	Test flight with BZA and EDS, including four dives
E	BW+CX	8.2.43	Test flight with BZA and EDS, including three dives
E	BW+CV	16.2.43	Test flight with wind measuring equipment
Do 217	GG+PF	19.2.43	Test flight with BZA-2, including three dives
Do 217	GG+PF	26–28.2.43	Test flight with BZA-2, including thirteen dives
E	RH+EQ	2.3.43	Test flight at an altitude of 6000 m with Lotfe 7D and SD 1 bombs
E	RH+EQ	15–16.3.43	MG 151 gunnery trials (two)
Do 217	DN+EA	22.2.44	Ballistic and Lotfe 7D trials
M	CL+UY	7.4.44	Test flight with Lotfe 7D at 6000 m
M	CL+UY	29.4.44	Test flight with Lotfe 7D at 4500 m
E	BW+CX	3.7.44	Test flight with Lotfe 7D and automatic pilot

Making the necessary improvement to the aft dive brake became an immediate objective, thereby avoiding any possible delays in getting series production under way.

The performance figures, produced by Dornier's test pilots, for Do 217s powered by DB 601A, Jumo 211A/B, or BMW 801A engines compared favourably also with those from the rigorous test programme, having minor deviations only. A Do 217E-1 (serial No 1002) and a Do 217E-2 (serial No 1132), both powered by BMW 801A-1 engines and fitted with combat systems and weaponry, were tested and proven under simulated operational conditions. Without their auxiliary, under-wing bomb racks, test flights at an altitude of 6000 m indicated that the aircrafts' operational ranges were 2400 km; with the addition of two 900-l fuel tanks, that range was increased to more than 3,700 km.

BMW 801A-1 engine tests could not begin until the first prototype of the Do 217 series was delivered, and a final assessment could not be made

The first Do 217E-1 which was built at Wismar, prior to its first flight on 1 April 1941 when it was piloted by Flugkapitän Robert Förster.

Internal view of the Do 217E-1's cockpit.

44

A Do 217E-1 pictured during loading practice with an aerial torpedo on 28 February 1941.

A view of the bomb bay of a Do 217E-1 which has been loaded with two SC 250 and SC 500 bombs.

until the summer of 1942 because of the frequent lack of replacement engines. In September 1941, tests with the flame retarder were almost complete. Flame dampeners were used often by Kampfgesch-wader 2 and by KG 40 and KG 100 also, for night operations. By that time, preliminary trials with the Rb 20/30 camera unit, which was to be installed in the Do 217E, were coming to an end.

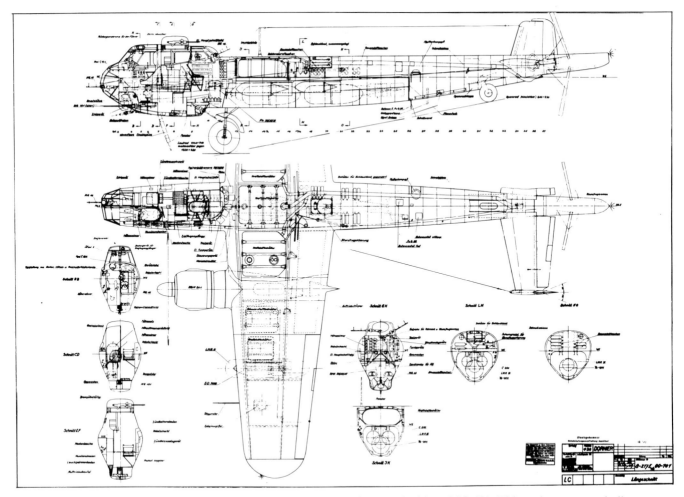

General arrangement of the Do 217E-1b, which was to be armed with an MG 131. This variant was not built.

Rechlin's final report on the Do 217E concentrated specifically on the aircraft's weapon systems and ordnance. The report stated that technicians had reached the conclusion, in 1942, that the weaponry met all of the specifications, including their ease and comfort of use. The technical systems of the two early Do 217Es were stated to be clear and easy to operate. The same was true of the bombing systems; successful bombing trials had tested all of the types of ordnance which was stored in the aircraft's spacious bomb bay. Trials with fixed and flexible weapons commenced in spring 1941. As had been expected from previous experiences of the Do 17 and 215, the trials ended with an extremely positive evaluation by the Luftwaffe.

In July 1941 approval was given for the temporary addition of one extra MG 131 in the front glazing of the cockpit of a Do 217E-1, and for trials using of an MG 131, in the B position, as a rear defensive weapon. The trial installation of MG FF 20-mm cannons was completed also. Following a further evaluation of the Do 217E-2's systems, a hot-air de-icing system was installed in the cabin and the tailplane. The subsequent extensive trials were not completed until February 1942. At Rechlin, engineers worked feverishly, re-equipping

46

One of the first Do 217E-2s
(RH+EJ; serial No 1136)
during flight trials over
Oberschwaben.

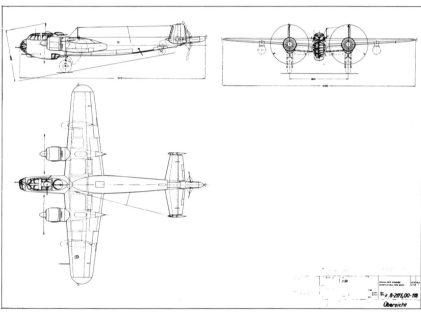

Plans for the Do 217E-2
which was to be equipped
with a defensive armament
in the sides of its fuselage,
and with drop tanks.

Photograph taken during
loading practice at
Friedrichshafen-Löwental,
showing an LMA stored
under the wing of the first
production Do 217E-1
(DD+LA).

47

the Do 217 with heated panes in the front canopy. All of these improvements benefited later E-series aircraft, the final K- and M- series of aircraft, and the night fighter versions of the Do 217 also.

Production of the Do 217E-2 series of aircraft commenced in March 1942, prior to the ending of the E-series' tests. This bomber series, which was later produced exclusively at Friedrichshafen, included 280 aircraft bearing the serial numbers 1101 to 1380. Most of these aircraft were test-flown by Dornier's test pilots Appel and Schropp, and by other Löwental pilots. They were transferred later to the Luftwaffe, when all their military systems had been installed.

In the meantime, tests were confined to the aircraft's combat systems, using twelve Do 217E-2s (serial Nos 1101–1112; call signs RE+CA to RE+CL). These were followed by further aircraft which had been allocated the call signs RH+EA to EY and RC+HA to HZ. The military testing unit flew a number of aircraft bearing the serial Nos 1212 onwards. BK-IA, in particular, had been equipped with greatly improved systems for diving operations, prior to its transfer to an operational unit.

At Friedrichshafen, Dornier had earmarked BK+II (serial No 1220) as a prototype for testing new equipment required by the constant changes to series specifications. Two aircraft (serial Nos 1221 and 1228) functioned as testbeds for BMW 801L-2 engines, and a Do 217 E-2 (BK+IO) was used mainly for bombing trials, and was equipped with 300-l, 900-l and 1200-l auxiliary fuel tanks.

That it was not a question of making a temporary improvements only was shown by the fact that, in June 1940, an 18.2-m long, more heavily armed Do 217E-2, equipped with lattice-type air brakes, appeared on the drawing board. Its weaponry

Löwental, spring 1942: behind the eighth Do 217E-1 prototype stands TC+ZC (which was later converted to become the Do 217 RV1 variant) and a prototype Do 217E-2 (CO+JO).

Prototype Do 217E-1 (serial No 1006; DD+LF) fitted with a skid control for trials.

A Do 217E-2 (serial No 1136) equipped with a complete weapons system which included a fixed MG 151/20.

49

Do 217 Production

Month	Year	Combat aircraft	Night fighters
December	1939	1	—
January	1940	—	—
February	1940	1	—
March	1940	—	—
April	1940	4	—
May	1940	—	—
June	1940	—	—
July	1940	—	—
August	1940	1	—
September	1940	2	—
October	1940	4	—
November	1940	1	—
December	1940	7	—
January	1941	1	—
February	1941	15	—
March	1941	31	—
April	1941	23	—
May	1941	13	—
June	1941	16	—
July	1941	37	—
August	1941	33	—
September	1941	35	—
October	1941	35	—
November	1941	16	—
December	1941	22	—
January	1942	16	—
February	1942	8	—
March	1942	75	8
April	1942	59	13
May	1942	50	35
June	1942	55	27
July	1942	55	21
August	1942	54	12
September	1942	51	13
October	1942	57	14
November	1942	35	4
December	1942	49	10
January	1943	54	23
February	1943	59	30
March	1943	74	17
April	1943	59	21
May	1943	67	20
June	1943	55	23
July	1943	56	28
August	1943	49	20
September	1943	30	25
October	1943	—	—
November	1943	—	—
December	1943	1	—
January to August 1944	1944	Conversions only	

consisted of a fixed MG 151, which was installed in its nose, an MG 15 in the A position, and three MG 131s, in separate rotating gun packs, one each in the B1, B2 and C position. The result was an aircraft which resembled greatly the Ju 188, which was a later development of the Ju 88E. For protection against enemy barrage balloon cables, many Do 217s were equipped later with cable cutting equipment (Kutonase).

Do 217s rolling off the production line were subjected to the scrutiny of construction supervisors also. Tests using four Do 217E-2s which flew at altitudes of 5300 m showed that the aircraft was capable of achieving a speed of 535 kmph (although the aircraft were not equipped with weapons, dive brakes, racks and flame dampers). Problems arose with the 12.5-ton Do 217 E-2 in single-engined flight. When it had an all-up weight of thirteen tons experienced pilots only, such as Boettcher of Rechlin's Test Establishment, were able to handle the aircraft. Aircraft with an all-up weight of less than twelve tons did not present any problems in maintaining altitude with the BMW 801 engine.

Most Do 217E-1 and E-2 aircraft were delivered to Kampfgeschwaders 2 and 40 in late summer 1941. These units had flown the Do 17 previously, and they acquainted themselves with the pleasant flying characteristics of the Do 217.

During the Blitz over the British Isles, the He 111 and the Do 17 had both shown themselves to be light and, in particular, vulnerable to enemy fire. The defensive armaments of these combat aircraft were not powerful enough, as was that of the earlier Ju 88, in spite of continuous additions and improvements. The lack of long-range fighter aircraft was a deciding factor in the failure of that campaign. Tactical errors and poor evaluations, especially concerning the strengths and effects of those German weapons used during the night raids over London and the other main cities of Britain, together with the constant changes in the choice of targets as an increasing number of crews were lost, could result with the campaign ending only badly.

From 1941 onwards, problems with the introduction of new aircraft became the rule, rather than the exception, and an air of mistrust spread through the Luftwaffe's leadership, each member blaming

A Do 217E-2 of KG 2, pictured in the Netherlands, awaiting engine trials (BA).

51

The fifteenth production Do 217E-2 (serial No 1226; BK+IO) which was the test aircraft for the BMW 801L-2 powerplant. This aircraft also underwent drop-tank trials.

another openly for the failures. The problems with the powerplants of the He 177 and those of other aircraft, together with the bitter set-backs encountered with the Me 210, destroyed completely the relationships between Göring, Udet and Milch. The feeling of hopelessness led to the suicide of Ernst Udet on 17 November 1941 and produced scepticism towards all new aircraft designs.

In 1941, the RLM went so far as to consider the Do 217 as the only aircraft capable of replacing

Close-up of a Do 217E-4 (serial No 5404), the fourth aircraft of the series to be equipped with a 20-mm MG FF in the A position at Wismar.

Pictured behind a Do 217 E-4 (serial No 4396) is a Do 217E-2 (BR+IQ).

both the He 111 and the Do 17. Concurrent with a cut-back in the production of the Ju 88, a start was to be made on the urgently-needed 'B Bomber'.

Returning to the development of the Do 217: Dornier was committed totally to producing a combat aircraft for the Western Offensive, as quickly as it was possible to do so. The need for an aircraft with more powerful weaponry was filled rapidly by the Do 217E-2. Together with an MG 15, which was installed in the A-position, the four-man crew each had an MG 131, positioned in the aft of the aircraft, and an MG 15 on bearings in the side windows. In addition to carrying an increased bomb load of 4000 kg (for accommodating which, a part of the fuselage tank had to be sacrificed), this variant was characterised by an effective DL 131 rotating turret. However, for long range operations, jettisonable tanks had to be fitted under the

An MG FF pictured in the cockpit of a Do 217E-4, one of the Luftwaffe's Atlantic combat aircraft.

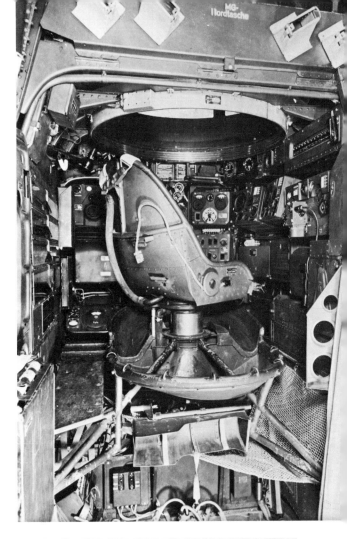

The radio operator's work station in the Do 217E. Note the swivel seat.

wing which resulted in a reduction of the aircraft's speed.

Originally, the Do 217E-1's radio equipment consisted of FuG X, 16, 25, PeilG V and FuBI 1. This was later replaced in the E-2 version by the FuBl2. A small number of aircraft were fitted with a Siemens FuG 101 electric altimeter also, enabling the pilot to make safer and more accurate low-level attacks.

For maritime and other types of operations where the possibility of having to ditch the aircraft into water existed, the aircraft was fitted with an R7 Equipment Pack, comprising of a four-man rubber dinghy and necessary life-saving equipment. It was not until later, when crew numbers increased and aircrews could no longer all reach the one dinghy safely from a fast-sinking aircraft, that one-man dinghies were supplied. The Do 217E-1 could be fitted also with other Equipment Packs such as the R1 (a rack for carrying 1800 kg ordnance), the R2 (wing rack), and the R3 (a rack for carrying 50-kg

A Do 217E-4 (serial No 4381) which was flown as F8-B4 by IV/KG 40 and was shot down over Sussex on 4 January 1943.

bombs), in addition to various types of auxiliary fuel tanks.

In the search for extra weaponry, Dornier collaborated with a group from the Technischen Aussendienst, who made frequent visits to Dornier during the development of the R20 Equipment Rack, which was comprised of two fixed MG 81Zs, positioned in the tail cone. The lattice-type dive brake, used on the Do 17 experimental prototype and the fourth Do 217 prototype never was a practical proposition for the E-2. The drag on the brake panels was often so great that it deformed the rear fuselage, making the aeroplane unsafe as a whole, and hastening the likelihood of metal fatigue.

Following a long meeting in May 1941, concerning improvements to the lattice brake and brake parachute, the test unit at Rechlin, together with the Graf Zeppelin Research Institute (which specialised in brake parachute testing), sent a telegram to the RLM at the end of June, because it was the RLM which decided the urgency of this and all similar projects. The parachute was to be tested for its suitability as a dive brake for the Ju 88, Do 217, Bf 210, Ar 240 and Fw 191 prototypes. A safety parachute for the He 177 was to be tested also, and an urgent need existed to test a landing drag parachute for the Me 321, DFS 230, Go 242 and the Ar 232. Despite the improvements made to the lattice brake, which were decided upon in June 1941, the results of tests, undertaken during the following spring, were far from satisfactory. While those tests were under way at Nellingen near Stuttgart, others were being carried out at the Research Institute, where a Do 217E-2 (serial No 0127) was damaged because of defective tyres. Following wind tunnel tests, using a smaller version of the ribbon parachute, practical tests using a converted Do 217E started in July 1942.

The R25 Equipment Pack, developed as a result of these tests, was fitted in the E-4, K-1 and M-1 variants of the Do 217, and later in the N-1 and N-2 night fighter variants, with satisfactory results. The ribbon parachute was deployed and recovered using an automatic release system in the diving attitude.

Constantly occurring new technical problems and weight-saving considerations resulted with the evaluation group having no other option than to remove the new air brakes from the aircraft when they came of the assembly line. Research into improving the Do 217's performance led to an unconventional way of attacking small, individual targets being found. A recoilless 35.5-cm cannon was to be installed in the fuselage of the Ju 288, and the Do 217E-1 was to have a retractable weapon. The 11.25-m long weapon would fire anti-tank rockets (weighing 1470-1600 kg, each having a 700-kg head) at naval targets specifically. Later, it was thought that the same weapon could be used when diving in to attack from a range of approximately 4000 m, enabling the aircraft to remain out of the range of the ships' anti-aircraft weapons, and keeping their crews in safety.

The first of these weapons, conceived originally in 1939, was fitted under the fuselage of a Do 17Z, at the Rheinmetall-Borsig firing range, between August and September 1940. Dornier had equipped the Do 17Z with instruments to measure the ordnance loading which the Do 217 could be expected to carry. The first tests took place on 9 September 1940. Unfortunately, the Gevät (Device) 104 'Münchhausen' not only destroyed the measuring and recording instruments, but it deformed the Do 17's tailplane and rear fuselage also. The experiments were continued using a Do 217 which had a strengthened fuselage and a tailplane which was 120-kg heavier than its predecessor.

A further fourteen rounds were fired, after which the research institutes came to the conclusion that a far greater chance of success would be achieving using anti-tank bombs and gliding weapons. Professor Sänger's numerous trials with a ramjet (which had been undergoing development since 1937) involving a Do 217 E-1 and an E-2 were very advanced when a ramjet was constructed on an Opel 'Blitz' truck. Seventy test flights were carried

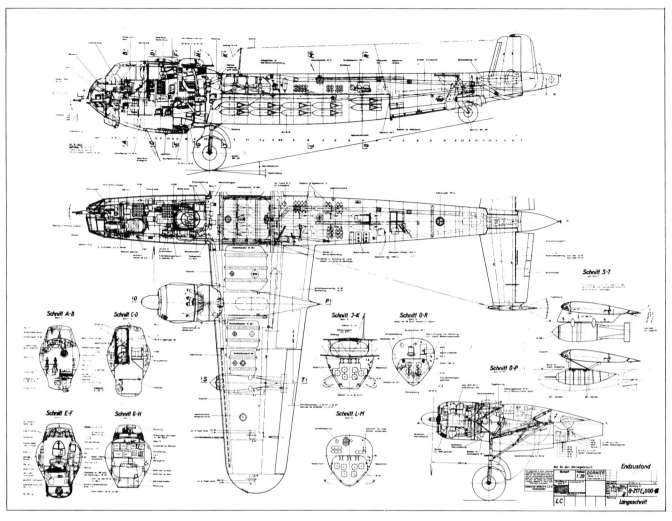

Detailed side view of a Do 217E-4 which was equipped with racks for carrying bombs up to and including the SC 1000.

out with the 50-cm diameter Sänger ramjet in a Do 17Z-1. The addition of an 81 l tank allowed a modest, five-minute test only.

The next aircraft to be used for tests was a higher-performance Do 217E-2 (serial No 1104; RE+CD), which had been operating at Löwental since April 1941. Flugkaptän Paul Spremberg collected the aircraft and, following the installation of a 100-cm ramjet on 6 March 1942, made the first

test flight. Twenty-four hours later, the first 'hot test', lasting twenty minutes, was carried out successfully, with Professor Eugen Sänger present in the cockpit as an observer. Numerous measurement flights were undertaken, using full thrust and at altitudes of up to 4000 m. These were followed by a series of both 'hot' and 'cold' flight tests at altitudes of up to 7000 m. The results from these tests showed very clearly that the ramjet's performance, like that of the Argus unit, was very much a function of both speed and altitude. Nonetheless, compared with the Do 217 E-2's normal range of speed, the ramjet boosted its maximum speed to almost 680 km/h in 1942.

During the eighth test flight with RE+CD, the pulse jet fuel supply line (which was ducted through the Do 217's cockpit, to enable the measurement of the aircraft's fuel consumption) failed. Petrol vapours engulfed the crew but, thanks to the skill of Paul Spremberg, the aircraft returned safely to the test centre.

Because of the increasing risk of encountering marauding Allied fighter aircraft, flight testing was transferred from Trauen, in the Lüneberger Heide, to Ainring near Bad Reichenhall, and to Hörsching near Linz. By the end of 1942 test flying at both establishments was well under way. In September 1943, Erich Klöckner made a number of test flights in the E-2, RE+CD, which had been fitted with a 10.6-m long, 1.5-m diameter, high-temperature ramjet. However, on 4 October of that year, RE+CD crashed as the result of engine failure. It was not repaired completely by Dornier until March 1944.

Developing 20,000 hp, the big ramjet was able to boost the Do 217's speed to approximatley 720

km/h. Underlying all of the trials conducted with the Sänger ramjet were proposals for a new generation of fighter aircraft, the powerplants for which were to be tested on a Do 217E-2. With a quick end nowhere in sight, the measurement and development programme of test flights was terminated prematurely at the end of August 1944.

Nevertheless, the series of aircraft tests was by no means brought to an end. One important development involved the installation of an FuG 200 'Hohentwiel' radar system for maritime reconnaissance operations. A Do 217 was flown to the DLH hangar at Staaken, where the system was to be installed using the same fittings as those which had been chosen for the Ju 88A. In spite of the rapid progress in development, the system was not installed in any aircraft series during 1943. In August 1943 the Heine Company fitted another Do 217 with flame throwing equipment for the ground attack role, and this was tested satisfactorily during runway-attack trials.

Together with these sometimes quite spectacular prototype conversions and the special equipment carried by the aircraft during testing, Dornier had been working, since 1941, on the adaptation of the Do 217 for operations in Arctic and tropical temperatures. Following gradual improvements to

Project drawing of a Do 217E-1 with underslung Münchhausen equipment.

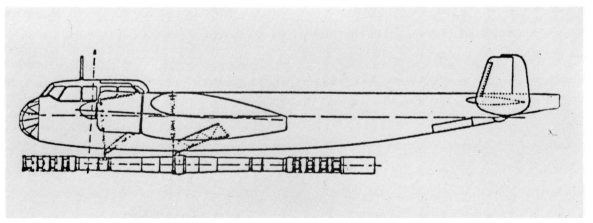

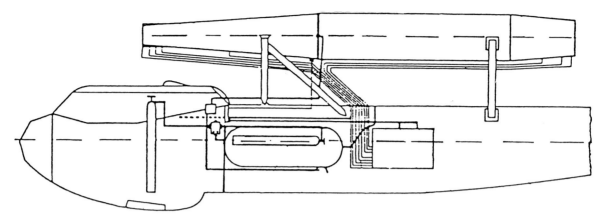

Fuel tank installation which was fitted for development testing of the Sänger ramjet on the Do 217E-1.

the cabin-heating and windscreen de-icing equipment, preparations were made, in the summer of 1942, for the Dornier bomber's entry into a Russian winter. A Do 217 fitted with skis appeared on the drawing board. The skis were to be fitted onto the strengthened struts of the landing gear, which had been lengthened to accommodate the sweep of the aircraft's propellers. Prior to this, a modified production aircraft underwent Arctic tests between January and April 1942, at Tartu (Dorpat) in Estonia, in temperatures ranging down to −25°C. The results were encouraging.

The particular objective of these trials was to determine whether or not the normal cold-start procedure for the BMW 801A-1 powerplant was sufficient, or if it would be necessary to use auxiliary batteries to start the aircraft. Some months later, in July and August 1942, trials were conducted in the shimmering heat of North Africa, using a Do 217 and an Fw 190A (both equipped with a BMW 801D powerplant), to evaluate different types of sand filter. The manufacturer also tested the performance spectrum of a Do 217E-2

powered by BMW 801A-1 engines, and fitted with GM-1 equipment. From July 1943, similar trials were carried out with BMW 801MG engines and improved Focke-Wulf sand filters. Germany's retreat from Africa eventually resulted with the termination of this series of trials.

During the final winter of the war, a Do 217 was used as a flying test bed to assist in the rapid completion of the prototype Ju 248 (Me 263) test programme. The Do 217 was used for practical trials of the bi-fuelled 109-509C rocket engine. It is not known if this intention was carried out by 1945. The Do 217 underwent trials with two As 014 pulsejets. The first tests took place towards the end of 1941 and showed an increase in speed of approximately 80 km/h. In January and February 1942, the tests pursued two lines of investigation: the pulsejet's capability as a short-term booster, and its use solely as an aid to take-off. In June, it had been planned to fit the Ju 88 also with this equipment. However, this engine never saw action, because it could be used only within Germany's borders, and nothing is known of any further tests.

A Do 217E-2 (RE+CD) during a test flight of a 20,000 hp ramjet over Hörsching. These flights took place between 16 September 1943 and 30 August 1944.

CHAPTER FOUR

The Bombing Offensive in the West

On 10 July 1940, the first comprehensive bombing attack on targets in the south of England were carried out by Luftflotten 2 (Kesselring) and 3 (Sperrle). During the first days of August, raids were carried out against several early warning units and the important ports of Southampton and Portsmouth. 13 August 1940 became known as the 'Eagle Day', and was followed a few days later by 'Black Thursday'.

The first daylight attacks on Greater London took place on 24 and 25 August. The first night raid, on 6 September, led to heavy losses for both sides, with neither being able to claim victory. A revenge raid against London, carried out by 300 bombers, did not produce a long-lasting triumph for Germany. Battle of Britain Day (15 September 1940) highlighted convincingly the effectiveness of Britain's fighter defences, and the futility of daylight raids without adequate fighter cover. Oddly enough, the air war seemed to ebb during October 1940, although further air raids against London,

between 15 and 19 October, appeared to have been very effective.

In spite of the heavy losses suffered by Luftflotte 2, the OKL issued orders that the attacks should continue. At the same time, the fifty bombers in operation with Luftflotte 2, together with Luftflotte 3's 150 bombers offered the potential of carrying out night raids to inflict massive economic damage to Britain, and erode the morale of her population. The task of attacking Allied shipping in the English Channel was given to Kampfgruppen 606 and 806, and to Stukastaffeln also, thereby enabling the air offensive to continue almost unceasingly.

Coventry was bombed on the night of 14/15 November, five days later the target was Birmingham and, at the end of the month, an attack was launched on Southampton. During 8 and 9 December, the incendiary bombing offensive launched against London, together with those against Manchester, Liverpool and other towns, left its tragic mark. The heavy air raids on London,

A Do 217E-1 (serial No 1209; F8+GN) of V/KG 40. This aircraft went missing on 2 October 1941.

60

executed by Luftflotte 2, continued until 16 May 1941, up to 460 twin-engined bombers having participated. Later, Liverpool was the target again, followed by Portsmouth and Bristol. The outbreak of hostilities on the Eastern Front did not result in any visible easing up of the Luftwaffe's activities over Britain.

From March 1940 onwards, the re-training of II/KG 2 began at Achmer and other places. A few months later, in June, I and III/KG 2 and two Staffeln of II/KG 2 followed suit. On 14 and 16 July 1941, II/KG 2 and II/KG 40 attacked various targets in Greater London, and a number of factories in Birmingham. By 21 August, five aircraft had been lost: apart from one Do 217 E-1 (U5+EM) lost by IV/KG 2 and one E-1 (U5+GN) lost by VI/KG 2, a third aircraft was lost by the Staff Squadron of II/KG 2. Two further Do 217E-1s, (F8+EC and F8+BP) were lost by KG 40.

Kampfgeschwader 40's story began when I/KG 40 crews began training in Bremen on 1 November 1939. In April 1940 the unit was equipped with FW 200s which had been the backbone of the entire group, until some of its units re-equipped with the He 177. Upon relinquishing its Fw 200s to III/KG 40 in May 1941, the unit took charge of its first Do 217s which represented an effective weapon against Allied targets on both land and sea. From

November 1941, Do 217 crews were instructed in the use of air torpedos at Grosseto, Italy. However, their instruction appears to have been in vain because, up to the time of writing this book, documentation of live aerial torpedo operations by the Do 217 has not been found.

Shortly after, II/KG 40 was placed under the command of the Angriffsführer England it left the Geschwader formation and instead became part of Kampfgeschwader 2. From the summer of 1943, it re-equipped with He 177s and started glider weapon training at Garz. In 1944, after having incurred heavy losses over England and the general area of the Allied invasion, the unit transferred to Gardermoen in Norway.

On 1 January 1941 III/KG 40 left the He 111 Group of the I/KG 1 and, from the winter of 1941, took Fw 200 long-range maritime reconnaissance bomber into commission. For a short while, work was undertaken on the re-arming of the He 177 order to later concentrate on all still available Fw 200 and to equip them with Hs 293.

The foregoing is a brief outline of the story of Kampfgeschwader 40. Up until November 1941, the crews of the II/KG 40 flew their Do 217s frequently over the Channel and convoy routes, and operated against any British coastal shipping found on major river estuaries.

A Do 217E-2 of II/KG 40 at Soesterberg.

61

Between 14 August 1941 and 4 March 1942 Albert Hain and his crew, flying in aircraft serial No 1175 of KG 2, sank three Allied ships and damaged one more.

In September 1941, two officers of KG 2 were decorated with the Ritterkreuz for their successes during the Western Offensive. The first Knight's Cross was awarded to Kommodore Walter Bradel, who later lost his life over Holland when returning from yet another raid over England. The second Knight's Cross was presented on 24 September to Hauptmann Alfred Kindler after he had taken part in no fewer than 230 raids and had attacked several naval vessels successfully.

On 12 October 1941, a 40-bomber raid was directed over Hull, Newcastle and Manchester, which bore its brunt. The same day, a Do 217E (U5+DN) of 5/KG 2 landed by mistake in Lydd, Kent, after taking part in a 'clearing-up' operation over the sea. However, the emergency landing caused only a small amount of damage to the aircraft itself.

On 10 January 1942, KG 40 lost its first Do 217 during a raid over Liverpool and the Merseyside area, when the crew of Oberfeldwebel Paul Wolf, all from KK/KG 40, went missing in action in F8+IN. Four days later, III/KG 2 lost its first Do 217E-2 (serial No 1153) over Schipol. During

Photograph showing two aircraft and the propellers of another, which were all allocated to IV/KG 40 in September 1940, including a Do 217E-4 (F8+DM) which failed to return from an operation over Allied territory on 16 December 1942.

January 1942, III Gruppe lost a total of eight of their Dornier bombers, five of these failing to return from bombing raids over enemy territory. In February, a further fourteen Do 217s had to be written off. Nine of these belonged to KG 2 and three to 4, 5 and 6 Staffeln of KG 40. The Staff Squadron of III/KG 2 had to write off U5+AD and U5+BD, and their crews (that of Oberleutnant Eckert, and that of Lt Roosen) remained missing. A third aircraft, F8+GP, was damaged severely and taken to Soesterberg for repairs. Between 1 and 27 March 1942, a further six Do 217s were lost and, on the night of 27 March the Royal Air Force launched a massive offensive. British bombers attacked almost all of the airfields operated by the Luftflotte 2. After accounting for the successful destruction of twelve British aircraft by anti-aircraft positions and night fighters, the Luftwaffe had sustained considerable damage. A few days later, on 5 April 1942, a Beaufighter crew had its first success using an AI Mark VII radar, shooting down a Do 217 E-2, piloted by Unteroffizer Fritz Meyer of III/KG 2, over the Thames.

During the first twenty-two days of April, KG 2 and KG 40 lost more than fifteen aircraft of the E-1 to E-4 types. Some of these crashed either during take-off, or on landing at Soesterberg. II Gruppe of Kampfgeschwader 40 sometimes had to operate without as many as nine bombers, some of them having sustained slight damage as the result of enemy anti-aircraft fire, and some having suffered minor engine trouble which was rectified easily.

A night raid on Exeter on 23 April 1942 was the start of a number of what the Germans termed 'revenge operations', in retaliation to the bombardment of the Hanse town Lübeck. Altogether, the Luftwaffe sent forty Do 217s from KG 2, a Ju 88 from Kampfgruppe 106 and an He 111 from I/KG 100. However, one aircraft only reached Exeter, and the entire operation was deemed to have been a complete failure. British night fighters had become more dangerous with each successive mission. A Do 217 received a direct hit from a No 64 Squadron fighter. The bomber, a Do 217E-4

(F8+AP, serial No 5368) of VI/KG 40, from which a few aircraft also took part in the action, flew to Soesterberg where it made an emergency landing.

On the night of 25/26 April 1942, a further raid was made on Exeter by twenty-five fighter bombers, flying for the first time with the new AB 500 canister bomb, which was filled with incendiary bombs. These 'Baedecker Raids', as they were called in Britain, continued throughout the following days of April over the centres of Bath, Norwich and York. Between sixty and seventy twin-engined bombers participated in these raids usually. During the night raid over York on 28/29 April the Luftwaffe lost three Do 217s, two of which had belonged to V/KG 40 at Soesterberg where they crashed into each other and were damaged badly. A Dornier with the call sign U5+QP went missing. That night, new British night-fighter operations, known as 'Turbinlite', were put into practice, but did not achieve any success. A Havoc of 1459 Flight, with a powerful searchlight, and a Hurricane both attempted to bring down a Do 217. However, the Dornier, which the Havoc had caught in its beam, disappeared into the darkness of the night.

In May 1942 the Staff Flight committed its Do 217s, together with those of I and III/KG 2, to yet another 'revenge operation'. Notwithstanding the rather negative attitude of Oberst Peltz*, many reliable sources have told of some of the crews having expressed the feeling that they had the sturdy construction of the Do 217 to thank for saving their lives. All that aside, there was not any immediate possibility of replacing the Dornier in the Western Offensive. The crews of KG 2 and KG 40 continued their armed reconnaissance operations over Britain, attacking shipping in both the Channel and the eastern Atlantic.

The next target on KG 2's list was the bearing factory at Chelmsford. Bomber crews had reported also that there was renewed shipping activity in the English Channel. The crews involved in the Chelmsford raid failed to find their target, as did

---

* Appointed "Angriffsführer England" in 1942.

A Do 217E-2 of KG 2 bearing temporary night markings under its fuselage.

the eleven bomber crews which had been detailed to attack the shipping.

Between 18 and 31 July 1942, Luftflotte 2 lost ten Dornier bombers, and, on 24 July, Hauptmann Marten and his crew crashed when flying in a Do 217E-4 (U5+FR). During the night of 26 July, twenty-two bombers, flying at altitudes of approximately 700–1500 m, dropped 22.4 tons of explosives and 5600 incendiary bombs over Middlesbrough, and did not encounter any fire from British fighters. Twenty-four hours later two night raids were made on the industrial centre of Birmingham, whose factories seemed to have had a magical attraction for the Junkers and Dornier bombers.

During the first days of August, the emphasis was placed on reconnaissance, individual raids and bombing operations against Aberdeen, Nottingham, and the port of Ipswich. However, Britain's air defences had not been caught napping. Seven Dornier crews, three from KG 2 and four from its neighbouring unit, KG 40, failed to return. Nevertheless, a new series of raids began in mid-August. Again, the main targets were Ipswich and the airfields at Nottingham and Great Yarmouth. Fifty fighter-bombers, of which half of this number only found their targets, took off in the direction of Portsmouth.

On the previous day, British and Canadian troops had landed at Dieppe, under heavy naval protection. The British bombardment of the airfields of Soesterberg, Deelen, Eindhoven and Gilze-Rijen, which together had a combined total

A Do 217E-2 (F8+KP) of VI/KG 40, taxying out for one of the night raids over Britain in the spring of 1943.

The crew of F8+EP, ready for battle, approach their aircraft on an airfield in north France, in 1942 (BA).

Personnel and aircraft of III/KG 2, prior to taking off to attack targets in southern England.

Two Do 217E-4s of VI/KG 2 'Holtzhammer', on an airfield in the Netherlands in the autumn of 1942 (BA).

Loading bombs on to a Do 217E of KG 2.

of 110 Do 217s, and the military ports of Creil, Beauvais, Chartres and Chateaudun, was an essential part of the landing operation. The bases of Jagdgeschwader 2 and 26 and other targets were also attacked by the enemy.

Air battles involving Spitfires Vs and XIs and Fw 190 fighters soon became the order of the day. Enemy bombers continued to drop their loads; KG 2, II and IV/KG 40, III/KG 53, KG 77 and, not least, Kampfgruppe 106 all fought back. Thirty-one Do 217s destroyed in the immediate vicinity of the landing area illustrated alone the bitterness of the battle. Together with Havoc bombers, four-engined B-17s bombarded Abbeville air base and other targets. Six of the Do 217 E-4s destroyed during this raid belonged to KG 40, and, in the air, the unit was defeated totally. The Holzhammer Geschwader was hit severely. Not only had it had several of its Do 217E-4s destroyed at Abbeville, a further five had been either damaged or shot down over Dieppe. The landings ended with over 1500 prisoners and the loss of thirty tanks and armoured vehicles.

Following an interlude, Luftflotte 2 concentrated its efforts again on British industrial centres. Bombs were dropped on Leeds, Sunderland, Colchester and Chesterfield.

At the beginning of September 1942, the first crisis arose in these units involved in the offensive over the British Isles: it had become almost impossible to replace the aircraft which were being lost constantly. Flying schools were able no longer to provide the Kampfgeschwaders with a sufficient number of trained personnel. KG 2 had twenty-three Do 217 crews only (!). Other units involved in the offensive were exactly in the same position. The planned disruptive and mine-laying operations had to be shelved until a later date.

In September, five Do 217s failed to return from operations over enemy territory; two of the aircraft, at least, were shot down by Mosquito night fighters over England. One Do 217E-4, a converted Do 217E-2, crashed near Cambridge, killing the entire crew. Another crew was more fortunate: its members parachuted to safety and were taken prisoner.

One of the participants in these late-summer operations was Wilhelm Schmitter, who was awarded the Knight's Cross for the part he played in the raids against the ports on 14 September 1942. One year later, on 8 November 1943, he was killed in action. The crews of U5+UR and U5+KR also lost their lives, on 18 and 19 September respectively, when their Do 217s crashed (presumably, the victims of enemy anti-aircraft fire). Their targets had been the towns of Yarmouth and Sunderland which were both attacked by a force of nineteen medium-range bombers.

In early October there was a lull in Luftflotte 2's night raids. Between 11 and 30 October 1942, the main thrust of the offensive was directed towards mine-laying operations in Britain's estuaries and on its railways, together with disruptive raids over its industrial targets and airfields. Small night raids over Sunderland and Middlesbrough only, on 17 October 1942, resulted in any success worth mentioning. Three members of KG 2 were decorated for their outstanding achievements: Peter Broich, of 3 Staffel, and Heinrich Meyer were each responsible for sinking a merchant vessel; while Oberfeldwebel Karl Müller had participated successfully in more than 280 operations. They were all awarded the Knight's Cross. A reprisal raid over Canterbury, in which 106 bombers took part, caused severe damage to that old city, and is also worth a mention.

In November 1942, adverse weather conditions precluded any larger operation. Often, the only operations which were possible were individual raids, undertaken by the best crews of KG 2. Many German explosives and incendiaries fell on Hull, Poole, Grimsby, Canterbury and Norwich, to name but a few. However, a price had to be paid: four Do 217s and their crews failed to return from the operations.

In June 1942, Ju 88s and Do 217s flew together in three raids over the heart of Canterbury. To repay the British for the massive RAF raid on Cologne on 29 June, Luftflotte 2 attacked with all of its modest strength. Relatively few bombs fell on

A Do 217E-4 (U5+AP) of 6./KG 2, at Schipol, Amsterdam, in May 1942.

Leutnant Walther's Do 217 E-4 (U5+DS) showing the damage it incurred during an aerial combat with a British night fighter.

One of three Do 217E-4s (serial No 4272) with a tail-mounted weapon system, which was allocated to KG 2, pictured at Soesterberg.

Ipswich, Birmingham, Norwich, Canterbury and Southampton. Although the small amount of bombs dropped was considered by the inhabitants of these cities to be too much, the Germans considered it to be not enough when compared with the total dropped on Cologne. Between one and three crews flew on various raids over British industrial targets, intending to disrupt night production totally by causing the air-raid sirens to sound. Any physical damage caused was slight. A raid on Avonmouth on the night of 30 June/1 July 1942 did not incur any losses for the Luftwaffe out of the forty-six Do 217s invlved. This was to be the last of the major raids over the British Isles for a while.

Oberst i. G.* Pelz participated in one of the final operations of June 1942:

> *Due to the use of new flares and battle plans, it is possible now to drop 80% of the bomb load over the target (as opposed to the previous 40%). During the last raid on Sunderland, three aircraft only were lost out of a total of seventy-six. The great advantage we have is the manoeuvrability of our aircraft. They circle in their waiting position, then strike suddenly against their target the moment they see the flares, to roll up and away again a few minutes later. During this time, the enemy defences are so smothered that they are practically helpless.*
>
> *The morale of the crews has risen considerably. It is a basic principle that losses should never be allowed to be greater than expected reinforcements. For large operations, the absolute percentage of losses cannot be any*

---

* i. G. = *in Generalstab.* German staff officer rank distinction bestowed to selected graduates of military academy.

greater, because the absolute limit of the effect the defence has been reached.

The Dornier Do 217 is not suitable for raids over Britain, even at night, because of certain flight performance problems. Training involves 30% more flying hours than that for other aircraft types; also there has been a marked increase in propeller failures recently. Therefore, I would request urgently that KG 2 be re-equipped with another aircraft type; the Ju 88, if that is possible. The DB 603 engines reduce greatly the range of the Do 217 (when the aircraft is not fitted with auxiliary fuel tanks), and cause a deterioration in flight and altitude performances. The Do 217's special properties make it more suitable for daylight raids over the Eastern Front.

During these raids, one Do 217E-4 of III/KG 2 was lost, and a further two were shot down over Hythe and elsewhere in Kent by British anti-aircraft fire. From early July, German operations went into a decline.

Each night from 15 November to 13 December 1942, between five and nine Ju 88s and Do 217s dropped LMB and BM 100 mines into the Thames and the Humber estuaries. Mines were also dropped over Tynemouth, the Isle of Wight, and off the south coast of England. During the last raid on 13 December 1942, sixteen twin-engined bombers of Luftflotte 2 dropped nine LMBs and fourteen BMs. In spite of the efforts of the British night fighters, twenty-four bombers attacked Hartlepool on 15 December, flying at altitudes of between 900 and 2000 m. Starting at 20.05 hr, they dropped three SC 1000s, sixteen SC 500s, thirty SD 500s and 1120 incendiary bombs. Following two raids against the York and Hull areas, German operations began to ebb gradually towards the end of the month.

At the end of the year, KG 40 lost another two of its crews. The Holzhammer Geschwader lost two Do 217s, one of which came into contact with the ground while flying at low altitude, and crashed on the Yorkshire Moors.

So much for the Western Offensive. The MG FF weapon, sited in the A position, had justified its use against small naval targets, and became the standard equipment for all Do 217 E-4s. Consideration had been given already to using the Do 217 as a torpedo-carrying bomber. This possibility had been contained in a data sheet, dated 30 January 1941, as soon as the designs for carrying airborne torpedos had become a reality. Apart from the loading tests, for which a Do 217 V6 was used at the Tarnewitz naval testing establishment, equipping Luftwaffe aircraft with the F5 aerial torpedo did not seem to be immediately in sight.

The minutes of a meeting, held on 17 May 1941, stated that, from the sixteenth Do 217E-1 production model onwards, aircraft should be capable of carrying an LT (aerial torpedo) without conversion, and that a further two torpedos should be carried under their wings. However, it had not been considered how the controls for the release of their torpedos should be constructed and fitted into the aircraft. In May 1941, a Do 217E-2 was equipped with five aerial torpedos at Dornier's factory at Bodensee, and made a demonstration flight in the presence of Generaloberst Udet. The Dornier works crew released all of the dummy torpedos over the Bay of Manzell. This led to a general feeling of agreement that the Do 217 would not have any problems undertaking operations carrying three LTs, one in the bomb bay and two under the wings.

Nine months later, in mid-April 1942, a representative of the Luftwaffe General Staff got together with the Dornier team to discuss again the possibilities of using the Do 217 as an aerial torpedo carrier. In the meantime, the RLM had demanded that the Do 217 should have a tactical range of 1000 km when carrying two externally mounted torpedos, and that it should be equipped with a mechanical release system, enabling the angle of the LT 60 to be adjusted to suit whatever tactical operation was being carried out. Because the Do 217 lacked such equipment, the LT's course had to be set by hand in the meantime.

70

The Dornier design office worked intensively on three new versions of the Do 217 in the LT carrying configuration: the Do 217E-4, M-2 and R-1. All three versions had been planned to carry auxiliary canisters in their bomb bays, and two torpedos, suspended from external ETCs between the fuselage and the engine.

In July 1942, Dornier agreed to have the electric remote-control system for the LT ready by the end of 1943, at the latest. However, although his crew

Dornier Do 217 Equipment Packs

Pack	Specification	Used on
R1	PVC 1006 rack to carry 1800 kg of ordnance (SC 1800 or SD 1800)	E-2, E-3
R2	Rack in wing ETC, for SC 250 and SD 250 ordnance	E-2, E-3
R3	Frame 8/XIIA — 2 XB clasps for 16x50 kg stores in fuselage	E-2, E-3
R4	PVC 1006B rack to carry F5 torpedo, or an (LM)A mine, in the bomb bay	E-1 to E-4, K-1
R5	Fixed MK 101 cannon in nose	E-1, E-2
R6	Store for camera unit (Rb) 20/30 in rear bomb compartment	E-1 to E-4, K-1, M-1
R7	Four-man dinghy with survival kit and emergency radio	E-1 to E-5, K and M
R8	Jettisonable 750 l auxiliary fuel tanks in forward bomb compartment	E-1 to E-4
R9	Jettisonable 750 l auxiliary fuel tanks in rear bomb compartment	E-1 to E-4
R10	Rack for external loads — TC 2000/XIIA under both wings	E-1 to E-5
R11	Frame 8/XIIX — 2 XB clasps for 16x50 kg stores in fuselage	E-5, J-1, K-1, M-1, N-1, M-9
R12	PVC 1006B rack for 1800 kg of ordnance with attachments (similar to R1)	E-4, K-1, M-1, M-3, M-9
R13, 13a	Auxiliary fuel tanks in forward bomb compartment	E-4, K-1, M-1, N-1, N-2
R14, 14a	Auxiliary fuel tanks in rear bomb compartment	E-4, K-1, M-1, N-1, N-2
R15	Special weapons unit (Hs 293 glider bomb) as extra equipment	E-2, E-5, K-2, K-3
R16	Exterior load rack ETC 2000/XIIA, sited under the inner wing	E-4, K and M
R17	Auxiliary fuel tanks for rear, or forward, bomb compartment	E-4, K and M
R18	Frame with 4 x 50/X locks in bomb compartment for 50 kg drop load	E-4, K-1, K-2, M-1, M-9
R19	Frame with 8 x 50/X locks in bomb compartment for 50 kg drop load	E-4, K-1, M-1
R20	Four racks, 4 x 500/100/XI, or 4 x 500/XI gun mounts	M-3
R21	Two racks, 2 x 500/100/XI, or 2 x 1000/XI gun mounts	M-3, M-9
R22	One rack, 1 x 500/100/XI, or 1 x 2000/XI gun mount	M-3
R22	Oblique firing weapons unit with four MG 151/20s	N-1, N-2
R23	Rear weapons unit with two MG 81Zs	E-2, K-2, K-3, M-9
R25	Attachment for external tanks (300 l, 900 l), similar to R10	E-4, K-1, M-1
R25	Brake parachute and two gliding tracks	E-4, M-1, K-1, N-1, N-2

This aircraft was flown by Leutnant Fahrefellner, and is pictured following a collision while landing during the night of 12 August 1942.

A Do 217E-4 (serial No 4263; U5+DT) after crashing at Schipol in August 1942.

Two Do 217E-4s of V/KG 2, flying at low altitude over Soesterberg.

were quite happy with the Do 217's performance over water, Oberstleutnant Petersen was against such a waste. He supported the Technisches Amt's suggestion to fit the Ju 88 with the LT unit, because the Junkers bomber had a far better dive-brake system in his opinion. The Dornier could dive in to attack at an angle of 50° only, while the Ju 88 was capable of doing so at much steeper angles. This disadvantage served to speed up the construction of more versions of the Do 217 with dive brakes under both wings, which was the normal configuration for the Ju 88. Tests performed by Dornier showed that

it was possible for the aircraft to land safely with unfired torpedos, but that it was not advisable for the aircraft to fly with one torpedo only, let alone return safely to the ground.

The first military demonstration took place at Kampfschulgeschwader 2's base in Grosseto, Italy, to where, together with several Ju 88s and He 111s, a single Do 217 had been assigned. Together with drop trials of mines and armour-piercing bombs, the trials unit at Travemünde carried out tests in November 1942 with a Do 217E-2 (serial No 1151) in the torpedo-carrying configuration.

A Do 217E-4 of V/KG 2, painted with a special camouflage for maritime operations.

The wreckage of a Do 217 E-4 (serial No 1213; U5+DP) of VI/KG 2 which crashed near Salthouse, Norfolk, on 30 July 1942.

A Do 217E-4 (U5+LS; serial No 5462) prior to transferring to a base in the south of France. The aircraft was operated at that time by 8 Staffel of the Holzhammer Geschwader.

During that time, the manufacture was under way of the LT-carrying aircraft, which was based on the Do 217M-1. The data sheet for this torpedo bomber was ready by 5 February 1943. A Do 217 M-1 bomber was converted to become the proto-type for carrying two LTs under the inner wings, and two 900 l auxiliary fuel tanks under the outer wing ETCs. Its defensive weaponry was to comprise an MG 81Z, capable of firing 1000 rounds, situated in the A position; a 500-round MG 131 in

Two Do 217E-4s of III/KG 2, pictured shortly before taking off.

Aircraft of VI/KG 2 flying over France.

the standard Do 217 rotating DL 131/1 gun mount; a second 1000-round MG 131 in the WL 131/1 cylindrical carriage; and two MG 81Is in the side-window positions.

The design did not meet with the approval of the Reichsluftfahrtministerium. One reason was that a tried and tested Ju 88 torpedo bomber existed already; also, an aircraft which could carry a glider bomb and a Fritz X missile was what was required. Another important factor was, that KG 2 required replacement for the number of Do 217s it had lost in action. Furthermore, a number of technical problems precluded equipping the Do 217M-2 with the new L 10 glider torpedos. These problems were

A black-painted Do 217 E-2 being rolled out of a maintenance shed.

76

The wreckage of a Do 217E-4 (serial No 4289; U5+IS) pictured at Southend, Essex, on 26 October 1942.

A Do 217E-4 of 7/KG 2.

highlighted during a number of trials with a Do 217 at the Torpedo Weapons Centre at Gotenhafen (Gdymia) on the Baltic Sea.

The prototype for the LT trials (serial No 56165) was fitted with the new, larger 67-m^2 wings, and arrived at Rechlin for performance trials in the late summer of 1943. The sixth Do 217 K-O (serial No 4406, RD+JF) was flown from Rechlin also, and on June 25 1943 was test-flown at Gotenhafen with four underslung cement torpedos. Performance tests, undertaken at between fifty and sixty metres above sea level, were made at an average speed of 320 km/h. However, as they had been with the Do 217M, plans to equip the Do 217K-1 as an aerial torpedo carrier were hampered severely by a serious shortage of combat aircraft in Luftflotte 2 on the Western Front.

In addition to attacks made against Allied shipping (by KG 40), one of the Do 217's important maritime tasks was that of bombing and mine laying, which were dropped by parachute mainly, over the sea lanes and convoy routes along the British coastline, concentrating on the Channel and the Humber and Thames Estuaries. These attacks were stepped up, following the issue of a directive by the Supreme Command after the Battle of Britain, which called for aerial attacks against targets in the Channel — not forgetting harbour and shipyard installations — to be intensified. To strengthen the attack force available, 9 Flieger-division was also assigned to these operations. At a meeting, held on 19 October 1940, the Luftwaffe High Command decided also to step up tactical raids against towns and industrial centres in Britain. Primary targets (such as those around the Liverpool area and the Bristol Channel), were also highlighted. KG 30 also took part in these attacks. A paper issued on 13 January 1941 by the Defence High Command examined the results of the air war up to that time, and dealt also with the minelaying operations performed by Ju 88s and Do 217s, which had resulted in the sinking of a considerable number of Allied merchant ships.

Air raids against the populated areas and the inner cities of Britain did not seem to be having the demoralising effect on the British people that had been hoped for originally. On the contrary, they appeared to have strengthened the morale and resistance of the civilian population. This was to prove true also, at a later stage of the war, when the devastating reprisal raids carried out by the RAF against German cities strengthened the will of the German people to hold out.

Given all of these observations, there was much to say in favour of the expansion of maritime operations by coastal units and of KG 2 and KG 40. It was hoped that such operations would help sever vital food supply lines to Britain, thereby starving its population. Operations against Allied naval shipping were relegated to second place.

This strategy was reflected in a directive issued on 4 February 1941, which concerned military operations in the West. According to this directive, 3000 mines dropped between 8 August and 19 December 1940 had resulted with almost 21,000 tons of Allied shipping being sunk in December 1940 alone. During the following weeks and months, most of Germany's combat aircraft strength was engaged in attacks (the majority of which were daylight attacks) against land-based targets in Britain, therefore the Luftwaffe High Command decided to carry out minelaying operations at night.

A large number of these minelaying sorties was undertaken, and commenced on the night of 15 November 1942, over the coastline of southern England. Initially, these operations involved groups of between twenty and thirty bombers. Later, smaller groups (less than ten, usually) were involved. On the night of 3/4 April 1943, a combined total of fifty Ju 88 and Do 217s took off, carrying 1000 kg and B-type aerial mines, for the Thames Estuary. Together with attacks against British targets (in the London area and the industrial Midlands, specifically) minelaying operations continued throughout April and May, and into June, although by that time there were not so many of them.

The real air war at sea (ie gunnery and bombing attacks against maritime targets) was conducted mainly by KG 40, supported by Do 217s from the Holzhammer Geschwader. These were predominantly of the E-4 type, but also included E-2s and E-3s. All three types had been built for combat operations in the Atlantic theatre. The E-3 was a modified version of the E-1 bomber (according to the production series designation). Its armament had been augmented by fitting an extra MG 15 in the A position. Most of the Do 217 E-4s were also fitted with MG FF cannon, and emergency equipment for the possibility of the aircraft having to ditch into the sea.

The seventh Do 217E-1 (serial No 1007, DD+LG) was used as the development aircraft for Atlantic operations, and was test-flown at Dornier's Löwenthal establishment from mid-May to July 1941. On 15 May 1941, a 20 mm MG FF cannon was fitted for weapons trials. This was manned by a flight observer and, no problems having arisen, a project commenced in August 1941 to study the incorporation of two MG 15s in the cabin side positions, and an MG 131 in the B position.

While serving with KG 2, the E-4 bore the brunt of operational duties, and it was one of the most mass-produced versions of the Do 217. The Do 217E-2 was fitted experimentally with a fixed MK 101 cannon and eight reserve magazine drums. This weapons configuration was issued later as the standard complement of Ordnance Pack 5. As was the Do 217E-2, the E-4 was fitted with a DL 131 turret in the rear B position.

The E-4 was also fitted with a wide range of radio equipment: the FuG X, 16, FuB1, 2H, a Peil GV direction finder and an FuG 101 precision altimeter.

The bomb load of the Do 217E-4, which went into operational service in the winter of 1942, consisted usually of four SC 500 bombs, giving the aircraft an all-up weight of approximately 15.2 tonnes. Armed with the SC/SD 1000, the E-4 had to be fitted with special electrically operated bomb racks and locks, and with two droptanks, fitted under the outer wing sections, the aircraft's

Do 217 Test Flights Undertaken at Rechlin

Type	Markings	Date	Comments	Type	Markings	Date	Comments
V2	D-ABWC	16.8.39	Performance tests	K-1	CF+PO	6.1.43	Endurance tests
V4	CN+HL	22.6.42	Equipment tests	K-1	TN+CI	30.1.43	Vibration measurement
V5	GM+AF	11.1.40	Drop tests	MV1	BK+IS	19.8.42	Engine tests of DB 603A1
V6	D-ADBE	25.9.41	Drop tests	M-0	BD+KO	31.7.42	Engine tests of DB 603A1
V7	CO+JK	9.5.42	Engine tests of BMW 801D	M-0	BD+KQ	14.5.43	Engine tests of DB 603A1
V8	CO+JL	5.10.43	Engine tests of BMW 801Ds	M-0/U1	BD+KR	5.3.43	Drop load tests
V9	CO+JM	10.12.41	Engine endurance tests	M-0/U1	BD+KS	4.9.43	Drop load tests
C-0	NF+UU	2.7.42	Drop tests	M-0	GB+CV	24.11.42	Endurance tests of DB 603A1
C-0	NF+UW	22.9.41	Drop and diving tests	M-1	CL+UY	9.2.44	Drop load tests
E-1	DD+LL	22.5.41	Basic evaluation	M-1/U2	DN+UA	2.3.43	Disc-brake tests
E-1	DD+LP	30.1.41	Altitude and heating trials	M-1/U2	DN+UG	8.5.43	Disc-brake tests
E-2	BK+IB	24.11.42	Performance tests	M	GC+BW	16.12.42	Performance tests
E-2	BK+IC	20.5.43	Engine tests	M	PG+UQ	17.9.43	Equipment tests
E-2	BK+IL	5.6.42	Equipment tests	M	PK+IG	28.1.44	Me P8 airscrew evaluation
E-2	BW+CU	1.7.42	Dive tests	M	PU+IP	23.5.44	High-altitude flight tests
E-2	BW+CV	7.9.42	Drop tests	M	RV+MP	15.6.44	Weapons testing
E-2	BW+CW	14.4.42	Dive tests	NV1	GG+YA	21.7.42	Engine tests of DB 603A1
E-2	BW+CX	19.5.42	Autopilot and drop tests	NV2	GG+YB	16.8.42	Engine tests of DB 603A1/2
E-2	BW+CZ	23.4.42	Dive tests	N	GG+PF	19.2.43	Dive tests
E-2	RB+YA	22.10.41	EK Lärz field tests	N	GI+ZL	10.9.42	Engine tests
E-2	RB+YD	10.12.41	EK Lärz field tests	RV1	TC+ZC	—	Dive tests
E-2	RB+YS	1.7.42	Flame retarder evaluation				
E-2	RC+IT	8.3.42	Engine tests of BMW 801L				
E-2	RH+EN	16.10.41	Dive and bomb sight trails				
E-2	RH+ED	11.11.41	Drop tests				
E-2	RH+EQ	23.6.42	Bomb sight evaluation				
E-2	RH+EV	18.12.43	Endurance tests				
E-2	RK+OY	10.11.41	EK Lärz field tests				
E-4	KE+ZD	1.7.42	Ordnance tests				
HV3	DD+LW	25.5.42	Engine tests of DB 603A, E				
J	TC+ZB	15.5.42	Engine tests				
KV1	RH+EI	3.7.42	Dive tests and bomb sight evelution				
K-01	KE+JA	27.7.42	Dive tests and equipment evaluation				
K-02	KE+JB	30.1.43	FT tests				

maximum flying weight could easily reach 16.5 tonnes. There was a wide range of stores configurations: from the R6 Equipment Pack (an Rb 20/30 camera unit), to the special Equipment Packs (11, 12, 18 and 19), which consisted of ordnance for the bomb bays, and externally mounted heavy PC 1000 and 1400 armour-piercing bombs which required pack types 10 and 16. The Lotfe 7C bomb aiming system was standard equipment on Do 217E aircraft, but it was replaced later by the improved Lotfe 7D system. Following minor modifications, the BZA 1 and Stuvi also became the standard bomb release

A Do 217E-4 of III/KG 40, fitted with cable-cutting equipment, which crash-landed in France at the end of 1942.

Two Do 217E-4s (U5+FN and UF+RM) pictured during an air raid over southern Britain. During a similar raid, on 16 February 1943, a Do 217E-4 (serial No 5532) was shot down over Dorset by an Allied night fighter.

A Do 217E-4 (F8+CN), pictured during a sortie over north-west Europe.

system for the Do 217. An aft-mounted dive brake had been planned for the aircraft, but this modification played little part in mass production.

The first Do 217E-4 was lost in action on 15 January 1942. U5+HS, stationed with 8 Staffel of the Holzhammer Geschwader, was piloted by Feldwebel Lehnis. This was followed by the loss of serial No 5314, on 17 January 1943, at Schipol Airport, Amsterdam. On 21 January, U5+GR, piloted by Leutnant Parel, failed to return to its base. KG 40 suffered its first Do 217 E-4 casualty, F8+FM of 4 Staffel which, together with its crew, fell victim to an enemy aircraft during an operation in the west. The first Do 217 losses sustained by KG 100 were serial Nos 1103 (a Do 217E-2 con-verted aircraft), 4256 and 4286. All three of these aircraft crash-landed while on training exercises with the Schwäbisch-Hall station flight, and were rebuilt later.

Three Do 217E-4s of KG 2 were something of a speciality, each being fitted with an MG 81Z 'twin' fixed tail gun. This 'watering can' unit, as it was called, was fitted in the tail cones of serial Nos 4320, 43272 and 5524. The gun was aimed using a rear-view telescopic sight which was mounted in the cabin roof. The first prototype aircraft, U5+NT, was in service with 9 Staffel of III Gruppe. However, as was the fixed aft-firing gun fitting in the He 111, this weapon configuration was the exception, rather than the rule.

CHAPTER FIVE
The Heavy Dornier Night Fighters

By October 1940, the production of heavy fighters, and night fighters (such as the Do 217 and its competitor, the Ju 88) had been the subject of comprehensive discussions which were concluded on 5 November 1941. On 23 November, the Technische Amt sprang a surprise: the Do 217 fighter was to be withdrawn from the bomber fleet and, in accordance with a decision made on 23 May of that year, the heavy fighter designated provisionally Do 217Z was to be produced at the rate of five machines per month during that year.

That the heavy fighter version (later to be designated Do 217J) had shown considerable promise was borne out by the fact that Japan had shown a great interest in procuring three Do 217s during the summer of 1942. Germany did not have any intention of supplying its Japanese allies with the emerging Dornier night fighter, therefore these aircraft were never exported to Japan.

Many hurdles had to be overcome before the design of the Do 217N-2 was settled finally. Its fiercest competitors were the Junkers Ju 88 C-2 to C-5, the B-3 and the later C-6 marks of the heavy fighters and night fighters. As it had with the Do 217, production at the Dessau plant was concentrated on the modification of bomber aircraft (the Ju 88A1 to A5 versions, together with the proposed Ju 88B-2). The Ju 88C2 and C4 were powered initially by Jumo 211B/F engines. Subsequently Junkers night fighter versions were to be powered by BMW 801 radial engines, generating 1560 hp for take off. However, because of the requirements for and production problems with the BMW 801 this was never fully realised.

The intention to equip the Do 217J with BMW engines also fell victim to the same problems. The subject of finding an alternative solution was a pressing one. The Ju 88C's speed was between 500 and 560 km/h, according to the manufacturer's somewhat optimistic performance calculations. Later, the design office at Dessau calculated it to be higher — 580 km/h. In contrast with the Do 217 J/N, which was armed with eight forward-mounted guns, the first few aircraft of the Ju 88C series were fitted mostly with only five fixed guns, which were mounted in the fuselage. In most cases, the armament comprised one MG 151 and up to four MG 17s.

From 1 January 1941, Junkers' delivery schedule was aimed towards producing a few Ju 88C-1 and C-2s, followed by sixty Ju 88C-4s, and 374 C-6s, powered by Jumo 211 engines. In Berlin and Dessau, consideration was given to the idea of equipping the C-6 night fighter with two BMW 801 engines, augmented by GM 1 auxiliary injection power boost units for extra performance or, alternatively, of making an early conversion to the more powerful Jumo 213. Both ideas remained to be preliminary projects.

From 1943, the Ju 88C-6's weaponry was improved by fitting one or two additional MG FFs in the fuselage. The radio equipment of the Ju 88C did not differ significantly from that of its Dornier competitor. Both fighters were fitted with the FuG 202 (Lichtenstein BC), but later Ju 88 models were equipped with the FuG 212 (Lichtenstein C1) and, subsequently, with the FuG 220 (SN 2). Up to the end of the war, Dornier night fighters were equipped almost exclusively with an improved version of the FuG 202.

Preliminary trials to evaluate the long- and short-range capabilities of the Dornier aircraft were conducted by Dornier at Löwental. A modified Dornier Do 217 E-1 (serial No 0042) was used to

A view of an open weapons bay of a Do 217Z-10 which was equipped with a Spanner IR sight, a spotlight, four MG 17s, and a 20 mm cannon.

The personnel of II/NJG 2 pictured in May 1942 in front of a Do 217B-5.

test the equipment for the forthcoming Do 217J. Of particular interest in these trials were the characteristics of the various types of fire extinguishing equipment used. Trials to determine the tactical suitability of the Do 217 in the night fighter role were carried out by a Dornier works crew in January 1942, using a suitably modified Do 217E-2 (serial No 1122).

Urgent trials were performed with a close-support night fighter, which Dornier intended to be ready for testing from February 1942. The prototype (serial No 1134), which was also a modified version of a Do 217E-2, was equipped with FuG 202 and 'Spanner' equipment. These systems enabled the detection of heat radiation at a limited range, thereby making the Do 217J a good candidate for night fighter defence operations over Germany. However, during flight tests at Travemünde, the prototype (RH+EH) crashed as the result of engine problems. The limited range of the 'Spanner' equipment (3 to 5 km), together with its slow development pace, precluded its use in the later J-1 version. Work on trying to perfect the IR equipment was in progress as late as the end of 1943. Modified infra-red AI equipment appeared in early 1945 and was installed in the Ju 88G-6.

From the very beginning, significant delays in the delivery of BMW 801 engines combined with similar delays being encountered in the development programme led to the point where the Do 217J also, at times without powerplants, had to be put to one side. In November 1941, two derivatives of the J version were planned: a Do 217J-1 equipped with a 'Spanner' system, and a Do 217J-2, fitted with a Lichtenstein radar. In early 1942, the radio equipment was changed. The Do 217J-1 was to be equipped with AI radar and 'Spanner' systems from the outset, and the technicians and radar specialists planned to equip the J-2 with the improved, higher performance AI radar.

The Technische Amt's production specifications for the two versions of the Do 217J were:

As well as four MG FF and MG 17 fuselage-mounted cannon, the defensive armament will comprise one 131 in both the B and the C positions. Furthermore, each aircraft shall carry eight 50-kg bombs.

FuG X, 16, 25, Peil G V, FuB1.1 and, if possible, FuG 101 radio equipment was to be fitted as standard. It was intended to equip the J-1 with the Lichtenstein DB (FuG 202) with a true range of 4000 m, three display tubes and a rear-mounted aerial. However, this would reduce the aircraft's speed by approximately 30–40 km/h. Therefore, in January 1942, a decision was made in favour of the installation of the 'Spanner' unit. A rear brake was dismissed as being unnecessary.

The first Do 217J was ready for works inspection on 5 January 1942, and completed its first flight successfully later in that month. Following a relatively

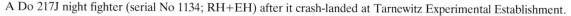

A Do 217J night fighter (serial No 1134; RH+EH) after it crash-landed at Tarnewitz Experimental Establishment.

Prototype of the Dornier night fighter, showing FuG Lichtenstein equipment in the nose.

This Do 217, its crew access doors open, was operated by IV/NJG 101 in Hungary.

A Do 217J, minus its FuG 202 equipment, pictured at a training establishment.

short period of works tests, the aircraft was delivered to Tarnewitz for gunnery trials of the four MG FFs and four MG 17s. Series production commenced in March 1942 with eight Do 217J-1s. In April, thirteen Dornier night fighters were manufactured, and these were followed by a further thirty-five aircraft in May 1942.

At the same time, monthly production had to be maximised. However, from June 1942 the production rate declined slowly until, in November 1942, four Do 217s only rolled off the assembly line. This was the result of a decision made by Air Supply Staff to withdraw the Do 217 airframes from the assembly line, enabling the rapid production of a large number of aircraft, in readiness for a Sondereinsatz (special operation). Reluctantly, the General of Night Fighters was forced to agree. By 31 December 1942, only 157 Do 217Js and a few N-series aircraft had been manufactured.

A Do 217J (serial No 1350) from the night-fighter production series 1251 to 1380 was used by Dornier for evaluating the changes to equipment

A Do 217J trainer, minus its forward-mounted 20 mm cannon.

and airframe construction during flight. During delivery of the first Do 217J-1 to a German air defence unit, General Kammhuber demanded that the Dornier night fighter's fuselage armament be modernised. The first investigations were carried out a few days later. A prototype (serial No 1365), armed with four MG 151s which replaced the usual MG FFs, designated J-1/U1, was modified in September 1942 and transferred to the Tarnewitz Experimental Establishment on 14 October 1942 for static gunnery trials. The new armament proved itself admirably during sustained firing tests, delivering 125,000 rounds without any significant problems. From the development viewpoint at last, there was not anything to stop adoption of the new ordnance, except, perhaps, the latent limitations of the firing pattern of the MG 151/20.

In 1943, further trials were carried out to investigate the effectiveness of increasing the aircraft's fire power by replacing the four MG 17s with cannon. However, the planned early production led the Techniches Amt to cancel all further trials. In spite of what must have been considered to be, from the beginning, an extremely effective combat aircraft, the new night fighter was the subject of some very strong criticism from the Luftwaffe. The first Do 217 J-1 was delivered to 4/NJG 1 at the end of March 1942. During their conversion to the much heavier aircraft, crews had criticised its difficult take-off and landing characteristics. The aircraft came also under attack from pilots who complained that it had too little performance reserve! The aircraft's very high surface loading and its poor manoeuvrability in aerial combat did not help to improve the general view of its capabilities.

Most of these criticisms stemmed from the aircraft's excessive all-up weight: when the aircraft had been converted from a bomber to a night fighter, the entire bomb release equipment had been retained. The two MG 131 defensive guns had also been retained, for the time being at least, as part of the aircraft's weapons complement. With the mounting of eight machine weapons in its fuselage and the resulting amount of ammunition required

A Do 217J-1 pictured in southern Germany undergoing armament maintenance.

to operate them, the night fighter outweighed the Do 217E bomber by approximately 750 kg.

The proposed Do 217J-2 differed from the three-seat Do 217J-1 only by its having an improved FuG 202 Lichtenstein C1 radar. The first C1 radar was tested extensively in Do 17Z-10 CD+PV in May 1942. Production of the Lichtenstein C1 radar commenced at the Telefunken works in the spring

A visit by Italian officers to NJG 2 shortly before acceptance of the first Do 217 night fighter.

of 1943 — that is to say, *after* production of the Do 217J had ceased! Consequently, from the spring of 1942, aircraft of III/NJG 101 and NJ-Schule 1 night-fighter training units, were equipped with the FuG 202 Lichtenstein radar. Even as late as when the N-2 version came off the assembly line, from the end of 1942, the radar equipment remained unchanged in the Dornier night fighters (that is if you can trust the manuals available). Accordingly, the J-2's performance proved to be no better than that of the J-1.

Aircrews soon began to experience for themselves the basic inferiority of the Dornier night fighters. Their reports flooded the desks of the Air Ministry and of the Luftwaffe High Command. The debate concerning the pros and cons of the heavy-weight night fighter was taken up again. Together with Luftwaffe High Command, the General of Night Fighters tried to bring pressure to bear on Erhard Milch. As the stock of Do 217Js became depleted, it was considered to be pointless to commence the mass production of the Do 217N. As the result of a meeting held on 12 May 1942, at Rechlin, with the Head of the Luftwaffe General Staff, Field Marshall Milch issued a directive which stated that all Dornier night fighters were to be withdrawn from the programme as quickly as it was possible to do so. However, notifying Dornier to that effect was considered to be totally unnecessary! Nevertheless, Major Storp informed Dornier's management that the Luftwaffe would concentrate solely on the Ju 88C-6, forthwith.

Major Herget, the commander of I/NJG 4, which was then operating a squadron of Do 217s, expressed his frustration at the aircraft's severe loss of performance, caused by the aerial array which reduced the aircraft's speed by as much as 30 km/h. The only way of overcoming this highly precarious situation seemed to be the immediate removal of the bombing apparatus and of both aft-facing guns. At the behest of the German Air Ministry, this equipment had to be retained, because it would enable the conversion of the night fighter to be a bomber, if and when this was required.

One of the few proponents of the Dornier night fighters was Hauptmann Schoenert, who was a night-fighter ace of III/NJG 3, who befriended the heavyweight Do 217 very quickly. In July 1942, Schoenert suggested to his superior officer (who relayed the request to General Kammhuber, the then incumbent chief of night fighters) that trials be made with slanting weapons, in the hope of improving the combat efficiency of his Do 217. This involved mounting four to six MG 151/20 guns, at an angle of approximately 70°, in the centre of the Do 217 night fighter's fuselage. Two mock-ups, one with four and one with six MG 151/20s, were presented to the representatives of the Luftwaffe and of the Technische Amt at Dornier on 5 August 1942. Dornier calculated that the first prototype could be ready towards the end of September 1942. The work was to be undertaken in close co-operation with the Mauser Company.

At the same time, trials with six MG 151/20s were apparently also carried out at Diepensee. Operational tests commenced at the beginning of 1943, and these were undertaken by Hauptmann Schoenert's squadron. The trials were entirely successful and led to the development of the Do 217J-1/U2 which was armed with four-barrelled, oblique-firing guns. A Do 217J (serial No 1364), powered by two BMW 801L engines, was used by Dornier as the prototype, at Löwental.

However, the idea of using oblique-firing guns did not come originally from Hauptmann Schoenert, but from Poppendieck, an engineer, who had suggested the use of this armament configuration in June 1942, in conjunction with 'Spanner' IR equipment and a powerful headlight. The objective was to introduce new tactics to combat Allied night bombers. Discussions with Oberleutnant Becker, who was then in charge of testing the Lichtenstein radar, resulted with the assertion that there were two basic modes of operation: one using 'Spanner', the other using an FuG 202 radar.

Using the infra-red equipment, German night fighters should have been able to attack enemy aircraft, as a rule climbing slowly to enable the pilot

A Do 217J-1 of the 41st Stormo Caccia Nocturno, pictured after having made a forced landing in northern Italy.

to open up with his oblique-firing guns at a range of 50 to 100 m. An added advantage of this tactic was that German crews were exposed to less risk than they would have been in a direct attack from behind, because British bombers were armed mostly with quadruple defensive guns in the rear fuselage. Because of the high technical costs in-

Fourth pre-series Do 217N-0, GG+YD, pictured during trials.

Side view of the Do 217N-04, equipped with FuG 202, at Löwenthal.

volved, future operations were flown with a further improved Lichtenstein AI radar and four oblique-firing guns. The Luftwaffe was sceptical of Poppendieck's idea of increasing the aircraft's armament to six MG 151s. The increased tactical advantage also helped trials involving rapid decreases in air-speed in order to adjust to the speed of the enemy aircraft.

As was the case with the Do 217J-1/U2 (serial No 1364), the Do 217J-1/U4 (serial No 1366) was fitted also with a semi-rigid brake parachute in October 1942. Three subsequent aircraft (serial

Three-view drawing of the Do 217N-2, dating from spring 1943. The 'Schräge Musik' armament was not contemplated at this time.

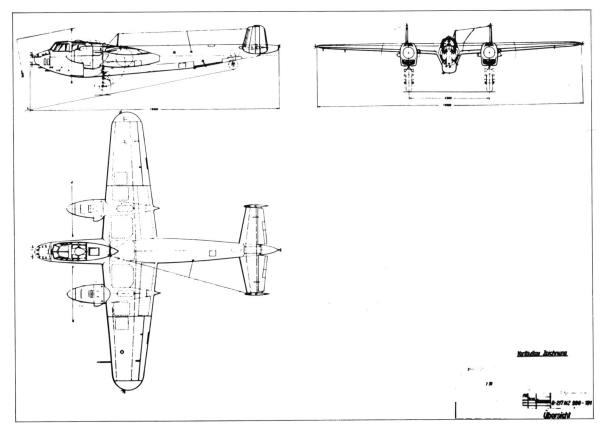

Nos 1370–1372) were equipped with the 'Schräge Musik' installation of six MG 151/20 guns, in addition to brake parachutes in the tail.

Each night fighter carried the type designation Do 217J1/U2, or /U4. These interim night-fighter variants were operated by Schoenert's Staffel and by the Staff Flight of IV Gruppe of NJG 2, 6/NJG 4, and the training flight of NJG 101.

Nachtjagdgeschwader 101 operated alongside the Operational Training Unit to the north of the Neusiedler See and in Hungary. Under the leadership of Haupmann Schwab, the OTU operated the Do 217J-1 — with and without nose armament — mainly as training aircraft, while the Do 217J-2 and a few Do 217Ns were used operationally, equipped with Lichtenstein radar.

The Staffelkapitän of 11/NJG 101, Hauptmann Hans Krause, scored several victories in a relatively short period while on operations with the Do 217 over Hungary and the Adriatic. He was awarded the Ritterkreuz following his twelfth kill. At the beginning of 1945, IV/NJG 101 exchanged its Do 217s for the Ju 88G-6 and moved to Nuremberg. The Dorniers were left behind in Hungary.

The operational history of the Do 217J also included the delivery of several examples to the Italian Air Force. In the summer of 1942, Germany agreed to hand over some Bf 110Cs and Do 217Js to the Commando Supremo for use as night fighters. So that Italian crews could become accustomed to the new equipment, a number of pilots and radio operators were sent to Venlo on 1 August 1942 for preliminary instruction, and ten days later they were sent to Stuttgart-Echterdingen for conversion training. The crews returned to Pozzola at the end of September 1942, having taken delivery of one Bf 110 and one Do 217. A few months later, the first Italian night-fighter squadron was cleared for operations with its German type.

On 1 January 1943, the equipment of 41° Stormo Caccia Noturno comprised four Do 217J-1s, three Bf 110Cs, a CR 42CN and a captured Bristol Beau-

General arrangement drawing of the Do 217N-2, dated 30 April 1944, featuring 'Schräge Musik' armament and a brake parachute.

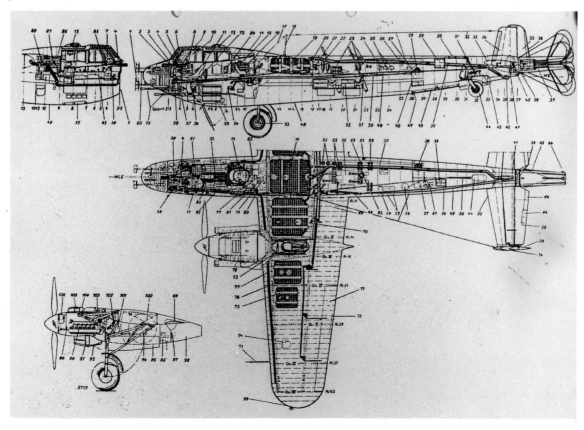

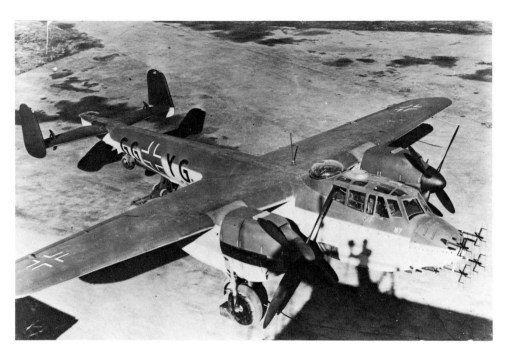

The seventh Do 217N-0 (GG+YG) seen factory-fresh at Dornier's plant.

fighter. After more crews had completed their training in southern Germany other types were delivered, among them another Do 217J-1 and, for the first time, a Do 217 equipped with FuG 202.

In the summer of 1943 there were several night engagements with Allied bombers attacking targets in northern Italy. For example, on the night of 16/17 July 1943, two Do 217J-1s attacked a formation of RAF Lancasters and destroyed one of them. On 31 July, 41° Stormo had an establishment of eleven Do 217Js, but of these only five were airworthy. Three were undergoing repair because of undercarriage defects, while the others lacked important spare parts.

The last Italian Do 217 sorties were flown on the night of 16 August 1943. Conversion to the single-engined Re 2001CN fighter was scheduled to begin in September.

Hungary also expressed an interest in the Do 217, a requirement for three examples of the night

Another shot of the Do 217N-07 with clearly discernible FuG 202.

92

fighter having been indicated during talks between Göring and Rakosi-Bela in Berlin on 13 January 1943. However, three Bf 110s were later delivered instead.

The story of the Dornier night fighters does not end with the Do 217J. From the beginning, it was planned to produce a further variant equipped with DB 603A-1 inline engines. Two aircraft were taken from the batch of ten pre-series aircraft and converted for trials work, being given the designations NV1/NV2, N1/N2, and then N-01/N-02. The first of the trials aircraft was located at Rechlin in the middle of 1942, and was joined on 16 August 1942 by the Do 217 NV2 from Friedrichshafen.

After the obligatory acceptance formalities, the NV1 (GG+YA) began performance trials with the DB 603A-1. The Daimler-Benz engines fitted in the second Do 217N (GG+YB) were subjected to endurance testing at various altitudes. The Do 217 NV1 (serial No 1401) crashed on 11 October 1942,

stalling with its undercarriage lowered and diving into the Müritz Lake. The pilot, Ritter, and his crew were killed.

The Do 217 NV2 (GG+YB) retained its engines until 12 November 1942. The 100-hour engine endurance trials began at Rechlin on 21 December 1942, the pistons burning through after 91 hours. Testing of the newly-installed DB 603A-2 inline engine was carried out between 28 April and 8 May 1943, but the programme was beset by continual breakdowns and defects and was abandoned. There is no further record of the trials aircraft after 20 June 1943.

In April, trials aimed at the replacement of the four MG FF guns had got under way, but they were not completed until late summer. The third Do 217N bore the type designation N-1/U1 and, in addition to displaying a number of small aerodynamic refinements, was fitted with the MG 151/20 nose armament. Dornier allocated the air-

General arrangement drawing of the Do 217N-2.

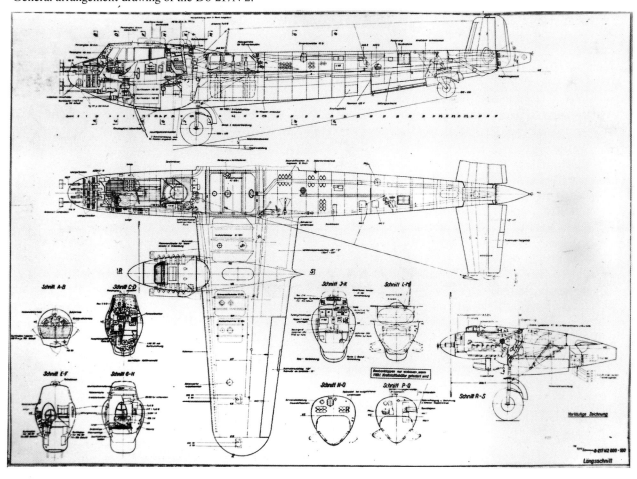

craft bearing the serial No 1404 for de-icing trials in the summer, while numbers 1406 and 1407 were assigned from the outset to operational trials. Aircraft number 1408 (GG+YH) was used to prove various systems; used initially for cold-start tests during March 1943, it was later employed in testing the installations of the 'Lichtenstein BCR' and 'Bernhardine' equipment.

In August 1943 the Oberpfaffenhofen factory completed the first ten mountings for the Do 217N's 'Schräge Musik' armament. The installation of the MG 151/20 cannon was undertaken between 27 and 31 August 1943 at Wismar and the Tarnewitz Test Establishment.

The tenth Do 217N-0 (serial No 1410), which was similar to the third aircraft in the trials batch (GG+YC), was used for radio trials in the late summer, being fitted with Peil G VI/APZ 6 automatic direction-finding equipment. Starting on 2 December 1943, and lasting until the spring of 1944, tactical trials were carried out also at Travemünde with infra-red target-illuminating equipment. The aircraft involved in these were GI+ZL, which had taken part in the DB 601 performance tests at Rechlin, GI+ZH, and two Do 217J-1s, RB+YH and BK+IO.

As a further measure in the development of the Dornier night fighter, the Technische Amt and the Kommando der Erprobungsstellen* requisitioned the workshops of Deutsche Lufthansa at the Werneuchen Test Centre and allotted the technicians there the task of designing an airborne installation for the SN 2 radar equipment in a converted Do 217E-4 (serial No 52041). The specification was finalised on 26 October 1943 following discussions between the Technische Amt, Dornier, Deutsche Lufthansa and representatives of the Kommando der Erprobungsstellen. As usual, the radar antenna was to be positioned so that the four dipoles projected ahead of the fuselage nose.

After a short flight test programme — including performance measurements with the antenna array

in place — the aircraft was handed over to Telefunken for the start of the radar trials proper.

Two basic versions of the series production aircraft — fitted with the FuG 202 — were envisaged: the Do 217N-1 and N-2, of which there were to be two sub-variants. Construction of the three-seat operational aircraft was to follow the pattern of the Do 217E-2/E-4 and the J-1/J-2, with much emphasis on improved range and endurance. Extra fuel tanks — the standard R 14a and R 17 types — were installed in the bomb bay.

For operations over water, the heavy night fighters were fitted with special sea-survival equipment, including a lifeboat and transmitter. The built-in radio apparatus comprised the FuG X with TZG 10, in addition to the FuG 16. IFF (Identification Friend or Foe) equipment was the FuG 25a. Finally, the Do 217N was fitted with the FuG 101 radio altimeter, blind-flying equipment developed from the FuB1 2 and the PeilG V. The AI search radar was the Lichtenstein FuG 202.

All this equipment — including some now useless items, such as the bomb release mechanism — brought the aircraft's take-off weight to fifteen tons, so that it was barely able to claw its way up to 7400 m. As the weight reduced gradually with fuel consumption, the maximum operational ceiling that could be achieved was approximately 8400 m. The aircraft could just about attain a maximum speed of 500 km/h at 6000 m. The picture improved with the appearance of the lighter and much refined Do 217N-2.

According to the data sheets, the various milestones in the development of this aircraft were as follows:
* It was first envisaged as a night fighter without 'Schräge Musik' armament, or a brake parachute.
* It was then decided to fit four 'Schräge Musik' guns and a semi-rigid brake parachute.
* Next, as the prototype of the N-2 version, Dornier flew a converted Do 217E-1, serial No 0174, coded PE+AW. Part 0 (General Information) of the Do 217N-2 handbook gives the date of this aircraft's appearance as April 1944.

* Command of Test Centres.

* Together with the much improved communications fit came the FuG 16 ZY and, in a separate installation, the FuG 214. The 'B' and 'C' cupolas were deleted and the positions faired over, the former with a Plexiglas panel and the latter with wood. The necessary modifications to the weapons stations were carried out by Dornier.

* A further improvement in the series production aircraft saw the use of four MG 151/20 cannon in place of the earlier MG FF weapons. The possibility of replacing the four MG 17s in the nose armament with newer, high-performance weapons was also considered, but the idea does not appear to have been adopted.

* At long last, the whole of the bomb-release mechanism was removed, together with the bomb-bay doors, and the latter were replaced by a light wooden fairing, saving considerable weight. Further modifications included changes to the main instrument panel in the cockpit and the provision of more protection for the crew. The whole of the forward fuselage was more heavily armoured than ever before.

As a consequence of the aerodynamic refinements, the aircraft's maximum speed rose to over 525 km/h, while at an average all-up weight of approximately 12.2 tons the aircraft could reach a ceiling of 9500 m.

Between the end of 1942 and September of the following year 210 Do 217Ns were produced at an average rate of between twenty and twenty-five examples per month. Approximately twenty-five were built from components and spares which Dornier had in stock already. The total number of Dornier night fighters produced — all variants — was 364.

On 31 January 1944 the Air Defence of Germany's resources included thirty-five Do 217N-1/N-2s, but only two Do 217J-2s. Up to May 1944, approximately thirty Dornier night fighters were in action continuously with the various front-line units.

Order of Battle statistics for 31 July and 30 September 1944 show that fifty-five and fifty-

Interior view of the Do 217N-2's cockpit.

Armament layout, comprising four MG 151/20 guns, of the third Do 217N–0 (serial No 1403; GG+YC). The aircraft was designated Do 217N-1/U1 also.

Several Do 217N night-fighters pictured during trials at Friedrichshafen.

four examples of the over-heavy Do 217N-1 were on the Luftwaffe inventory on those respective dates. Numerous Do 217N-1s were in service with 4/NJG 3 (Code D5+AM to D5+MM), 5/NJG 3 (Code D5+AN to D5+MM) and also with 6/NJG 2 and 11/NJG 5. The majority of the Do 217N-2s were flown by 4/NJG 3, the Staff Flight of NJG 100 and 18/NJG 101. Occasionally, single Do 217 night fighters were also used by NJG 200 (8V+NO) as well as by the 9th-11th and 14th Squadrons of Operational Training Wing 101, where they served both as conversion types and operational aircraft.

The short-lived career of the Do 217N, and its limited service status — compared with those of the Bf 110 and the Ju 88 — resulted, in part, from its unsatisfactory flight characteristics, but above all from technical and delivery problems with its DB 603A-1 and A-2 engines.

As early as 2 June 1942 — at least from the viewpoint of Generalingenieur Eisenlohr — the DB 603 was at a stage of development which was far removed from any possible introduction into the series. Defects in the transmission, oil circulation system and supercharger coupling all combined to frustrate the smooth perforrmance that had been

An armament trials Do 217 with DB 601A-1 engines, and Hs 298 air-to-air missiles under the wings.

96

expected. Of the ten DB 603-engined Do 217s which should have been available between the autumn of 1942 and the spring of 1943, all but three had been cancelled by the Technische Amt. The same fate overtook all five DB 603-powered Ju 88 trials aircraft.

It was unfortunate that a small stock of these engines was placed at the disposal of the Rechlin Test Centre. Milch, as the man responsible, expressed his displeasure at several conferences, complaining about the protracted development programme and demanding that trials must continue by day and night. Despite this narrow-minded attitude over the DB 603, the decision was taken in October 1942 to equip the Ju 88 with BMW 801 engines. These were diverted from Do 217E production, which resulted in further delays to the programme.

At the armaments conference which took place on 29 June 1943, it was realised finally that the DB 603's unreliability and its unfitness for series production had thrown the entire programme into disarray. Only a modest requirement for equipping the He 219 with the powerplant was assured of going ahead, albeit with many misgivings. Production extended no longer to the Do 217M and N. Having taken into account the wildly optimistic estimates of the armaments leadership, it was not anticipated, in the summer of 1943, that there would be any improvement in the engine situation.

The position looked even gloomier when the latest development statistics were presented on 16 July 1943. In the case of the Do 217N there would be serious disruption of the production schedule, and in fact the backlog would not be cleared until late spring 1944. For a few weeks in August, it seemed as though all Do 217 variants which had been planned to have DB 603 engines would have to be abandoned. Because an immediate improvement was not anticipated, the Technische Amt, as an emergency measure, ordered an

A Do 217N-2 (serial No 1570; 3C+IP) which, piloted by Feldwebel G. Konzac, laned in Switzerland.

A Do 217N-2 which landed at Basle-Birsfelden, seen in Swiss national markings in 1946.

increase in the Ju 88C-6 production run from forty to sixty aircraft per month.

In September, fresh reports had been submitted to the Luftwaffe leadership detailing the mass of defects in the DB 603. One such report, for example, originating in July, stated that all fourteen Do 217Ns of II/NJG 3 had been grounded with severe engine troubles. By October the situation had deteriorated further, and it was decided that production of the Do 217 with DB 603 engines was to end with the final ten series aircraft in February. After that, higher priority would be given to the BMW 801-equipped Ju 88C-6, which was then allocated the designation Ju 88R-1 and R-2.

Because of lengthy delays in the supply of replacement motors, temporary measures were introduced in 1944 by IV/NJG 101 and the remaining OTUs, which re-fitted their aircraft with the lower-powered BMW 801 radial engine, thereby having part of their complement available at least, for training and operations.

Problems were experienced also with the use of the R 25 equipment. The dive brake, in the form of a ribbon parachute — which in addition to the Do 217N and a few Do 217Es was also fitted to the

98

K-1, M-1 and M-11 — needed a number of modifications, creating an extra workload for the base workshops. The brake parachute, which was deployed by the effect of the slipstream, was attached by eight ribs to its housing in the round, sheet metal-skinned tail cone. The disadvantage was that it was released by the flight engineer by means of a wheel behind the pilot's seat, a layout which put it out of the pilot's reach.

In contrast, limitations were not experienced with the 'Schräge Musik' armament, installed in many Do 217Ns as standard R 22 equipment. For sighting while flying beneath the target aircraft, a second reflector sight was fitted in the middle of the cockpit enclosure.

Despite a large number of modifications and improvements to the Do 217N, many German air defence crews chose to remain with Ju 88 or Bf 110 units, at their own request. In July 1943, there were barely thirty Do 217Ns on the inventory, and in terms of operational aircraft this figure dropped to between fifteen and twenty on several occasions. XII Fliegerkorps summed up the position in concise terms:

Replacement stocks of Do 27Ns have dried up completely. The type can no longer be considered as an operational aircraft. It lacks engines!

From the summer of 1943, flying accidents became increasingly numerous, as did the total of unserviceable Do 217Ns. One example was serial No 52006, which set out from Tarnewitz to Oberpfaffenhofen but only got as far as Fürth. Other noteworthy examples of losses were Rehm's crew of III/NJG 2, who failed to return from operations in their Do 217N-1 on 16 July 1943, and Do 217 JU-1 of IV Lehrgruppe NJG 101 (Code KI+LV), which was badly damaged in a forced landing in Hungary. Many aircraft were repairable and were used later by the Luftwaffe's courier and mail units.

In the autumn of 1943 the Oberkommando der Luftwaffe concentrated the remaining Dornier night fighters in NJG 4 and NJG 100 on the Eastern Front, where, as a consequence of extremely bad airfield surfaces, several of the heavy aircraft suffered smashed undercarriages. In the end, because of the spares problem and also because the

One of the last surviving examples of the Do 217N-1, seen in southern Germany, 1945.

Do 217N-1 (ASO+QY) after it was captured by American troops at Straubing, May 1945.

Dorniers had little in the way of opposition, they were withdrawn. In October 1943 the German night fighters began to carry out daylight operations, but, despite its exceptionally heavy nose armament, the Do 217 did not have any real prospect of success against types such as the B-17, and it was no different for the Bf 110. Therefore, it was hardly surprising that scarcely any Do 217s were to be found in front-line units by the end of 1944. The majorty of the night-fighter squadrons used the Bf 110G-4 and the Ju 88G-1 with BMW 801s, in addition to the Ju 88G-6 with Jumo 213s, all of which engines possessed greater reserves of power.

The story of the Dornier night fighters would be incomplete without mention of a range of high-altitude night fighters, developed from the Do 217P-1, which were at the project stage in 1943 at a time when series production was coming to an end. However, parallel developments by Heinkel (the He 219), Junkers (the Ju 388), and Dornier's Do 335 offered more favourable prospects.

Also included in the story of the Do 217's employment as a fighter aircraft is its role in testing various air-to-air missiles such as the Henschel Hs 293H and the Hs 298. Testing of the Hs 293H, a converted glider bomb, in the air-to-air role began shortly after the arrival of the first suitable equipped Dornier Do 217 K-2/U-1 at Peenemünde on 17 July 1943. It was followed soon afterwards by a second aircraft (serial No 4558) and, at the beginning of August, by another aircraft bearing the serial No 4541. After overall checks of the missile's systems, the next stage was to prove the heating system of the weapon, which was to be carried under the centre fuselage of the parent aircraft, and the FuG 203e radio-guidance equipment before research into the flight characteristics could get under way.

The aircraft itself was partially cleared only for later operations that were envisaged against enemy bombers, for its poor service ceiling and its rate of climb, which was tactically too slow, meant that it could gain no real advantage. Other disadvantages were the altitude performance of the two BMW

100

801ML engines, in addition to technical problems with the missile. For example, there was a tendency of the glider weapon's tracking flares to fail at altitudes of approximately 9000 m.

Nevertheless, when one considers that the missile-carrier was to fly only marginally higher than the attacking enemy formations, the other disadvantages did not seem especially important.

After one of the trials aircraft (serial No 4558) had been handed over to Erprobungskommando 100 at Garz on 1 August 1943, it was found necessary to iron out a number of circuit faults in the weapon system before missile testing could begin. The trials with the Hs 298 were carried out at Karlshagen. A preliminary series of five launches took place from a Do 217 between the end of August and 4 September 1944. All launches were made from pylons mounted under the outer wing sections.

The first live launch took place at an altitude of 2000 m, the missile accelerating away under the power of its booster and sustainer motors. However, soon after leaving the launch pylon, the missile veered sharply off course to the right and went out of control, crashing a few seconds later. The three following launched were not crowned with success either. It was only on the fifth shot that the Hs 298 flew for approximately 30 seconds, at an altitude of 4000 m; then it, too, crashed.

At the beginning of September 1944 the next projectile exploded after only five seconds. Thirteen further trials were carried out from the Do 217 in October, and for the first time two were completely successful. In December 1944 a Ju 88 (NS+RZ) assumed the role of trials aircraft.

CHAPTER SIX

Dornier Bombers in Special Combat Operations

In the spring of 1939, Dr Herbert Wagner began working on the concept of a new generation of weapons which would revolutionise more than just warfare at sea. In Berlin-Schöneberg, Henschel produced a remote-controlled gliding bomb, after studying Wagner's designs for a flying bomb for use on specific targets at sea.

Thanks to the remote-control facility, greater accuracy and an increase in the number of direct hits on specified targets than experienced hitherto with free-falling bombs, was expected. The development of the Hs 293 was given a very high priority listing therefore by German research officers. The high degree of accuracy was not the only factor in favour of the new gliding bomb. It rendered any attacking flight over vessels with heavy flak defences, or convoys, unnecessary, because the bomb could be steered directly to its target from a safe distance. Furthermore, the compact body of the gliding bomb presented a difficult target for the flak defences.

In spring 1940, following the completion of the preliminary studies, the production of the first mock-up and the plans for the first series of prototypes were in hand. At the same time, intensive efforts were directed towards the transmission and reception parts of the remote-control system. Practical trials were carried out from May to September 1940, using a modified He 111 (KC+NX) fitted with Kehl communications equipment. Following extensive tests, the first (albeit uncontrolled) drop test of the Hs 293 was carried out over Peenemünde from an He 111 (DC+CD). During September and October, further drop tests were made using a new version, the Hs 293 V2/3-11, to investigate the stability and structural strength of the device.

The first remote-controlled test firing took place on 16 December 1940, using an Hs 293 V2/12 gliding bomb. However, because the ground crew had switched two electrical connections inadvertently, the test was a failure. It was repeated two days later, the Hs 293 V2/13 missile narrowly missing its target, a large barn. A third test series (V3) with a Henschel Hs 293 was launched successfully in the spring of 1941, a direct hit being made on its target, a 6000-ton ship off the Pommeranian coast.

Even so, tests with this new weapon had only begun. Test launches of the modified Henschel Hs 293 bombs, in the V3 and V4 series, had to be completed by the end of October 1941. Following the final demonstration of the Hs 293 on 10 August 1941, even the last remaining sceptics in the RLM appeared to be convinced, and the first production series of the Hs 293 A-0 could begin on schedule, at the Berlin-Schönefeld factory.

On 1 November 1940, the Luftwaffe High Command assigned the task of evaluating the new weapon system operationally to Lehr-und Versuchsstaffel 293 (Training and Experimental Squadron), which was later to become Erprobungskommando (EK) 15 (Experimental Detachment). In January 1942, Henschel began the mass production of the Hs 293A-1.

Meanwhile, three He 111H-12s, fitted with Kehl equipment, were to undergo operational tests by the Weser Flight. On 7 February four aircraft had been assigned to the Training and Experimental Squadron, including the 43rd prototype He 111.

Fresh from the factory, a Do 217E-4 of V/KG 40, newly arrived on the Western Front.

Pilot training and the training of the first nine missile controllers then commenced. Between February and May 1942, the crews test-fired the Hs 293A-1 on forty-three occasions, of which eighteen were unsuccessful as the result of technical problems; the remainder worked perfectly. Those crews which had trained at the Lehrstaffel (Training Squadron) were then seconded to EK 15 for conversion to the new weapon system.

Ground testing of the PC 1400 X, formerly designated PC 1400, was carried out from 1 February to 15 May 1942. As had been the Henschel gliding bomb tests, the PC 1400 X was assigned for tests to the Peenemünde-Süd Experimental Establishment at Karlshagen. With the formation of EK 15, from Lehrstaffel 293 on 7 March 1942, operational training began in earnest. The tactical evaluation of the PC 1400 X Fritz-X (referred to

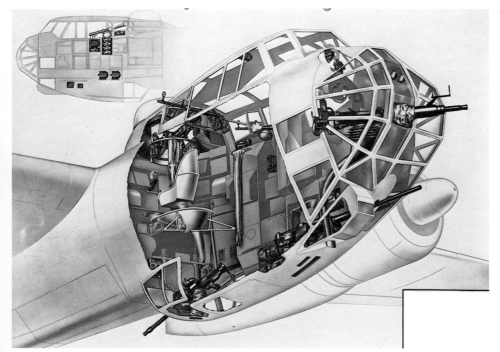

The armament of the Atlantic Do 217E-4 bomber comprised of one fixed and five flexible guns.

103

A Do 217E-1 (serial No 1044; TC+KR) equipped with two underwing bombs and auxiliary fuel tanks.

occasionally 'FX') was conducted in the same manner.

Ten missiles in April 1942, and thirteen in May, were launched from the He 111H-12. Forty-nine of the 100 missiles launched under laboratory conditions scored direct hits, or very near misses, on their prescribed targets.

Thirty per cent only suffered direct control problems and missed their targets. Impressed with these results, the Director of Operational Requirements decided in favour of equipping a total of forty He 177s and forty Do 217s with Hs 293 and Fritz-X missiles, in readiness for the front-line operation which was expected to take place soon. Thirty-four aircraft of each type were to be adapted, without delay, to carry the Henschel bomb, and six of each type were to carry the PC 1400 X.

Meanwhile, detailed training and operational guidelines were to be drawn up, and handbooks, relevant to this special weaponry, were to be produced. Operations against land-based targets

were punishable, because the Germans did not want the technology to fall into enemy hands. Despite considerable groundwork, new problems arose every week: moisture was having an unfavourable effect on those missiles which were held in store; at high altitude, the rocket motors were prone to icing and, consequently, would cut out; the temperamental electrical system failed; and the radio valve in the control unit fell victim to vibration. This situation was summarized in a Peenemünde report, dated May 1942: the target hit rate was approximately 50%, and the failure rate was considered to be much too high.

The first Do 217E-5 was available in April, and the second in May 1942. These were to be operated by the Peenemünde Experimental Establishment, which had to determine the aircraft's operating range with a variety of stores configurations, auxiliary fuel tanks and fuselage-mounted missiles, which together gave all-up weights of between 15.4 and 16.5 tonnes. This was augmented by tests using

A Do 217 (serial No 5552) with an MG 17 in the A position, and an Hs 293 slung under the starboard wing.

A Do 217E-5 special operations aircraft, camouflaged for night-flying operations with II/KG 100 at Istres.

This Do 217 was fitted with submarine-detecting equipment in 1943.

single-engined aircraft with suspended stores, and, in July 1942, by the evaluation of a heating unit for the Hs 293 gliding bomb. By August 1942, all the data necessary had been collated, and the handbook 'Heavy Combat Aircraft for Special Operations', together with a construction manual and a modified equipment specification, were all ready for publication.

The Do 217E-5 was similar basically to the Do 217 E-2, although weight considerations precluded it being equipped with a dive brake. Production aircraft were fitted with Equipment Pack 10 in the front fuselage, and a heating unit for the cold-sensitive gliding bomb. With external ETCs and without a gliding bomb or auxiliary fuel tanks, the Do 217E-5 could attain a speed of 480 km/h at an altitude of 5000 m. With two external stores, its maximum speed was reduced to 445 km/h, and its weight, including 4300 litres of fuel, was 16.85 tonnes. In this respect, the Do 217E-2/U1, which was serving as the prototype of the E-5, equipped with a remote-controlled torpedo bomb, could have been of some interest, but whether or not a Do 217E was used to launch an Hs 294 is uncertain. The only certain fact is that a Do 217 carrying an Hs 294 flew into Berlin-Schönefeld in May 1943.

The first test launch took place on 7 August 1942, from a Bf 110, and was succeeded by further test launches from the He 177. Subsequently, a statement, issued by Henschel, stated that suspending the torpedo bomb under the fuselage necessitated a corresponding reduction in the fuel carried in the fuselage tanks; the resulting loss in range precluded the operational value of the aircraft.

Following the delivery of the two aforementioned Do 217E-5s, the intention was to modify a further fifteen aircraft by 20 June 1942, and a further twenty-three aircraft by 31 July 1942. On 17 July, Milch issued a directive to the effect that the glider bomb was to be put into operation against merchant shipping in the Atlantic by the spring of 1943. The Luftwaffe High Command intended also to use the Fritz X in operations against Allied naval shipping primarily, before the end of the year. The opinion was that the FX was capable of dealing with battleships of the *King George* class. The 1600-kg Peter X was also being developed, as was the SD 2500 bomb which was to be used for attacking *Iowa* class battleships.

The HS 293 and FX missiles could be launched from two aircraft only: the Do 217 and the He 177. Later, they were launched from the Fw 200 Condor.

Regardless of the type of launch aircraft used, the minimum launch altitude for the Fritz X was 4000 m and that for the Henschel gliding bomb was 300 m.

Meanwhile, bringing these missiles into operation was delayed further since the first few special operations aircraft were used for crew training, and therefore could not be assigned to units operating on the Western Front. Consequently, it is hardly surprising that, during the summer, the Luftwaffe High Command was pressing harder than ever for the conversion of Dornier aircraft to E-5 standard. These aircraft were destined to operate against targets in the Mediterranean theatre. Operations over the Atlantic were allocated to the He 177. Consideration was also given to equipping Ju 88s with missiles to attack shipping off the coast of Britain.

In addition to the 40 Dornier bombers already on order a further 80 aircraft, each fitted with Kehl-III units were to be procured before the end of December 1942: the failure rate during test launches had been reduced to the point where the tactical deployment of these missiles was fast becoming a practical proposition.

In the 27 July 1942 meeting the Generalluftzeugmeister assigned the highest level of priority to both air-to-surface missiles with immediate effect. Only by doing this was was it possible to secure additional labour and materials at such short notice.

A decision could not be put off much longer. But they were agreed that further delays could not be tolerated: presupposing that it would be possible to organise a properly-functioning ground-support and supply organisation. Furthermore, it would be necessary to provide service and maintenance crews for the new, and still rather failure-prone, weapons technology in France and Italy.

From 1 August 1942, FX tests were transferred from EK 15 to EK 21, which had been formed for that purpose. In the meantime, the OKL intended operational training to be undergone in Cazeaux, France, although this was delayed with the withdrawal to Bordeaux. Training consisted of weekly courses for groups of six missile controllers at Peenemünde-West in release techniques. Six men practised the stand-off bombing technique at Anklam, using the Do 217. Nevertheless, by November it had become clear that, despite all of the efforts put into such training, the number of trained personnel was insufficient. Also, there were not enough missiles available for operations. Consequently, Dornier was surprised when it received a communication from the RLM to the effect that the thirty-four Do 217E-5s, then on order, were to be delivered. The 107 aircraft then in production in southern Germany were to be manufactured as conventional bomber aircraft.

Grabert and his crew, pictured in 1944, in front of their Do 217E-5. The aircraft was fitted with an auxiliary fuel tank, to increase the aircraft's range, under the port wing.

107

Do 217K-06 (RD+JE; serial No 4406) which was used in January 1943 to test three aerial torpedos at Gotenhafen.

Plans of the Do 217K-2 special operations aircraft which was equipped with rear guns and could carry two PC 1400 X (Fritz-X) stand-off bombs.

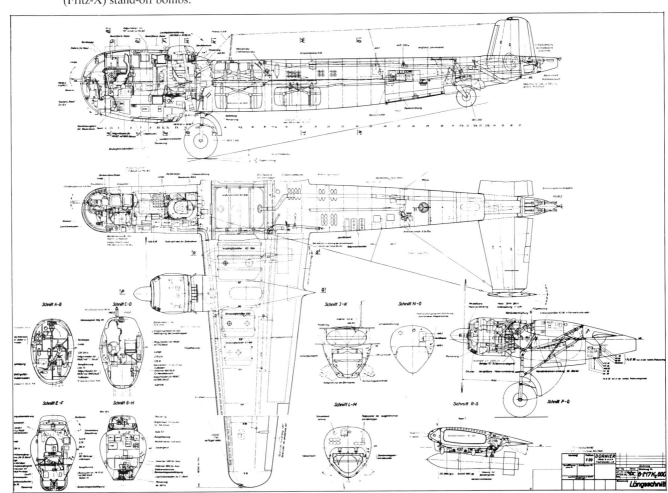

Do 217K-0 (serial No 4407) was stationed for a while at TWP Gotenhafen as an evaluation aircraft for testing LT 950 B aerial torpedos.

Do 217K-2 (serial No 4572) was equipped with an MG 81Z for operational evaluation.

To replace the Do 217, the RLM focussed its attention on the He 177A-3 and A-5 to be the long-range carrier aircraft for both missiles, specifically because the situation pertaining to the BMW 801 powerplant was so stressed that many Do 217s came off the Dornier assembly line without engines. Also, the ambitious undertaking to produce 450 more Hs 293s each month (bringing the total number produced to 900 units) was doomed to failure. The rapid retraining programme fell apart as the result of the Battle of Stalingrad. Part of Kampfgruppe 21 had to be transferred from EK 21 to take part in operations to supply the trapped 6th Army.

A small, residual command only remained at Schwäbisch-Hall to carry out trials with the improved FX bomb, instead of the original retraining programme. The remainder of Kampfgruppe 21 did not return to Schwäbisch-Hall until March 1943, when I/KG 40's conversion to the He 177 got under way rapidly. However, because of a variety of problems encountered with the new operational aircraft (not least, the tendency of the engines to catch fire!), Do 217s were delivered to replace the He 177.

The general situation at KG 100 did not look too good, either. On 20 February 1943, in the wake of the Stalingrad operation, the Gruppe HQ did not have any operational aircraft available. The same applied to I Gruppe. Only EK 15 (which had been integrated into II/KG 100 on 10 February 1943) could field twenty-one He 111s. A few days later, Erhard Milch focussed his attention again on the Do 217 and demanded a greater number of Do 217K-2s for missile operations in the near future. Practical testing of this version was to get under way as soon as it was possible to do so.

In March 1943 tests were in progress already with the special weapons equipment. At BMW, the possibilities of improving the performance of the Do 217K-2 were being examined. By replacing the BMW 801A-1 powerplant with the uprated BMW 801G, the engine specialists thought that the aircraft could possibly achieve easily an operating

ceiling of 7000 m, notwithstanding an all-up weight of 16.8 tonnes. Preliminary tests, using one, or two FX missiles, were carried out by the Luftwaffe at Peenemünde in June and July 1943. The results showed that with one engine only and carrying one PC 1400 X stand-off bomb, the Do 217 K-2 was still controllable.

In the meantime, units of II/KG 100 practised at Garz/Usedom and rehearsed missile operations on eight flight simulators. The Wiking Kampfgeschwader finally took charge of all of the Do 217s there, and completed the training programme itself. Meanwhile, III Gruppe flew the Do 217 from Schwäbisch-Hall and Giebelstadt. The chief pilot of what was formerly EK 21, now 4 Kampfgruppe of 13/KG 100 was there also. The amalgamation of EK 21 with II/KG 100 meant that there was no longer an experimental detachment available for the missile development programme.

Bombing trials, planned for the summer of 1943, were sacrificed in favour of satisfying rapidly operational requirements, and the missile controllers' training programme suffered accordingly. Under the leadership of Major Fritz Auffhammer (Geschwaderkommodore of KG 100), Majors Class and Zimmer (commanding officers of I and IV Gruppen), and Hauptleute Hetzel and Hollweck, numerous war games were conducted in preparation for the new operational section. Incidentally, Hollweck was the former and very reliable leader of EK 15; thanks to his initiative, the basic tests of the new weapons were brought to a speedy conclusion, despite the many drawbacks encountered on the way. At the same time, missile depots were established in places such as Kalamaki in Greece (for future attacks in the Aegean and East Mediterranean theatres); in Foggia, Italy (to cover the Sicily and Malta areas); and in Istres, Toulouse and Cognac, France (to support operations in the Atlantic theatre). Finally, a missile depot was set up in Trondheim, Norway to cover operations over the North Sea and the North Atlantic.

Because operational training rested solely with the Gruppe, the lack of expert training and teaching

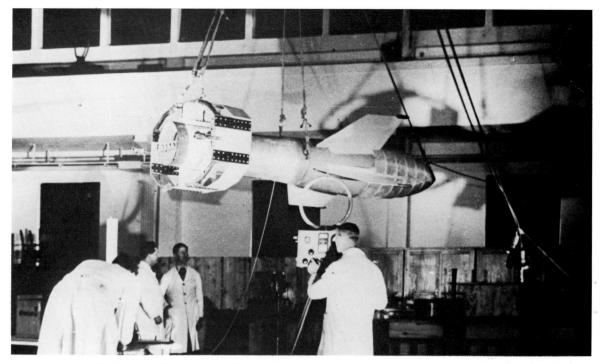

Testing the PC 1400 X stand-off bomb at the DVL research unit.

personnel became increasingly more noticeable from February 1943 onwards.

At a meeting of 14 May 1945, between representatives of the Director of Operational Requirements, the Technische Amt, the Experimental Establishment Command and the generals of the bomber units, agreement was reached quickly on the need to establish a new Experimental Detachment. This was to be formed within 13/KG 100 and designated EK 36. The unit would come under the command of the General of the bombers, but technically, it was responsible to the German Air Ministry. Major Baumbach proposed the immediate appointment of Hauptmann Hollweck as the commander of this future group. It was expected that the problems remaining with the ignition and remote-control systems would be resolved within a few weeks.

Together with the lack of Do 217s and He 177s, further delays occurred as the result of replacing the tubes in the receiver part of the remote-control unit, and of the attendant delivery problems. Mov-

ing the entire Hs 293 programme away from the endangered airspace of Berlin also resulted in occasional delays in the total number of deliveries. Nevertheless, according to figures published at that time, more than 1200 Hs 293s were ready for the coming operations. Also, Henschel produced a further 603 wire-guided gliding bombs.

By mid-May 1943, however, only 100 armed Fritz-X stand-off bombs were available. As a result of the extremely low production rate at the Rheinmetall factory, Fritz-X tests could not proceed as had been planned originally. Up until the end of October 1942 evaluation prototypes of the Fritz-X only were being delivered. Between August 1942 and May 1943, 135 devices were tested — of these, 50% were unsuccessful. Delays were caused also by the snail's pace at which the missiles were filled with explosives, and over-zealous pre-delivery inspections.

With eighty-five Do 217s available, an 'Advance Command' was formed, as part of KG 100, in the summer of 1943, and it was moved to Istres on

The tail guns of this Do 217K-2 consisted of two MG 81 Zwillings which did not prove to be effective.

Sketch depicting the Do 217K-3 which had a 67 m² wing area, and carried a special armament.

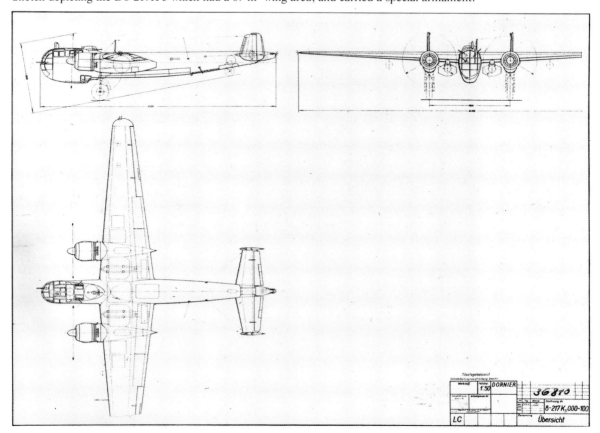

Major Bernhard Jope talking with his maintenance crew. In the background is an aircraft of II/KG 100 which was based at Toulouse.

5 July. A large part of III Gruppe followed seven days later. Operational units of II and III Gruppen transferred to Foggia, the preliminary launch base, on 17 July 1943. The first operational deployment of the PC 1400 X was planned to be part of a twilight raid of 21 July, involving an attack by three Do 217Ks on Allied shipping in the lanes between Augusta and Sicily. Following the failure of another operation, and after 23 July 1943, only the operational unit of III Gruppe remained in Foggia for a

short time. II/KG 100 had returned to its Group during the last days of July, when it reached the Cognac airfield from Istres with a total of forty-six Do 217s.

Further operations took place on 1, 10 and 20 August, against naval targets off Palermo, Syracuse and other ports in southern Italy. These were followed by Britain's commencing of *Operation Percussion*. From 23 August onwards, the 5th and 40th Escort Groups of the Royal Navy, with

Radio operator's station in the Do 217K. The seat has been removed to reveal the equipment.

cover from one battle cruiser at least, took part in a campaign to destroy all German submarines on their way to French ports. A first attack, on 23 August, led by He 177s, proved to be a failure, but two days later, a raid by twelve Do 217E-5s, loaded with Henschel glider bombs, ended with the first success. Under the leadership of Major Auffhammer and Hauptmann Molinnus, aircraft belonging to both the Staff Flight and III/KG 100 reached the Bay of Biscay. The British sloop *Landguard* suffered substantial damage starboard, caused by an Hs 293, while the *Bideford* and the *Waverney* both escaped with light damage only, caused by bombs falling at close quarters.

Following a pause of forty-eight hours, the 40th Escort Group, comprising two destroyers and three small sloops, was the target of a further missile attack. At approximately 14.15 hr, the Do 217E-5s reached the Allied anti-submarine unit. The Germans' first move was to divide themselves into three groups, in order to disperse enemy

MG 131 on its rotating ring and WL 131 anti-friction carriage.

114

An MG 81 mounted in the side window of a Do 217K-2.

defensive fire. Their first victim was the sloop *Egret*. No fewer than seven Hs 293 A-1 glider bombs were aimed at the *Egret*. Its guns were able to destroy the first bomb before it reached its goal, and the following five bombs fell into the sea. However, the seventh reached its goal to devastating effect. A direct hit on the munitions store caused a massive explosion — not one of her British crew survived.

The result of the Germans' concerted efforts, during which they did not suffer any losses, was the withdrawal of the Allied anti-submarine force to the Atlantic, immediately following a direct hit on the Canadian destroyer *Athabascan*. Had another such operation been necessary within a short period of time, the guided-missile squadrons would have been faced with tremendous problems. Particularly

troublesome was the continuing shortage of Do 217 special operations aircraft, required by KG 2 and KG 40 to replace the heavy losses incurred during previous operations. However, the squadrons waited, almost in vain, for larger aircraft, such as the Do 217K-2.

At that time Henschel, together with the testing units, was working intensively on the problems of adapting steered glider bombs to wire guidance, basing its work on the assumption that interference by enemy radio waves could be expected in the very near future. It was decided that, in order to test the EK 36, six Do 217s and He 177s should be fitted with wire-guidance equipment. The engineers applied themselves to the job of improving the wire-guidance system for the Henschel bombs which were to be launched from the He 177A-3. Similar equipment was being developed for the Fw 200 and Ju 290. The transmission unit for the wire-guidance system was given the code-name 'Duisburg-Dortmund', while the entire system was code-named 'Düren-Detmold'.

It had been presumed that Allied reconnaissance had discovered the whereabouts of the missile depots, the launching posts for missile operations, and the experimental and test centres involved in the development of new guided missiles. According to a comprehensive report, the possibility of reconnaissance raids by commando troops, or airborne attacks could no longer be ruled out. Should this occur, a back-up station and depot were established in Jesau, eastern Prussia, to enable the continuation tests.

In the Mediterranean theatre, the focal point of events during late summer was the entire airspace of southern Italy. After the armistice between the Italians and the Allied nations on 3 September 1943, and the landing of heavy, motorized units at Salerno and in the Gulf of Taranto area, KG 100 carried out fourteen missile attacks against naval units and convoys.

Following the official armistice announcement by General Eisenhower on 8 September 1943, most of the Italian Navy's personnel tried to go over to the

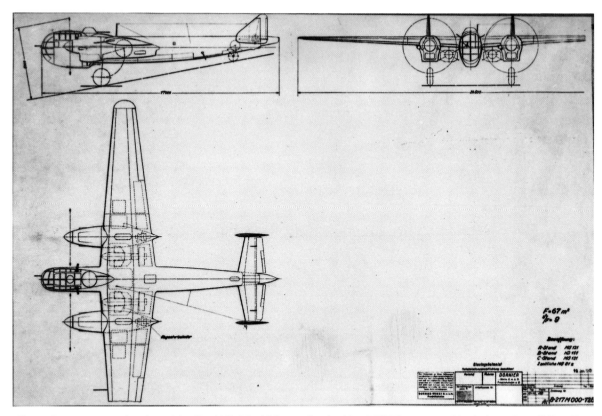

General arrangement drawing of the Do 217M-8 which was fitted with a TK II booster and had triangular tail fins. Two aircraft only of this variant were manufactured.

Allies and head towards Malta. The result was what proved to be the most successful missile attacks carried out so far by the Germans. Early in the afternoon of 9 September, eleven Do 217s attacked and put out of action the modern battleship *Roma* which was sailing in a convoy west of the Strait of

The Do 217M-8's powerplant, which consisted of a DB 603 and a TK II booster.

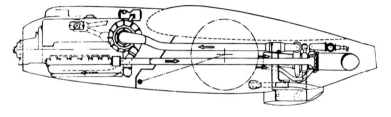

Bonifacio, between Sardinia and Corsica. Two Fritz-X missiles punctured the ship's armour, fire broke out and the ship sank, following an explosion in the ammunition store. A short while later, a second wave of seven Do 217Ks scored a direct hit on the *Roma*'s sister ship which, due to flooding, was forced to reduce her speed substantially.

On 11 September 1943, III/KG 100, having been transferred from Cognac to Istres, carried out a missile attack over the Gulf of Salerno where the American cruisers the *USS Philadelphia*, which had suffered slight damage following a near miss, and the *USS Savannah* were operating. Between 9 and 30 September, three daylight and six night raids were carried out by twenty-eight Do 217s of KG 100. The most successful raid took place on 13 September, hits being scored on the cruiser *USS Savannah* and on *HMS Uganda*. Two Allied destroyers were also damaged. The hospital ship *Newfoundland* was also hit inadvertently and sank with a great loss of life. The price of this action was the loss of four experienced crews from II/KG 100, together with two Do 217E-5s and two Do 217K-2s.

Attacks using the Fritz-X resulted in the sinking of a number of freighters, and an attack against the British battleship *HMS Warspite*, on 16 September 1943, resulted in a direct hit on her stern section. Another PC 1400 X scored a hit on the *Warspite*'s sister ship, *HMS Valiant*, which was operating in the vicinity. Allied fighters (superior in numbers to German aircraft) took their toll in battles over southern Italy: two Do 215E-2s and one Do 217K-2 failed to return to their bases. At the end of September, crews from the Wiking Geschwader sank two armoured landing craft, LST 79 and 2231, in Ajaccio harbour.

Increasing losses to enemy fighter action, however, meant that missile attack operations were carried out at dawn, or at night. During one of these attacks, the British freighter *Fort Fitzgerald* was sunk by an Hs 293 A-1. A further three merchant ships, travelling in convoy, also were hit. Together with the loss of Hauptmann Molinnus and his crew (who were killed when their aircraft crash-landed at Istres), four Dornier bombers were lost. During this stage of operations, a number of gliding bombs crashed as the result of either control failure, or poor maintenance. Furthermore, supplies of the Hs 293 began to dry up, and the same applied to the deliveries of Do 217K-2s. Notwithstanding, the Chief of Staff (Operations) having pressed hard for the delivery of 150 wing sets for the conversion of the Do 217K-1, the situation remained the same.

At a development meeting of 12 October 1943 the, decision was made not to produce any more Do 217/Kehl aircraft, because its engines were needed more urgently to equip the Fw 190. In addition, giving the aircraft a greater wing area would have resulted with extra work and effort.

So that the supply of Do 217s to KG 2 would not be jeopardized, Oberstleutnant Peltz argued very strongly against the production of the Do 217K-2, and demanded more Do 217E-4 aircraft instead. At a critical meeting which took place on 25 October 1943, a tribute was paid to those missile squadrons which were operating in the Mediterranean theatre. An increasing number of Do 217s were being shot down, especially in the skies above the Allied beachheads, which were ruled by enemy fighters. Following a number of successful night raids over the Aegean Sea, during which a total of forty gliding bombs were launched from twenty-two Do 217s, the He 177 was sent to bolster operations against Allied convoys. On 29 December 1943, Do 217 bombers were being operated by 5 and 6 Staffeln of the second Gruppe, 7/KG 100, and some sections of the Wiking Geschwader.

At the beginning of 1944, the first Do 217K-3s, modified versions of the Do 217M-1, rolled off the Dornier assembly line. Due solely to a limited production capacity, only a very small number of the Do 217M-11, intended as the new standard version for missile operations, left the factory.

On 22 January 1944, and coincidental with the conversion phase to the new Dornier aircraft, new landing operations were in progress at Anzio and Nettuno, south of Rome. More than 250 vessels were deployed to land the American 6th Army, which suffered heavy casualties during the early stages of the landing. In addition to the Do 217s of II/KG 100, the Luftwaffe sent the Ju 88s, He 111s and He 177s of KG 1, 26 and 40 into battle. Between 23 January and 1 March 1944, Dornier bombers carried out twelve missile attacks against Allied shipping massed off the Anzio and Nettuno beaches. Because of the Allies' air superiority, most of these raids (including one on 24 January 1944 involving seven Do 217s and four He 177s) were carried out under the cover of darkness.

On returning from a 24 January raid, crews reported that the destroyer *HMS Janus* had been sunk and that hits had been made on another destroyer, *HMS Jervis*. A Do 217E-5 of 4/KG 100

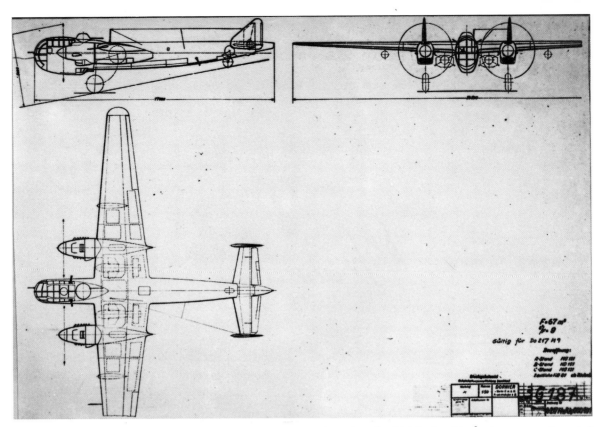

General arrangement drawing of the Do 217M-9 special operations aircraft which had a 67 m² wing area, and carried MG 151/20 armament. Below: Side view of the Do 217M-9, which could be adapted to carry Fritz-X and Hs 293 stores.

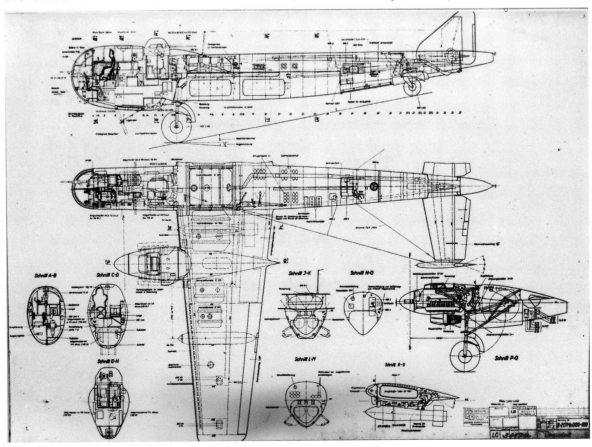

Prototype of the Do 217M-9, pictured at Flensburg in 1945.

had been damaged by an enemy night fighter, and had crashed not far from Rome. The cruiser *HMS Spartan* and a Liberty ship were both sunk in the lanes outside the landing bay. During these operations the effectiveness of jamming was experienced. Consequently, the supply of 200 Hs 293 wire-guided missiles was given high priority, so that missile attacks would not be rendered ineffective because of this jamming.

During dusk raids on 7 and 12 February, experienced crews of II/KG 100 attacked a supply ship and an armoured landing craft, in spite of Spitfire

This Do 217M-11 crashed in northern France in the summer of 1944 while returning from a bombing operation over southern France.

fighter defence. Including a destroyer that was damaged on 16 February, and the three merchantmen, twelve Luftwaffe raids against shipping off the Anzio and Nettuno beaches resulted in the loss of eighteen Allied ships, either sunk or so badly damaged that they were out of commission for several months. The failure rate of the Hs 293 also diminished, and, after the installation of more durable tubes, it finally dropped to 25%. In April 1943, during raids on some large Allied convoys off Cape Tenes and the North African coast, two Do 217s crashed as the result of technical problems.

German aircrew were beginning to suffer in two ways: first, by losing many good crews and comrades; second, as the result of the declining operational strength of their squadrons. The supply of Do 217s was also very poor. Lacking engines, more than 210 Dornier bombers were dispersed to a number of airfields. This deplorable state of affairs was raised at a meeting of the Rüstungsstab (Armaments Staff) on 14 January 1944, after which they wanted to discipline the manufacturer for not having fulfilled the delivery quota of aircraft ordered. Neither had the many skilled workers that had been requested materialized. Forty wing sets only for the Do 217M-11 could be converted by Dornier.

So much for the supply situation and the first missile operations in the Mediterranean.

A comprehensive report issued by Karlshagen Erprobungsstelle (Experimental Establishment) covered all aspects of Fritz-X and Hs 293 operations between 25 August 1943 and 30 April 1944.

General arrangement drawing of the Do 217M-11 which carried a PC 1400 X underneath its modified fuselage centre section.

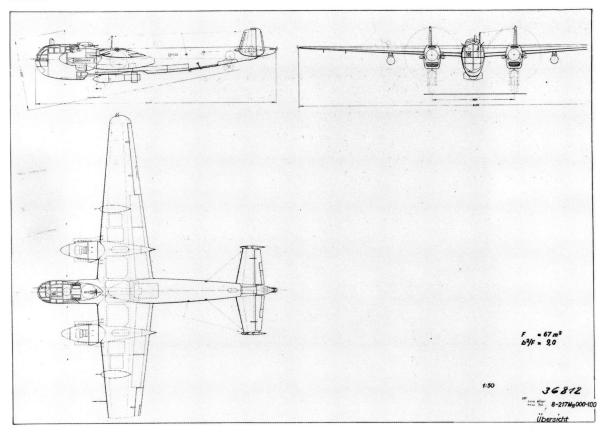

A total of sixty-five missile operations had been carried out, using a total of 487 aircraft, over southern England, the Bay of Biscay and the Mediterranean. 137 aircraft (27.6%) had returned before completing their missions: twenty-nine aircraft (21.6%) suffered engine and technical problems, and in ten of these cases the missile equipment was non-operational. Because of unfavourable tactical conditions over the target area a force of ninety-two Do 217s and He 177s failed to deliver their attacks. Three crews only released their missiles, jettisoning them in the face of heavy flak and enemy fighter attacks. 313 aircraft (64.4% of the original main force) reached the target area. Of these, forty-eight were lost, as the result of one reason or another, between taking off and landing. KG 100 alone lost 123 aircrew.

In that nine-month period, a combined total of 500 PC 1400 X and Hs 293 missiles had been delivered: 100 of them went out of control, and a further forty-six were brought back, unfired. Of the 319 missiles launched, 215 only were 'live', and with these the bomb controllers succeeded in scoring sixty-six direct hits and forty near misses, resulting with targets being damaged effectively.

Included in this 49.3% success rate was the sinking of a modern battleship, two cruisers, ten destroyers, a flak ship, three armoured landing craft, numerous smaller vessels and 76,000 tons of merchant shipping. A further four battleships, six cruisers, twelve destroyers and twenty-nine merchant ships totalling 215,000 tons were either damaged, or hit badly. Additionally, the breakwater areas in the harbours of Messina and Ajaccio, and a big fuel dump near Anzio-Nettuno were attacked successfully. Roughly equal percentages of Hs 293A-1 and Fritz-X missiles were deployed, and one in every 6.25 drops, for both missile types, resulted in a direct hit. Nevertheless, at the beginning of April, KG 100 and its Do 217s was withdrawn from operations in the Mediterranean theatre.

Losses to a superior number of enemy fighter groups became intolerably high and, in order to refurbish the missile units, they had to be withdrawn temporarily from operational duty. During the Normandy landings, and later during the despairing raids carried out by Versuchskommando 200 (Trials Unit), missile attacks were revived, albeit for a short time only.

CHAPTER SEVEN
The Bomber with All-Round Vision

By January 1942 the development of the Do 217E's replacements, the K and M bombers with fully glazed cockpits, was in full swing. The two prototypes differed in their powerplants only.

Early in 1942, the new-style canopy was tested for watertightness, as was that of the Ju 288, at the Shipbuilding Institute in Hamburg. These tests involved loading the glass panelling with a water pressure corresponding to a speed of more than 700 km/h. A few only of the small glass panels failed as the result of inadequate mounting. All in all, the new cabin construction passed the test with flying colours.

As the prototype of the Do 217 having a canopy to give all-round vision, Dornier modified a Do 217 E-2 (c/n 2170521135), RH+EI, at Friedrichshafen, and this was to be ready for works evaluation by February 1942. However, as the result of structural problems, it rolled out only on 31 March of that year.

The Do 217K V1, powered by BMW 801A-1 engines initially, underwent basic testing in Löwental, after which it underwent flight tests at Rechlin during July and August 1943. Dornier used the first prototype to also improve the aircraft's flying characteristics. Dynamic pressure measurements were made in June 1943. In the meantime, the prototype, powered by two BMW 801 L-1 engines, was so designed that the control pressure was reduced substantially. In addition, a series of tests were carried out using a modified, tail-mounted brake parachute, to evaluate the dive-brake release equipment. Following trials with a changed BZA unit, activation of the dive brake was both simplified and improved at the same time.

At the end of April 1944, and before being re-equipped with more powerful engines, the Do 217 K V1 flew as part of the Do 335 research programme. Later, Dornier's management began to consider modifying the Do 217K V1 to become a high-speed courier aircraft. Together with the first prototype, an initial batch of ten 0-series aircraft were manufactured, of which the first four Do 217 K-0s were assigned the markings KE+JA to KE+JD. Subsequent aircraft carried the markings RD+JD to RD+JK.

A Do 217K-01 (serial No 4401) joined the K V1 aircraft at Rechlin for evaluation. Between 9 July and 28 August 1942, the first V-series aircraft had undergone diving trials, carrying BZA 1 equipment, and later underwent tests using Lotfe 7D and SD 70 ordnance. The Do 217K-01 also performed numerous diving test drops of the SD 70, specifically between July and December 1942. Further tests were carried out to perfect target location with the automatic pilot engaged. Gradual improvements in the cabin heating, the use of different heated panels and more powerful de-icing systems were the subjects of the second series of evaluation trials.

From the beginning of August 1942, a Do 217 K-02 (serial No 4402), KE+JB, was based at the Müritz Lake Experimental Establishment. Starting on 25 August 1942, several week-long tests were carried out with FT equipment which, in the meantime, had been augmented by the Siemens precision altimeter. A few Luftwaffe pilots took advantage of whatever opportunities the test schedule presented and flew the Do 217K. In addition to bombing and loading trials, and drop tests of different, special loads, one Do 217 K-0 at least, was flown operationally by KG 2 over the Western Front. On 15 May 1944, the tenth K-0-series aircraft, U5+MR, of 7/KG 2, fell victim to a night fighter and was shot down, crashing in flames over Yeovil in Somerset. All but one of the crew managed to escape by parachute. In the wreckage British specialists found four 500 kg bombs, MG 81 and 131 guns, and the remains of the FuG 10, 16, 101a and FuBl.2H equipment.

Nine aircraft were evaluated operationally, and performed a variety of other tasks also. Do 217 K-03 (KE+JC), for example, was used as a launch aircraft for the rocket-propelled DFS 228 high-altitude reconnaissance aircraft and the Me 328 fighter.

Dornier bomber versions with an all-round vision canopy

Type	Deployment
Do 217K V1	Evaluation prototype, heavy combat aircraft with all-round vision canopy, and BMW 801A powerplants
Do 217K-0	0-series heavy bomber, similar to Do 217KV1
Do 217K-1	Heavy bomber, no brake parachute; armed with MG 81 and MG 131
Do 217K-2	Special bomber, carrying a PC 1400X missile; same armament as the K-1 but with two MG 81Z tail-mounted guns
Do 217K-2/U1	Special bomber, Hs 293H under-fuselage attachment; otherwise the same as the K-2
Do 217K-2/U2	Special bomber equipped with FuG 203e for use with either the PC 1400X or Hs 293; otherwise, the same as the K-2
Do 217K-3	Special bomber equipped to carry the PC 1400X (intended for the K-2/U2)
Do 217M V1	Evaluation prototype, heavy bomber with all-round vision canopy, and a DB 603A powerplant
Do 217M-0	0-series heavy bomber, similar to the Do 217M V1
Do 217M-0/U1	Special bomber carrying Hs 293A; same armament as the Do 217M-0
Do 217M-1	Heavy, level- and dive-bomber, carrying the same defensive armament as the Do 217M-0
Do 217M-1/U1	Heavy, level- and dive-bomber equipped with a tail parachute and heavier armament
Do 217M-1/U2	Special bomber with simplified equipment for wire-guided missiles; otherwise the same as the Do 217 M-1
Do 217M-1/U5	High-altitude bomber, with a turbo-supercharger and the same missile-launching equipment as the Do 217 K-2/U1 (Hs 293H, stored in the fuselage)
Do 217M-2	Torpedo bomber, carrying three aerial torpedos; airframe and equipment the same as that on the Do 217M-1
Do 217M-3	Heavy bomber with a tail parachute, triangular planform, and HD 151 turret; otherwise, the same as the Do 217M-1

Type	Deployment
Do 217M-4	Special bomber with a TK 11 turbo-supercharger; a prototype only was built
Do 217M-5	Special bomber equipped with Hs 293A; otherwise, the same as the Do 217M-1
Do 217M-6	Not known
Do 217M-7	Not known
Do 217M-8	High-altitude bomber with a TK 11 turbo-supercharger, triangular planform, a 67 m^2 wing area, and the same armament as that of the Do 217M-3
Do 217M-9	Special bomber, similar to the M-8, but without the turbo-supercharger and triangular planform.
Do 217M-10	Special bomber, converted from the Do 217M-1 and given a new wing design (steel and wood construction)
Do 217M-11	Special bomber, carrying a PC 1400 X missile, and having standard wings and the same armament as the Do 217K-2

The development of the DFS 228 started with various high-altitude flights, during which Erich Klöckner took a DFS 54 to an altitude of 11,400 m. From 1940 onwards, a still higher performance aircraft was needed, and the development of a suitable, high-altitude reconnaissance aircraft as quickly as it was possible to do so, became a matter of importance. The result was the DFS 228 which, according to performance calculations, having a maximum all-up weight of 5500 kg, could reach a maximum speed of 865 km/h. At a gliding angle of 1:20, the aircraft's expected speed was approximately 610 km/h.

Initially, the DFS 228 was taken to its operational altitude by a Do 217K-03. Later, the development team decided to use a Do 217 with a greater surface area and equipped with a TK 11 exhaust turbo charger (turbo-supercharger). On its release from the launch aircraft, at an altitude of approximately 10,000 m, the pilot, who was seated in a pressure cabin, could switch to rocket drive and take the aircraft to an altitude of 25,000 m.

Using an 0-series Do 217 to launch the aircraft to an altitude of 4000 m tripled the flying time of the DFS 228. It took the K-03 the best part of eighteen minutes to reach an altitude of 4000 metres above sea level. The disadvantage of the system used,

The first 0-series aircraft (Do 217K-0), KE+JA, pictured during initial tests with Dornier.

A Do 217K-04 (KE+JD) armed with two MG 81s.

124

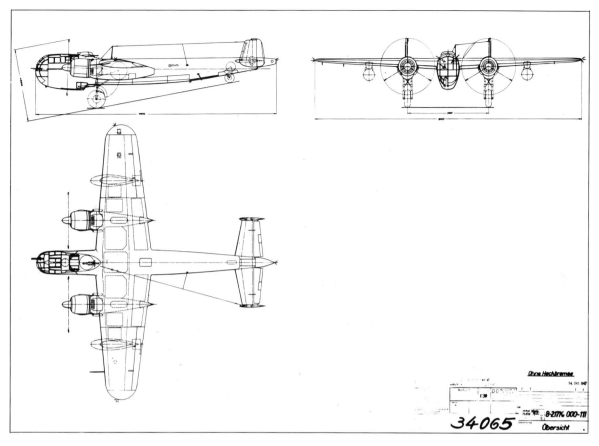

34065

General arrangement drawing of the future Do 217K-1 production model, dated 13 October 1942.

A Do 217K-1 (serial No 4452) pictured in France during the spring of 1943.

125

One of KG 2's operations aircraft, wearing a temporary protective paint scheme, and having had its Geschwader crest painted out.

which affected future planned operations, was that the coupling of the DFS to the Dornier led to an enormous increase in the Dornier's weight. It became obvious that the DFS 228 was not ready for live operations. Following the first prototype, (D-IBFQ), a further aircraft was in the process of being built during December 1942. Also, Schmetz at Griesheim, Darmstadt, was preparing ten 0-series, high-altitude aircraft. The Do 217 was also being tested as a launch aircraft for the small, general-purpose Me 328. The Me 328's roles ranged from that of a fighter; a ground attack, or reconnaissance aircraft; a high-speed bomber, to that of a suicide aircraft, if the need arose. The first trials took place using a Do 217E-4 (JT+EL). After clearing a few basic details, the tests were carried out with the close co-operation of DFS.

Initially, an investigation was made into the design of three fighter variations, all of which should have a flight-refuelling capability. The Me 328, which was first tested in Ainring, was flown by DFS in 1943, and later arrived at Hörsching.

Stability and performance tests, without the use of engines, were carried out at altitudes of between 3000 m and 6000 m. Subsequently, a vast number of towing tests were carried out using a Do 217 E-4.

Following the cancellation of the Me 328 fighter, work commenced on a high-speed bomber which was to be powered by between two and four pulse-jets. A Do 217K-0, RL+TY, was to be used as the host aircraft for the Me 328B. However, the Me 328B's actual performance (500 km/h) differed so drastically from that which had been calculated (800 km/h) that the Technische Amt in Berlin cancelled the aircraft. Thereafter, the fourth Do 217K-0 was used in a more conventional role, for undergoing tests as the prototype of the future Do 217K-1 bomber.

By mid-November 1942, the fifth Do 217K-0 was in production. From 1943, it was used almost exclusively for gunnery trials with the MG 81 Z and MG 131. The sixth Do 217K-0 aircraft was powered by two BMW 801A-2 engines, and was used to evaluate the Keil IV. Prior to being handed over

126

Layout of the cockpit of the Do 217K-1, dating from April 1943.

1 Blindfluggerätetafel
2 Gerätetafel vor Bedienbank
3 Bedienbank
4 Gerätetafel Spant 4 oben
5 Triebwerksgerätetafel
6 Sturzvisier Stuvi 5 B
7 Abwerfbarer Dachteil
8 Ladeklappenhandkuppelhebel
9 Abwurfhebel zu „7"

10 Notkompaß
11 Spant 4
12 Steuerschwenkarm (Normalstellung)
13 Steuerschwenkarm rechts ausgeschwenkt
14 Borduhr
15 Beleuchtungsdruckknopf zu „14"
16 Elektrischer Schalterkasten
17 Seitensteuerpedale
18 Führersitzunterbau

19 Funkpeilanzeigegerät
20 MG 81 Z
21 Lotfe 7D
22 Feststellhandschraube für Steuerschwenkarm
23 Bombenknopf BK XI
24 Sprechknopf Fu G 16
25 Richtungsgeber LRi 2
26 Abfeuerknopf (starre Schußwaffe)
27 Steuerverstellrad (Pedale)   T 407 L 135

Do 217 K-1
Besatzungsraum
Blick nach vorn

Stand vom April 1943
Inzwischen eingetretene Änderungen beachten
und dazu I. hinweisen

127

to EK 21 at Schwäbisch-Hall for operational evaluation with the PC 1400 X, the K-07 was used to evaluate aerial torpedos. RD+JF, particularly, was used for flight tests with new heating equipment for the 'special stores', which Dornier fitted in November 1942. Finally, the aircraft took part also in investigations to determine the optimum dropping conditions for the Fritz X. Tests with the PC 1400 X in January 1943 showed that to enabled the new guided weapon to be launched, it was necessary to reduce the aircraft's speed by extending the flaps and simultaneously cutting back the engine revs.

Do 217K-08 and K-09 were used by Dornier as development aircraft for the on-going K series. Following a month-long series of tests to evaluate a wide variety of brake parachutes, the tenth, and last, K-0 aircraft (serial No 4410) was transferred to Kampfschulgeschwader 3 in Italy, where it was used for training Luftwaffe aircrews in the use of the brake parachute. In addition to the Do 217K V1 and K-01, a Do 217K-1, CF+PO, was also allocated to an Experimental Establishment, and

was used for endurance testing of its BMW engines; as was TN+CI which, having larger wings, was used, between 30 January and 17 February 1943 for vibration measurements.

At this time, production of the Do 217K-1 was under way at Dornier's factory in Wismar, northern Germany. According to the manuals, the aircraft was a heavy bomber, and had a crew of four. Many types of armament could be fitted, taking into account the tactical requirements at that time. Dornier had chosen BMW 801L engines, generating 1560 hp take-off power, as the aircraft's powerplant which, according to the works specification, would provide a maximum speed of 430 km/h at ground level, and 520 km/h at the aircraft's operating ceiling of 5200 m with an average all-up weight. As it did in the preceding aircraft (specifically, RD+JC), the aircraft's defensive armament comprised an MG 81 Z (located in the A position) which was operated by a gunner/observer; while in the B and C positions, the radio operator and the flight engineer protected the rear with an MG 131 each.

The heavily armour-plated pilot's seat in the cockpit of a Do 217K-1. The observer sat to the pilot's right in a folding seat (BA).

Up to that time one production series only of K-1s had been produced with consecutive construction numbers. This series ran from serials Nos 4411 to 4500, of which the majority were stationed with units of KG 2 on the Western Front.

The shortage of BMW 801 engines resulted with the RLM terminating the K-1 programme in favour of that for the Do 217M-1. The so-called command unit, which engaged the booster switch, the ignition timing and the weak-rich mixture control automatically, made the BMW 801ML powerplant easy to operate. A few Do 217K-1s were also fitted with an independent, propeller-pitch adjustment unit, which many squadron commanders in the Holzhammer Geschwader had had fitted during late summer 1942. However, because the daylight glider bomb attacks were being abandoned to an ever-increasing extent in favour of level-flight, night bombing raids, this device became increasingly less important. The oil-pressure activated VDM propeller with electrical manual control had a diameter of 3.9 m; a 3.8 m diameter wooden propeller could be used as an alternative.

The standard, 2,165-l capacity fuel tank could be augmented by either one, or two fuselage tanks, each having a capacity of 750 l, or external tanks having a capacity of between 300 and 900 l. With an all-up weight of 15 to 16.5 tonnes, the Do 217K-1 needed 850 to 1100 m to get airborne. Taking off from a grass strip, an altitude of 20 m was reached after 1500 m and from a concrete runway, after 1300 m. With an average weight of 12.7 tonnes, the bomber approached the target at 510 kmph, at an altitude of 5200 m. However, with two external auxiliary fuel tanks, its speed dropped by approximately 4.5%, and by 6% with two externally mounted bombs. The fire-extinguishing equipment caused an additional 7% speed reduction in low-level flight, and 9% when flying at its operational ceiling.

It is known that a number of Do 217K-1s were converted to E-4 standard. According to C Amt's programme, forty-one Do 217s, powered by BMW 801 engines, were to be produced each month between 6 July 1941 and October 1942, and fifty-eight per month between September 1942 and

From 1943, low-level flying became one of the focal points of KG 2's training programme on the Western Front.

March 1944, in the Wismar and Oberpfaffenhofen factories. Most of these bomber aircraft were assigned to KG 2. The first of them, U5+EM (serial No 4478), operated by 4/KG 2, fell victim to a vastly superior RAF Mosquito night fighter.

The policy of increasing the operational performances of aircraft applied also to the Do 217K-1. During late summer 1943, the first tests using a production aircraft fitted with an auxiliary GM 1 had been completed. The results showed that at 100 g/sec, the GM 1 boosted the K-1's maximum speed by 84 km/h at an altitude of 8000 m. With 50 g/sec only, the aircraft's operating ceiling could be extended easily from 8400 to 9800 m. However, because the failure rate of the GM 1 was very high and because attention was being focussed on other versions of the Do 217, use of this equipment never got beyond the testing stage.

The Do 217K-1 was succeeded by the K-2, which was a bomber aircraft, having a wing area of 67 m^2 to give an improved high-altitude performance. The Do 217K-2 (the first of which were converted K-1 aircraft), was used almost exclusively for Fritz-X missile operations in the Mediterranean theatre,

being equipped with Kehl for just that purpose. The aircraft operated by KG 100 were fitted with auxiliary fuel tanks also, which were mounted in the bomb bay, using the R14 and R17 equipment packs used on other Do 217s.

The K-1's defensive armament consisted usually of mobile guns only. MG 81Zs were mounted in gun positions, one each on the port and starboard sides of the cockpit, and one in the fuselage. A DL 131/1C rotating turret was mounted in the B position, and an MG 131, in a WL 131/1 cylindrical carriage, in the C position. The production aircraft of both versions of the Do 217K were also armed with two fixed MG 81Zs, in the tail section. Each barrel was supplied with 350 rounds of ammunition. The guns were aimed by the use of an RF 1 rear-view telescope, mounted in the forward section of the jettisonable cockpit canopy, left of the pilot. The firing buttons for the additional tail guns could be activated by either the pilot, or the rear gunner. In an emergency (for example, if one of the BMW 801 engines failed), the rear fuselage fairing and the tail gun could be jettisoned (as they could when dive braking) by activating a special release winch.

A Do 217K-1 (serial No 4425) on a training flight in adverse weather conditions.

130

Other than a few unimportant details, the armament and equipment of the K-2 was the same as those in the K-1.

Most of the Do 217K-2s were assigned to Kampfgeschwader 100, to be used in raids against enemy shipping, and operating over a range of between 800 and 1100 km, on average, depending upon the load carried. Following the K-2, the Do 217E-5 was the second version to be fitted with remote-control equipment as standard for missile operations. This equipment consisted of an FuG 203 (Kehl) transmitter, and an FuG 230 (Strassburg) receiver, used to transmit control signals to the missile's rudder.

There were five versions of the Kehl equipment, designated FuG 203a to FuG 203e, which all differed in their use. Using the FuG 203a (Kehl I), one PC 1400 X missile only could be guided; using the FuG 203b (Kehl III), one Henschel gliding bomb only could be steered towards the target. The designation Kehl IV covered three versions of the FuG 203, the first of which, the FuG 203c, could be used to control either Fritz-X, or Hs 293 bombs. Using the FuG 203d, a maximum of four missiles could be controlled. The FuG 203e was developed for operations involving greater numbers of PC 1400X and Hs 293 missiles. Kehl equipment was installed in forty Fw 200s, 107 He 177s, and in a combined total of 140 E, K and M versions of the Do 217.

The Do 217K-2 could carry two Fritz-Xs only on inner wing pylons. Evaluation tests to investigate the performance of this special bomber version were performed, using either one, or two PC 1400 X bombs, at West Peenemünde in June 1943. In July, additional tests of the aircraft's performance in single-engined flight were carried out; the results showed that, carrying one Fritz-X only, it was possible for the aircraft to maintain its operating ceiling, without any significant alteration to its handling characteristics.

To provide a broader performance spectrum for the Do 217K-2 and K-3 in the event of an emergency, BMW increased its efforts to have the BMW 801MG available for the production of these aircraft. With a weapon load comprising two Fritz-X bombs, and an all-up weight of 16.8 tonnes,

131

This aircraft (serial No 4586) was operated by 7/KG 2 on the Western Front. Although it was intended for night operations, flame retarders were not installed.

An aircraft of II/KG 2 pictured on a Dutch air-field at the beginning of 1943.

Dornier Works Friedrichshafen
Aircraft Programme No. 222/2 (status as of 1 November 1942)

Type	No of Engines	Version	Serial No.	Status	Comments
Do 217E-1	2 BMW 801A	V 12	0012	—	In accordance with RLM directive, transferred 29.10.1942 to DW Ausbildungswesen (training unit). Aileron trials completed
Do 217V2	2 DB 601E	V2	688	—	Scrapped/released for spares utilization for DW trials 29.10.1942, in accordance with RLM directive
Do 217V4	2 Jumo 211B	V4	690	On test	Rapid-release engines. Preparation for drop tests completed. 5-panel parachute made up
Do 217K	2 BMW 801	KV1	1135	On test	Test of semi-rigid brake chute and use of dive-brake release system
Do 217M	2 DB 603	M-02	1242	On test	DW testing of increased wing area and enlarged empannage
Do 217P	2 DB 603	PV1	1229	On test	High-altitude reconnaissance version, with DB 605 booster in flight testing
Do 217P	2 DB 603	PV2	0024	On test	High-altitude reconnaissance version with DB 605 booster, to be delivered to Daimler-Benz following short test programme at DW.
Do 217P	2 DB 603	PV3	0025	On test	High-altitude reconnaissance version of Do 217PV1
Do 217P	2 DB 603	PV4	0026	In production	High-altitude reconnaissance version of Do 217PV1
Do 217P	2 DB 603	PV5	0027	In production	High-altitude reconnaissance version of Do 217PV1
Do 217P	2 DB 603	PV6	0028	In production	High-altitude reconnaissance version of Do 217PV1
Do 217R	2 BMW 801	RV1	0029	On test	Dive-brake testing
Do 217R	2 BMW 801	RV2	0030	On test	Dive-brake testing
Do 217R	2 BMW 801	RV3	0031	In production	Dive-brake testing
Do 217R	2 DB 603	RV4	0032	—	Schedule not specified at that time. Dive-brake testing
Do 217A	2 DB 601F	—	2704	On test	Conversion to troop transport. Delivered to Southern Command Centre 30.12.1942
Do 217E-1	2 BMW 801	—	0042	On test	Endurance testing of flame-retarder unit (Do 217J)
Do 217E-2	2 BMW 801	—	1151	On test	Aerial torpedo evaluation trials, and adapted accordingly
Do 217E-2	2 BMW 801	—	1185	On test	Conversion to Hs 294 carrier. Delivered to Landsberg 21.10.1942
Do 217E-2	2 BMW 801	—	1212	On test	To be handed over to RLM following dive-brake release unit testing
Do 217E-2	2 BMW 801	—	1214	On test	Endurance testing of flame-retarder unit (Do 217Z) with BMW 801 engines
Do 217E-2	2 BMW 801	—	1220	On test	Development aircraft for evaluation of on-going production aircraft modifications
Do 217E-2	2 BMW 801	—	1221	On test	In-flight vibration measurements with Do 217P wing
Do 217E-2	2 BMW 801	—	1226	On test	Drop tests with external auxiliary fuel tanks (300-l and 1260-l capacity)
Do 217J	2 BMW 801L	J-1/U2	1364	On test	Night fighter with additional armament; 4 x MG 151s, oblique- and upward-firing, jettisonable from bomb bay
Do 217J	2 BMW 801L	J-1/U1	1365	On test	Night fighter with 4 x MG 151 forward-mounted, fixed guns. Delivered to Tarnewitz 14.10.1942
Do 217J	2 BMW 801L	J-1/U2	1366	In production	Night fighter version, as serial No 1364, but with semi-rigid brake parachute
Do 217J	2 BMW 801L	J-1/U2/U4	1372	In production	Night fighter with six fixed MG 151s
Do 217J	2 BMW 801L	J-1/U4	1370	In production	Semi-rigid brake parachute added for field evaluation
Do 217J	2 BMW 801L	J-1/U4	1371	In production	Semi-rigid brake parachute added for field evaluation
Do 217N	2 DB 603A-1	N-1/U2	1403	In production	Night fighter with four forward-mounted, fixed MG 151s, and aerodynamic improvements
Do 217N	2 DB 603A-1	N-1/U2	1409	In production	Night fighter version as serial No 1403, modified to carry Peil G VI with APZ6
Do 217N	2 DB 603A-1	N-1	1404	On test	Switchable wing tip heating. Completed and released for series production
Do 217N	2 DB 603A-1	N-1	1405	In production	To be delivered 3.11.1942 for tests at Rechlin Experimental Establishment
Do 217N	2 DB 603A-1	N-1	1408	On test	Development aircraft. Replacement for Do 217J, serial No 1350
Do 217K	2 BMW 801	K-03	1233	In production	New version of switch for dive-brake release unit. (Assigned to Rechlin for tests)
Do 217K	2 BMW 801	—	4405	In production	Weapons testing aircraft for Tarnemünde, incorporating cabin-mounted MG 81Z and standard fittings

Type	No of Engines	Version	Serial No.	Status	Comments
Do 217K	2 BMW 801	—	4406	In production	Conversion to Kehl IV
Do 217K	2 BMW 801	—	4407	In production	Torpedo-carrying test aircraft (3 mechanical torpedos) for Experimental Establishments
Do 217K	2 BMW 801	—	4410	In production	Installation of parachute brake
Do 217E	2 BMW 801A-2	—	4272	In production	'Watering-can' (MG 81Z pod) installation for Soesterberg, air gunnery trials
Do 217E	2 BMW 801A-2	—	4320	In production	See data for serial No 4272
Do 217E	2 BMW 801A-2	—	5524	In production	See data for serial No 4272

an operational ceiling of 7000 m for the aircraft was the ultimate aim. One Do 217 K-2, at least, was fitted with a remote-control unit (in August 1943) for wire-guided missiles. Basically, this involved simplifying the transmitter by dispensing with the high-frequency module. The control unit consisted of an FuG 207 (Dortmund) transmitter and an FuG 237 (Duisburg) receiver and both were equally compatible with the control of Fritz-X and Hs 293 missiles. More simple equipment, the Düren-Detmold (comprising an FuG 208 transmitter and an FuG 238 receiver), was developed and installed, albeit in prototype form, in a Do 217K-2 during late summer 1943. Compared with its predecessors, the equipment was to be used in conjunction with the Fritz-X only.

The first few K-2 aircraft with larger wing areas started to arrive at training and experimental establishments in the spring of 1943. However, heavy landings resulted in a number of problems with their landing gear. Other Do 217s either suffered engine problems, or were lost for other, unknown reasons (for example, serial No 4559 which crashed on 24 June 1943).

By mid-March 1943, two topics were being discussed hotly; offensive operations over the Mediterranean, and the use of the gliding bomb against Allied four-engined aircraft. Tactical studies, together with a search for the method of of installing the Hs 293 H were under way at the Air Ministry, at Henschel and at Dornier.

Kampfgeschwader 100 had to relinquish three of its recently-delivered Do 217K-2s which were to be converted to three prototypes. In June and July

1943 these special combat aircraft were ferried from Giebelstadt to Friedrichshafen for conversion. Having been converted to carry the Hs 293H, the aircraft were transferred, with the designation Do 217K-2/U1, to the Peenemünde Experimental Establishment, where they were assigned the serial numbers 4541, 4558 and 4570, in readiness for tactical evaluations. Do 217Es and Ks underwent realistic bombing trials also, at Rechlin and similar locations. Following Germany's withdrawal from Foggia, the testing of all types of thick-walled bombs was transferred, in the autumn of 1943, to the rocky Chausses du Larzac near Millan in the South of France.

In addition to trials with SD 250 and SD 500 ordnance, the casing strengths of both the SE 500 and SC 250 JA were tested thoroughly during a series of high- and low-level drops, and the quality of their steel was examined closely. Apart from an He 111H-11 (GL+ET, which crashed on 10 November 1943), and aircraft GL+EJ (which replaced it), Hauptmann Weldelt flew the Ju 88. It was not until October 1943 that a Do 217K from the VOH Research Group, arrived in the South of France, having been flown there by Hauptmann Spremberg.

Subsequent to the Do 217K-2 special-combat aircraft (of which relatively few were stationed with Kampfgeschwader 2), which were not fitted with Kehl equipment, a third version of K-series aircraft appeared in Dornier's production programme in 1943. The K-3 was also a guided-weapons carrier, and Dornier had stated that it would be possible to manufacture and equip this aircraft by July

Trenkle and his crew standing in front of a Do 217K-1 (serial No 4518) in Bordeaux. The aircraft had been intended for delivery to Japan.

The Do 217K-1 which was used by Field Marshal Kesselring for travelling to southern Italy.

One of the three Do 217Hs which were tested with DB 603 engines.

1943. By that time, one of the first few conversion aircraft was operational and configured to carry Fritz-X and Henschel missiles. The K-3 programme involved the conversion of forty Do 217M-1 bombers, equipped with Kehl III. The conversion was to be done at Dornier's factory in northern Germany, where larger, 67 m^2 wings were to be fitted also.

Not enough Do 217K-1s were available for operations, and it was necessary to convert Do 217M-1 bombers to solve this problem. This is also referred to in Part 0, General Instructions of the K-3's manual. A decision was made to convert fifty Do 217K-1s to K-2 standard, in Friedrichshafen. The aircraft were to be equipped with guided weapons and Kehl IV equipment.

General arrangement drawing of the Do 217M-1, dated 24 September 1943. An MG 131 replaced the MG 81Z of earlier Do 217 variants.

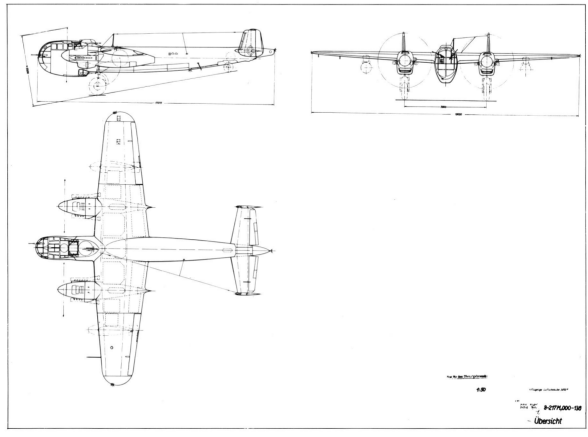

By August 1943, at Wismar, work on an additional Do 217K-3 prototype, with Kehl IV equipment, had not been completed because of a delay in the delivery of a Fritz-X mock-up from Schwäbisch-Hall; a wooden mock-up of the Hs 293 had to be made also. The fuel jettisoning equipment of the K-2 was omitted on the K-3. Minor changes were made to the aircraft's armament, and the heating equipment for the Hs 293 and the PC 1400X guided weapons, which could be used interchangeably, had also to be modified.

On 6 August 1943, it was agreed between the German Air Ministry and Dornier that forty K-3 special combat aircraft were to be manufactured. It had been decided to manufacture these aircraft without an ETC-fuselage attachment. Instead, standard R20 equipment, comprising jettisonable auxiliary tanks mounted under both wings, was incorporated on production aircraft. By the beginning of December 1943, however, the plan for twenty Do 217K-3s to be configured to carry a single, ventrally-mounted Hs 293 had won ground. The remaining twenty aircraft were to be equipped with underwing attachments only. In the end, a few K-3s only were produced with fuselage attachments, and these aircraft were designated Do 217 K-3/U1s.

The reduction in the fuel capacity of the Do 217 M-11, caused by eliminating the tank under the aircraft's fuselage, resulted with a few only of these special combat aircraft being used in operations against short-range targets. Further changes to the Do 217K-2 (such as the installation of an MG 131, instead of the usual MG 81Z in the A position) did not affect the aircraft's total weight.

The new Do 217K-3s (serial Nos 4701 to 4740) flew together with K-2s often, and, in 1944, with Do 217 E-5 special operations aircraft over the west Mediterranean, the Channel and southern England. In spite of the aircrafts' superb equipment, these actions against superior Allied air power were very risky. The first Do 217K-3, belonging to the 9/KG 100, was lost on 20 October 1943, when Lt Kemmer and his crew crashed in

serial No 4704, in the vicinity of Montelimar. Another K-3 of 9 Staffel met its fate in a lonely Devon field, in the early morning of 30 April 1944.

A special bomber, 6N+IT (formerly RO+YD, serial No 4716), carried more defensive armament: together with two MG 131s, in the B and C positions, and MG 81Zs in the side windows, an additional MG 81Z, and an MG 8I1 were mounted in the aircraft's nose. Nevertheless, after taking off from Vannes, for a raid against Plymouth, the aircraft was hit and burst into flames and, after the captain tried vainly to evade the searchlights, it was lost irrevocably. The crew, with the exception of the observer, Unteroffizier Erich Katzenberger, managed to parachute to safety.

The main burden of the battle over southern England and the Channel was borne by the Do 217 K-1, which succeeded the Do 217E-4 in the summer of 1943 (following an adjustment adaptation period of several months' duration), when it was assigned to KG 2 and KG 40. A short time later, the new Do 217M-1 was supplied also in greater numbers.

According to RLM plans, production of the M model, which was powered by two DB 601A-1s, was due to commence with two aircraft in May 1942, followed by approximately ten Do 217M-1s in the summer 1942. By March 1943, a production target of forty-two aircraft per month was to be achieved. Apart from its increased performance, another convincing argument for the use of the Daimler-Benz engine was the then-current bottleneck in the production of the BMW 801A, which had arisen during its prioritized mounting in the Fw 190A. Therefore, the DB 603A-1 powerplant was chosen for the aircraft; however, this had not been tested fully, consequently a number of technical problems arose. It was intended that the first three Do 217Hs (a glider-bomber for land operations, having a Do 217E-1 airframe) should be used for the endurance testing of the powerplant. From the beginning, considerable delays were experienced in the building of the first prototypes. Flight tests had been planned originally for December 1940;

A view of the crew area on a Do 217M-1, dated April 1943.

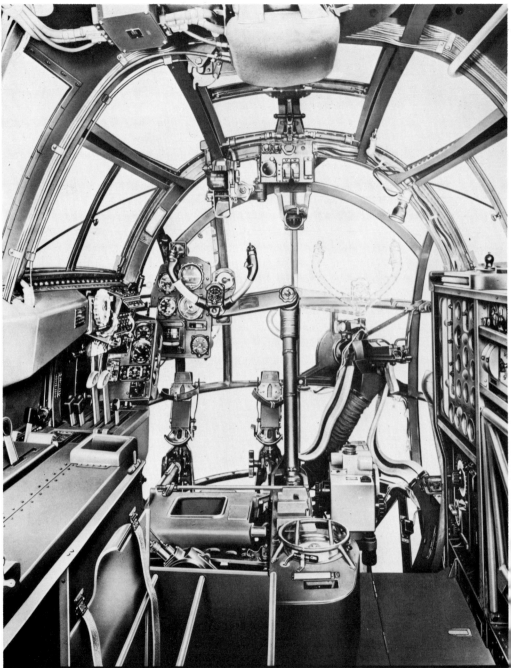

1 Blindfluggerätetafel	10 Notkompaß	19 Funkpeilanzeigegerät
2 Gerätetafel vor Bedienbank	11 Spant 4	20 MG 81 Z
3 Bedienbank	12 Steuerschwenkarm (Normalstellung)	21 Lotfe 7D
4 Gerätetafel Spant 4 oben	13 Steuerschwenkarm rechts ausgeschwenkt	22 Feststellhandschraube für Steuerschwenkarm
5 Triebwerksgerätetafel	14 Borduhr	23 Bombenknopf BK XI
6 Sturzvisier Stuvi 5 B	15 Beleuchtungsdruckknopf zu „14"	24 Sprechknopf Fu G 16
7 Abwerfbarer Dachteil	16 Elektrischer Schalterkasten	25 Richtungsgeber LRi 2
8 Ladeklappenhandkuppelhebel	17 Seitensteuerpedale	26 Abfeuerknopf (starre Schußwaffe)
9 Abwurfhebel zu „7"	18 Führersitzunterbau	27 Steuerverstellrad (Pedale)

T 407 L 137

Do 217 M-1
Besatzungsraum
Blick nach vorn

Stand vom April 1943
Inzwischen eingetretene Änderungen beachten
und darauf hinweisen

however, these did not take place until the late summer of 1941.

The specifications for the H V1 to H V3 versions of the Do 217 (serial Nos 21780021 to 21780023) called for unarmed bombers, powered by Daimler-Benz engines, having 3.8-m diameter VDM propellers, instead of the BMW 801A powerplant, and the aircraft were to carry crews of four. Bomb attachment locks, the dive brake and the Rb 50/30 camera unit were all dispensable. Breathing apparatus was provided and necessary to perform high-altitude tests on the engines.

The Do 217H V1 was delivered to Daimler-Benz in Stuttgart-Echterdingen in September 1941; but, shortly thereafter, it crashed as the result of technical problems with the propellers. After the aircraft had been repaired and the cause of the accident had been investigated, engine-evaluation tests finally got under way in 1942. To achieve a higher level of performance, it was decided to re-fit the H V1 with larger, 67-m^2 wings; Dornier began this conversion in the summer of 1943, which was to be completed as quickly as it was possible to do so. In September 1943, the H V1 was fitted with DB 603G prototype engines. However, its story ends at this point because the subsequent fate of the aircraft is unknown.

The second Do 217H (H V2) should have been delivered immediately to Rechlin but, during a works proving flight on 25 October 1942, a problem arose with the propellers and the aircraft crashed as the result. The crew survived, but sustained quite severe injuries.

The third, and last, Do 217H was assigned the designation H V3 and bore the markings DD+LW. This aircraft was flown from Friedrichshafen to Rechlin by Fliegeroberingenieur Huber on 25 May 1942. Following the usual post-delivery inspection, the aircraft was used to test different versions of the DB 603. These tests continued to the end of November 1944 at least. The first high-altitude test was carried out at 7000 m on 9 June 1942. Shortly before this, Daimler-Benz had fitted and tested thoroughly different types of twin exhausts and pulse jets, at Echterdingen.

Four months later, tests were carried out using different types of propeller. In addition to 3- and 4-bladed duralumin propellers, different types of wooden propellers were fitted, at Rechlin, during October 1942. Because of its better vibration characteristics, it was concluded that the four-bladed, adjustable-pitch VDM propeller was the best.

The first aircraft to be fitted with a central control unit, which was allocated to 3 Kampfschulgeschwader (Combat School Group) — KSG 3.

A Do 217M-1 (serial No 56040) equipped with a FIST ribbon parachute in the tail cone.

Testing a brake parachute on a Do 217.

A Do 217M-1 on a KG 2 training exercise.

On 11 October 1942, the third Do 217H flew at 8000 m for the first time, before receiving the engines from the severely damaged Ar 240 V4. After the engines had been fitted, test flights at 9000 m and above were carried out in July and September 1943, before they, too, were replaced with the new DB 603E, which had an improved supercharger giving a better high-altitude performance. Up until October of that year, the H V3 made numerous test flights (including several at altitudes of up to ten kilometers), carried out at Rechlin by test pilots Cuno, Huber and Baist. However, following a number of long-range flights, the remaining Do 217H aircraft were cancelled because of a fuel shortage.

The next aircraft to be produced was the Do 217 M V1, which had a cockpit canopy giving all-round vision, and which was powered by DB 603 engines. The first Do 217M was produced by converting a Do 217 E-2 (serial No 217521220), which bore the identification BK+IK. Following initial flight tests at Dornier, the aircraft was transferred to Rechlin where it was operated from September 1942. A critical assessment of the new bomber's performance, together with the pressing through of a DB 603 testing programme, followed. A series of high-altitude tests were performed during November 1943, and these were followed by numerous, long-range flights. During one of these flight, on 16 November 1942, the aircraft was forced to make an emergency landing at Ahlimbs-Mühle. Subsequent to its return to Rechlin, the endurance-test programme (which included climbing-performance measurements, and heating tests) continued, according to plan, until 1943.

Parallel to the high-altitude, test-flight programme, tests were carried out to evaluate different designs of cooling systems. The results of these tests showed that the design under consideration at that time was too small and would have to be replaced by a larger system. Tests with a flame retarder showed a drop in the aircraft's performance amounting to between 15 and 25 kmph, depending on altitude.

Six 0-series aircraft, at least, were manufactured. Their serial numbers ran from 1241 to 1245, and they carried the identifications BD+KO to BD+KS. The first 0-series aircraft (M-01) crashed into Lake Müritz, near Rechlin, on 9 September 1942, while on an engine-test flight. It had been the predecessor of the later Do 217M-1. The second 0-series aircraft, M-02, was fitted with the new-design, 59 m^2 wings, thereby becoming the predecessor of the M-3 bomber.

After initial flight tests with Dornier, Do 217 M-03 (BD+KQ) was used to complete the DB 603A-1 test programme. On 14 May 1943, the aircraft collided in mid-air with a Do 215 (NO+TO) and crashed. Structurally, this 0-series aircraft

Dornier Do 217H V3
(serial No 217080023; DD+LW)

Test Programme, 1942–44

25.5.42	Transferred to Friedrichshafen-Rechlin
9.6.42	DB 603A test flight at an altitude of 7000 m (Rechlin)
11.6.42	DB 603A test flight, (Rechlin)
30.6.42	High-altitude, one hour flight, at 8000 m (Rechlin)
5.7.42	Test flight (Rechlin)
6.7.42	Test flight (Rechlin)
6.7.42	High-altitude flight at 6000 m (Rechlin)
7.7.42	High-altitude flight at 6000 m (Rechlin)
10.7.42	DB 603A endurance test (Rechlin)
1.8.42	High-altitude flight at 6000 m (Rechlin)
2.8.42	High-altitude flight at 6000 m (Rechlin)
6.8.42	High-altitude flight at 8000 m (Rechlin)
7.8.42	Two high-altitude flights at 6000 m (Rechlin)
9.9.42	Test flight (Rechlin)
19.9.42	Test flight (Rechlin)
21.9.42	Test flight (Rechlin)
25.9.42	Test flight (Rechlin)
29.9.42	Test flight (Rechlin)
1.10.42	Test flight (Rechlin)
2.10.42	Test flight (Rechlin)
5.10.42	Two test flights (Rechlin)
8.10.42	Test flight (Rechlin)
11.10.42	Two test flights at an altitude of 8000 m (Rechlin)
18.10.42	DB 603A endurance test (Rechlin)
20.10.42	DB 603A endurance test (Rechlin)
20.10.42	High-altitude flight at 8000 m (Rechlin)
30.10.42	High-altitude flight at 8000 m (Rechlin)
5.12.42	Endurance test at an altitude of 5000 m (Rechlin)
8.12.42	Endurance test at an altitude of 6500 m (Rechlin)
10.12.42	Endurance test flight (Rechlin)
23.12.42	High-altitude flight at 6500 m (Rechlin)
9.3.43	Engine test (Rechlin)
21.4.43	Endurance test (Rechlin)
29.4.43	Test flight (Rechlin)
3.5.43	Endurance test (Rechlin)
11.5.43	Endurance test (Rechlin)
25.6.43	Endurance test (Rechlin)
28.6.43	Transferred from Rechlin to Leipzig-Mockau

29.6.42	Climbing tests to 8400 m
1.7.43	High-altitude flight at 9000 m (Rechlin)
5.7.43	High-altitude flight at 8500 m (Rechlin)
12.7.43	High-altitude flight at 9000 m (Rechlin)
16.7.43	High-altitude flight at 9000 m (Rechlin)
17.7.43	High-altitude flight at 8000 m (Rechlin)
19.7.43	Endurance test (Rechlin)
22.7.43	Endurance test (Rechlin)
23.7.43	Two flights at 9000 m (Rechlin)
26.7.43	Endurance test (Rechlin)
27.7.43	Three endurance test flights (Rechlin)
12.8.43	Two endurance test flights (Rechlin)
18.8.43	DB 603 test flight (Rechlin)
19.8.43	DB 603 test flight (Rechlin)
28.3.44	Test flight with DB 603E (Rechlin)
23.4.44	DB 603E endurance test (Rechlin)
19.6.44	High-altitude flight at 8500 m (Rechlin)
22.6.44	DB 603E endurance test (Rechlin-Oranienburg)
26.6.44	Test flight (Oranienburg)
27.6.44	DB 603E endurance test (Oranienburg)
28.6.44	DB 603E endurance test (Oranienburg)
29.6.44	Three test flights (Oranienburg)
30.6.44	Transferred from Oranienburg to Rechlin
9.7.44	Endurance test (Rechlin)
12.7.44	Endurance test (Rechlin)
13.7.44	Endurance test at 9700 m (Rechlin)
8.8.44	High-altitude flight at 9600 m (Rechlin)
13.8.44	DB 603E endurance test — night flight — (Rechlin)
18.8.44	DB 603E endurance test (Rechlin)
19.8.44	DB 603E endurance test (Rechlin)
27.9.44	High-altitude flight at 10,000 m (Rechlin)
30.9.44	DB 603E endurance test (Rechlin)
12.10.44	DB 603E endurance test (Rechlin)
13.10.44	DB 603E endurance test at 2800 m (Rechlin)
14.10.44	DB 603E endurance test (Rechlin)
2.11.44	Long-range (Rechlin-Staaken-Rechlin)
8.11.44	Long-range flight (Rechlin-Staaken-Rechlin)
9.11.44	Endurance test (Rechlin)
21.11.44	Endurance test (Rechlin)

differed from the M-1 standard bomber, in the way that it had some rather odd modifications to its wings and tailplane. In many ways, it was the forerunner to both the Do 217M-9 and M-11.

The log books of Rechlin pilots include frequent references to a Do 217M-04 (GB+CV) from December 1942 and May 1943. In addition to tailplane tests, this aircraft was used to test modifications to cabin heating and de-icing equipment, and also to perform tests with the DB 603 engines. During the summer of 1943, two additional M-0 aircraft were used to evaluate gliding-bomb operations. These aircraft (serial Nos 1244 and 1245) were designated M-0/U1s, and were each armed with an ETC 2000 XII, which was slung under the fuselage.

The 0-series was followed by the Do 217M-1 series. As the new, standard heavy bomber, the M-1 differed mainly from the Do 217K-1 in that it was powered by DB 603A-1 engines. Besides the standard M-1 series of aircraft, several other versions were produced. The first of these was the Do 217M-1/U1, which appeared on the drawing board at Dornier in January 1942. This version incorporated the lattice-type air brake of the Do 217E, and the defensive armament of the M-1. The MG 81Z and MG 131 were to be replaced by the much more effective MG 151 in the A position. However, adverse experiences with the aft-mounted brakes precluded serial conversion.

By November 1943, the M-1/U1 had matured into a bomber aircraft with the final equipment configuration of the M-1. This was a night bomber, fitted with anti-glare protection in the forward cabin. The lattice-type brake had been dispensed with long ago. Its defensive armament consisted of an MG 131 in the nose, two MG 81Is in the cabin side-window positions and two MG 131s in the B and C positions. The installation of an ETC 2000/XII C under each wing was planned also, for carrying heavy bombs, or drop tanks with a capacity of up to 900 l. At least one Do 217M-1/U1 aircraft was used as a prototype with DB 603A-1 engines and a TK 9 turbo-supercharger; and at least one Do 217M-1/U5, having the same armament as the K-2/U-1 and intended for the carrying of air-to-air guided weapons, was fitted with the same equipment.

An aircraft (serial No 722753) operated by 7/KG 2, equipped with a rear-looking FuG 216 'Neptun R' radar.

U5+LK of Kampfgeschwader 2, waiting to be loaded with a canister of AB 1000 incendiaries (BA).

A small number of Do 217M-1/U2s (a version of the Do 217M-1 fitted with Kehl IV equipment) were produced also. Like the Do 217K-3, this version could carry two PC 1400X, or Hs 293 gliding bombs. The prototype (serial No 56010, DN+UB) was followed by at least six special bomber aircraft, modified Do 217 M-1s, one of which, PU+IP, flew together with a Do 217 M, CL+UY, at Rechlin in 1943. Apart from further drop tests using weapons, the Do 217M undertook a series of flights at altitudes of more than 7000 m with various bomb loads, and with and without a flame retarder system.

Most of the Do 217M-1s produced were stationed with Kampfgeschwader 2 during 1943, and took part in raids on London and against targets in the south of England. Raids carried out between July and December proved to be especially costly: more than a dozen Do 217M-1s of the Holzhammer Geschwader were shot down by Mosquito night fighters, two of them on the night of 13 July 1943. In the meantime, most Do 217s had been supplied to III/KG 2. Six months earlier, during January and February, the number of aircrew losses had reduced drastically the number of crews available.

For example, 7/KG 2 only had three full crews. On 15 March III/Gruppe was withdrawn from Deelen, near Arnheim, where it had been stationed since September 1942, to Soesterberg for resting and refurbishment. Altogether, the three Staffeln had fifteen crews only and, in order to go some way towards reducing the effects of crew losses, it had to fall back on personnel from IV/KG 2. Nevertheless, KG 2 continued with its offensive operations, but between 15 and 24 March, a further four crews failed to return.

At this time Do 217Ks and Ms were being delivered fresh from the factory, and crew training was in full swing. During German operations of that time, raids were carried out against targets on the coast of southern England, and much further afield. For example, there was a night raid on Edinburgh in which four Do 217s of 7/KG 2 took part. Because of the long distance to the target,

A Do 217 having suffered undercarriage failure.

each aircraft had an auxiliary fuel tank installed in the fuselage. In addition to two AB 500, or SC 500 bombs, the bomb load included four SC 50 bombs. Having completed this mission, Kampfgeschwader 2 reported the loss of one of its crew, whose Do 217E-4 crashed in Kircudbrightshire before reaching its target, Edinburgh. From April 1943, raids against targets in Britain to be carried out by the crews of III/KG 2, began to be divided among I and II/KG 2.

Meanwhile, III/KG 2 was re-grouped to Coulomiers where newly-arrived crews underwent a fourteen-week long training programme, amassing approximately eighty flying hours. Particular emphasis was placed on practising long-range navigation, dive-bombing attacks, and emergency procedures. During this phase, III Gruppe suffered the loss of six more crews. In addition to conversion Do 217K-1s, KG 2 began to take delivery of Do 217M-1s which were fitted with a brake parachute which, in almost every case, was removed and stored because it would not be required for the forthcoming night raid operations. This helped to reduce the aircraft's weight and improve its performance also. Additionally, the nose-mounted MG 81Z was replaced with the more effective MG 131.

The re-grouping of III/KG 2 came to an end officially on 5 August 1943, and its flight units were transferred to Gilze-Rijen, where they began operations shortly thereafter. On 15 August 1943, Do 217s belonging to 2 and 7/KG 2 took off from Dreux for a night raid on Portsmouth; five Do 217 M-1s failed to return. Three days later, on 18 August, the target was Lincoln. One of the crews of 2 Staffel was shot down during this, its tenth,

General arrangement drawing of the Do 217M-2 which could carry three aerial torpedos.

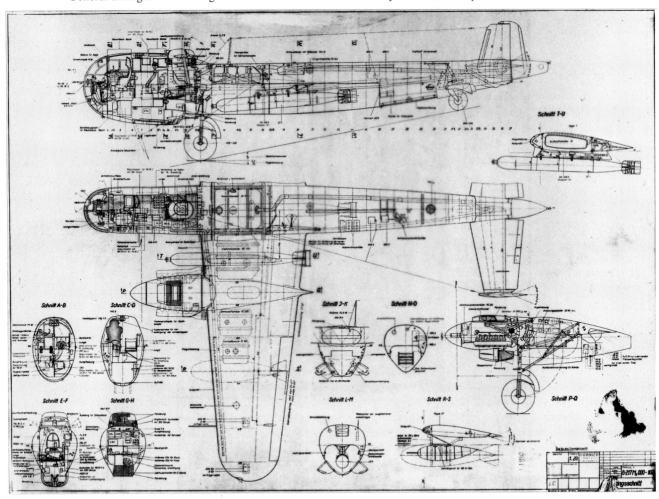

146

Front view of a Do 217M-1 (DN+UE) during tests with Dornier in 1943.

mission. 7/KG 2 also lost a Do 217 M-1, (U5+DR), which was carrying four SC 500 stores and three AB 36 canisters. In all, these night raids cost Kampfgeschwader 2 the loss of eight crews: one from I Gruppe, two from II Gruppe and five from III/KG 2. One Do 217 was shot down by a British long-range night fighter after take-off, and failed to reach the Channel. Considering that forty Do 217s only took off, Germany's losses amounted to 20% of its strike force. Those crews who were neither killed nor injured were captured and became prisoners in Britain. On the night of 19 August 1943, the Holzhammer-Geschwader lost two Do 217s, both of which fell victims to enemy night-fighters.

Hardly any Do 217K-1s and M-1s were operated by Kampfgeschwader 100, because the K-2s and K-3s were far more suitable for operations using guided missiles. This, briefly, was the status of Dornier bomber operations against Britain. For test purposes only, a long radius of action was unnecessary; therefore a few K and M aircraft were

allocated to EK 36 where, in the summer of 1943, and in close liaison with Dornier, plans were drawn up for the practical testing of wire-guided missiles, using a Do 217K-2 (serial No 4569), an M-1/U2 and an M-1 (serial No 56015). In the course of these trials, the Do 217M-1 (5K+BW) was written off totally.

The next production series was that of the M-2, which was a bomber having the same fuselage and wings as those of the M-1, but was adapted to carry aerial torpedos. Together with the Ju 87D, the He 111 H-6/H-11, the Ju 88A-4 and the Fw 190 A-5/U11, a prototype Do 217M-2 was in the line-up of aerial bomb-and-torpedo-aircraft inspected by Erhard Milch in Gotenhafen on 20 and 21 May 1943. Besides the Do 217 K-0 (which could carry five LTF 5Bs), Erhard Milch also inspected the M-2 and was given a flight demonstration later. The maintenance crew of Gotenhafen Experimental Establishment fitted the aircraft with two LT 950Cs on outboard underwing pylons, and, later, with two LTF 5Bs on inboard pylons. In both cases, electrically operated ETC 1000-type pylons carried Blohm & Voss stand-off torpedos, which were dropped successfully from a height of 600 m. Subsequently, the LTF 5Bs were fitted onto PVC 1006D pylons and released at a height of 50 m above sea level.

When the Air Ministry decided finally in favour of the Ju 88 becoming the future standard torpedo bomber, the plans to put the Do 217M-2 into series production were dropped. A prototype aircraft (serial No 56165) was fitted with the larger wings of the K-2, and was test-flown at Rechlin. However, on 26 March 1943, it crashed whilst landing at Dessau and was badly damaged. The flight engineer, Unteroffizier Kozian, was killed.

The next Do 217M version, the M-3, was the subject of a major discussion which took place at a meeting with the Generalluftzeugmeister (Air Supply Department) on 30 January 1943. Shortly before this meeting took place, an internal memorandum had been drawn up, on 18 December 1942, stating that the proposed M-3 was to be a heavy bomber, having a crew of four. It had a wingspan of 19.8 m and a wing area of 59 m^2, and was the first Do 217-series aircraft to be fitted with triangular tail fins as standard. With an all-up weight of 15,855 kg, powered by two DB 603 engines and fitted with 3.7 m diameter propellers, it was hoped that the aerodynamic improvements incorporated in the design would result with better performance figures.

The first M-2 prototype was made by fitting K-2-type version wings to Do 217M-1 (serial No 56015) at the Friedrichshafen plant. In June 1943, the aircraft made five test flights at Löwental.

Plans were drawn up to begin the serial production of the M-3 in June 1943, at a rate of two aircraft per month. This was to be stepped up to a peak production of seventy-five aircraft by the summer of 1944. However, Oberst iG Peltz continued to warn of the risks involved in undertaking the mass production of the M-3 because he had not been impressed with its performance data to date. At the same time, it was becoming clear that the

bombing offensive in the West must consist of night and twilight raids, for which the Ju 188 offered the promise of a better performance in the long term.

Due mainly to the proposed installation of a brake parachute in the tail and a revolving turret with an MG 151/20, the all-up weight of the M-3 increased to just under sixteen tonnes, reducing further its performance capability. The bomb equipment of the M-3 consisted of the Lotfe 7D bomb sight, the Navi 3, a BZA 1 unit, and two inboard, electrically-operated underwing pylons for carrying heavy bombs, such as the SC 1000, or SC 1800.

The M-3's radio equipment was essentially similar to that installed in other versions of the Do 217M; although, together with the FuG 101, it was intended to include the FuG 202R in production aircraft.

On 8 November 1943, the Technische Amt cancelled all those versions of the Do 217M which were equipped with two fixed MG 81Zs mounted in the tail, a configuration which featured on the Do 217K-2. Dornier's proposal to fit the aircraft with 59 m^2 wings was also scratched, and committed to the files. This decision was attributed to the high production costs involved in manufacturing a variety of wing types with widely differing wingspans. So, the heavy Do 217M-3 dive-bomber disappeared from the production schedule also.

The next proposal submitted to Berlin was that for the Do 217M-4. This aircraft offset the high costs involved in using engines with a TK 9 turbo-supercharger with its possible tactical advantages. The calculated performance figures for the M-4 (the first production series of which had been proposed at the beginning of 1943) were so impressive that, on 26 January 1943, Generalfeldmarschall Erhard Milch pressed unconditionally for his requirement that forty Do 217M-4s per month be produced.

Production plans from 10 February 1943 contained two further Do 217 versions only, together with a Do 217E powered by BMW 801ML engines, of which 235 had been built each year, and which were due to be phased out of production by August 1944. The production of the Do 217M-1 with a DB

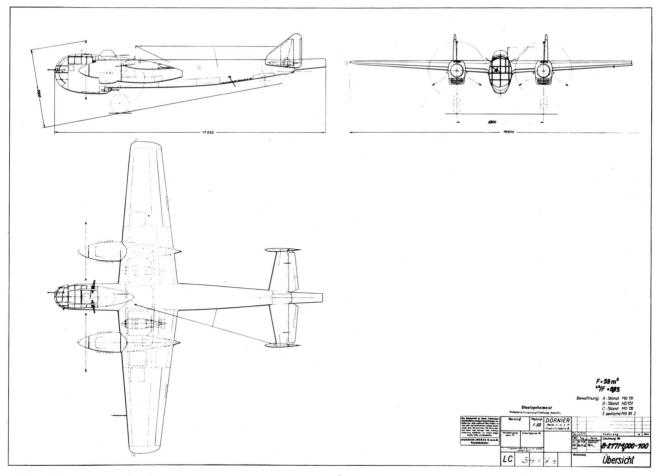

General arrangement drawing of the Do 217M-3 which had 58 m^2 wings and triangular tail fins.

603A powerplant was intended to reach a figure of more than 1000 aircraft by August 1944, and two Do 217M-4s were to be produced by May 1944. Subsequently, the plan was to build forty Do 217 M-4s per month, between September 1944 and June 1945. The last of a total of 505 high-altitude bombers were to be built in September 1945.

Early plans included the production of two Do 217 M-4s in June 1943, and the re-equipping of two Do 217s per month, at least, at Dornier. It was planned to double this figure from the summer of 1944.

Targets such as important, military and civil installations, especially British industrial centres, were considered to be especially suitable for the guided-weapons carrying M-4. However, development work on the turbo-supercharger and its installation in the Do 217 was fraught with technical difficulties and it was quite clear that it would not be possible to complete this part of the project on schedule. This, together with the fact that the Do 217M-8, fitted with a TK turbo-supercharger, was waiting in the wings, led finally to the cancellation of the M-4.

The Do 217M-02 was the pattern aircraft for the M-3 series, first flying at Rechlin in September 1942

The Do 217M-5, a special bomber version intended for operations with the Hs 293, also did not get beyond the prototype stage. The M-5 was very similar in its design to the M-4, but it included an R15 equipment pack as standard. However, its performance figures failed to meet the RLM's requirements totally. To date there was not any information available for the Do 217 M-6 and M-7.

The next version, designated M-8, represented the final Dornier bomber configuration with a turbo-supercharger. Planning for the M-8 started at the same time as plans for the development of the M-4, in the spring of 1941. The objective was to produce different bomber versions, carrying TK 9 equipment and having high-altitude DB 603E engines with a turbo-supercharger. Initial studies concerned the use of a Hirth 9-2281 supercharger. Unforeseen technical problems with the supercharger (which was complicated to operate), together with problems with the air-cooling system, and several other problems led to interminable delays at Daimler-Benz, Heinkel-Hirth and Henschel.

The first prototype Do 217 V13 (serial No 0032, DG+BC) was intended originally to be part of the

Do 217R programme, but was fitted with a turbo-supercharger also to increase the aircraft's performance. Since December 1941, engine specialists at Manzell had been considering actively the idea of installing a Hirth turbo-supercharger and cooler in the rear section of the engine nacelle. With this configuration, the combustion gasses from the DB 603 powerplant would be channelled to the turbo-supercharger by a feeder duct which ran along the undercarriage bay, after which the compressed and cooled gas would be piped back to the Daimler-Benz engine by a return duct. In the initial stages of its development this aircraft was designed provisionally as a Do 217 with a DB 603 power-plant and was designated Project 1.

Despite the intense efforts of the designers, studies had not been completed satisfactorily by 1942; the Hirth supercharger still had numerous shortcomings. In November 1942, the turbo-supercharger had been improved sufficiently to begin practical tests. During March and April 1943, an engine mock-up with a TK 9 supercharger was produced for the Do 217 V13; but, following an inspection on 21 April 1943, it was agreed that the aircraft's final configuration was a long way off.

The new engines were fitted in the thirteenth prototype on 21 June 1943, and two flights, each lasting twenty minutes, were made on 29 June. By 13 September, the aircraft had made twenty-four test flights, totalling twenty hours' flying, during which frequent faults occurred in the supercharger, the engine overheated, there was a piston fire and other breakdowns. Some of these test flights were carried out at the Henschel works, to which the Do 217 V14 was later delivered also. By the end of 1943, the development schedule had fallen apart at the seams completely. In 1944, it was intended to transfer the Do 217 V13's powerplant to the first M-8 prototype. This required the modification of its engine mountings, and the installation of a new fire bulkhead.

Accordingly, an initial Do 217M-8 prototype (DN+UG) was transferred to Rechlin in May 1943 for evaluation by its engine department. In June, the aircraft was fitted with an oil centrifuge to maintain a uniform supply of oil while climbing. By late summer 1943, the first Do 217M-8 had suffered numerous problems and also faults. Together with numerous cable fires (caused by temperatures which were too high), cooling-system failures, the overheating of the Daimler-Benz engines and the, by now, quite clearly, useless oil centrifuge, it was becoming apparent increasingly that the possibility of the aircraft attaining an operational ceiling of 12,000 m would not be realized.

According to the specialists at Rechlin, the final report concerning the merits of the turbo-supercharger would be available to the RLM at the end of the year. At best, one could fall back on the calculated values quoted in the data sheet, dated 6 March 1943 for the M-8, citing also an operating range of 2000 km, carrying 2000 kg of stores.

One thing was certain: this four-seater bomber, having a wingspan of 24.5 m, a wing area of 67 m^2, and an all-up weight of 17.2 tonnes would be compatible with high-altitude operations. Its defensive armament consisted of an MG 151 with 750 rounds of ammunition in the A and B positions, and an MG 131 in a WL 131 cylindrical carriage in the C position. An MG 81 could also be installed in each of the cabin side windows.

As was the Do 217M-3, the M-8 was fitted with new triangular tailfins. Any firm decisions concerning the installation of flame-retarding equipment, a reaction jet and a fixed tail gun could not be made until the spring. Trials with the Do 217 V13 left no doubt in the design department that the aft section of the engine nacelles would have to be modified to accommodate exhaust ducting. Contrary to what was being considered at that time, the boost air cooler was to be installed under the DB 603A powerplant, rather than under the supercharger.

Despite the conscientious groundwork which was done at Dornier, the RLM deferred the Do 217 M-8 project on 20 May 1943, because of an insufficient production capacity for the manufacture of the 67 m^2 wings and because most of the larger-area wings would be required for the Do 217K-2 and K-3 special bombers.

Production of Do 217s equipped with a turbo-supercharger was planned to commence at Dornier's factory in north Germany in the summer of 1943. However, Generalfeldmarschall Milch cancelled the entire project, in spite of the fact that performance data, gathered in the meantime, was not looking so poor. It became apparent that progress on the second prototype, the Do 217 V14, with a turbo-supercharger, was dragging its heels. Consequently, Dornier and the Technische Amt both agreed to cease any further development of a Do 217M equipped with the DB 603 and the TK 11. Both of the prototypes, together with the two Do 217M-8 conversion aircraft, had to be stripped by Dornier and their proposed transfer to Henschel, for engine tests, was dropped.

By the end of April 1944 development work concerned almost exclusively the high-altitude capabilities of aircraft. The conclusion had been reached finally that high-performance, high-altitude aero-engines were the thing of the future. The problem now was building them!

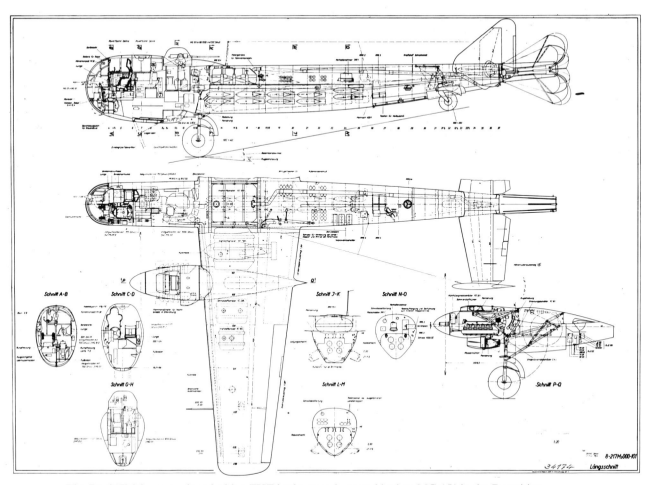

The Do 217M-3 was equipped with a FIST brake parachute and had an MG 151 in the B position.

The Do 217M-9 was a special bomber version which, according to the drawings, could be armed with either the PC 1400 X, or the Hs 293. It was a modified version of the M-3, basically, having a larger wing area and carrying FuG 203e equipment. It was intended to use the M-3's fuselage for the M-9, virtually without any modifications, to keep production costs as low as it was possible to do so. However, to improve the bomber's ability to fend off enemy fighter aircraft, more effective defensive armament was required. As was the M-8, the M-9 was equipped with a rotating MG 151,

mounted in the rear gun position. Because of weight limitations, one MG 131 was mounted in the nose, instead of two MG 151s. Four jettisonable, auxiliary fuel tanks were mounted in the bomb bay to increase the aircraft's radius of action.

In addition to providing an armoured seat for the pilot, Dornier's design team intended to provide armour protection against enemy gunfire in other parts of the cabin. Both of the cooling systems under the DB 603 engines were also to be protected with armour. The M-9's communications equipment consisted of an FuG X, 16, and 25, an

FuBl.2F, a PeilG 6, the fine FuG 101 altimeter, together with the previously-mentioned missile-control equipment. To further improve the aircraft's operating range, two outboard, underwing drop tanks were to be installed by using Equipment Pack R 21. For example, on the Do 217K-2, a PC 1400 X was mounted on an inboard, underwing pylon.

The Do 217M-9's performance was superior to that of most of its predecessors. A data sheet dated 9 August 1943 cited a maximum speed of 540 kmph at 6500 m and a maximum operating ceiling of approximately 10,000 m. Nevertheless, by 8 August 1943 it had become abundantly clear to the RLM that the M-9 would never go into production. Consequently, a directive was issued to Dornier which ordered the scrapping of all existing M-9 components. However, British troops captured an M-9 (serial No 0040), KE+JN, on Flensburg airfield in May 1945!

The proposed Do 217M-10 was a conversion of the M-1. The modification consisted of fitting steel and wooden components in the wing structure, to conserve other, more valuable materials. As had been the other Do 217 special bomber versions, the M-10 was to be equipped with Kehl. Following completion of the basic design work in Wismar, the RLM cancelled all further work on this version, too.

The M-11 special bomber version, with a Fritz-X weapon carried under the fuselage, did go into production.

The plans for the Do 217M-11, dated November 1943, showed an aircraft powered by DB 603A-2 engines, fitted with four-bladed propellers, and flame-retarder tubes. The design of the bomb bay's doors had been modified to accommodate the tail unit of the Fritz-X stand-off bomb. The M-11's defensive armament consisted of three MG 131s and two MG 81s. The same fixed guns as those on the Do 217K-2 and K-3 were mounted in the tail section.

In the meantime, however, production had become a major problem. On 14 January 1944, the

A Do 217M-1 (U5+DR) which was operated by II/KG 2 in 1943.

1400 X was mounted on an inboard, underwing pylon.

The Do 217M-9's performance was superior to that of most of its predecessors. A data sheet dated 9 August 1943 cited a maximum speed of 540 kmph at 6500 m and a maximum operating ceiling of approximately 10,000 m. Nevertheless, by 8 August 1943 it had become abundantly clear to the RLM that the M-9 would never go into production. Consequently, a directive was issued to Dornier which ordered the scrapping of all existing M-9 components. However, British troops captured an M-9 (serial No 0040), KE+JN, on Flensburg airfield in May 1945!

The proposed Do 217M-10 was a conversion of the M-1. The modification consisted of fitting steel and wooden components in the wing structure, to conserve other, more valuable materials. As had been the other Do 217 special bomber versions, the M-10 was to be equipped with Kehl. Following completion of the basic design work in Wismar, the RLM cancelled all further work on this version, too.

The M-11 special bomber version, with a Fritz-X weapon carried under the fuselage, did go into production.

The plans for the Do 217M-11, dated November 1943, showed an aircraft powered by DB 603A-2 engines, fitted with four-bladed propellers, and flame-retarder tubes. The design of the bomb bay's doors had been modified to accommodate the tail unit of the Fritz-X stand-off bomb. The M-11's defensive armament consisted of three MG 131s and two MG 81s. The same fixed guns as those on the Do 217K-2 and K-3 were mounted in the tail section.

In the meantime, however, production had become a major problem. On 14 January 1944, the lack of skilled workers and materials restricted wing production to forty sets only! It was not possible to produce the required 150 sets of 67 [2] wing. Furthermore, on 10 February 1944, 270 Do 217s, lacking engines, were cancelled. At a crisis meeting, it was decided to alter the procurement schedule for aero-engines, to reduce the number of engines available for the Do 217 by 100 at least.

Most M-11 production aircraft were delivered to Kampfgeschwader 100 'Wiking' from May 1944 and went into operation at the beginning of June 1944. The first losses were incurred on 10 June 1944, when a Do 217M-11 (serial No 723052) was shot

Little remained of Do 217 M-1 (U5+MR; serial No 6335) of 7/KG 2 after it crashed in Sussex on 14 March 1944.

Mistel trials involving a Do 217K-03 (KE+JC) and an Me 328 (RL+TY).

down by flak over Britain, and an M-11 (serial No 336473), 6N+JP, belonging to 6 Staffel, Kampfgeschwader 100 failed to return also. More than eight of KG 100's special bomber aircraft were lost over Britain or the English Channel on 21 July and 15 August 1944. On 23 August a Do 217M-11 was brought down by heavy flak over Kent. The aircraft, which was powered by two DB 603 A-3 engines and armed with three MG 131s and two MG 81s, was found by British salvage and rescue services.

As the production situation in 1944 came to a head, consideration was given to discontinuing production of the M-11 in favour of the Ju 188. Given the situation on the Western Front, in the light of the events of 6 June 1944, this remained an idea only.

CHAPTER EIGHT

Back as a Dive-Bomber?

Beginning in the winter of 1941/42, Dornier's design department at Friedrichshafen examined a number of proposals for a heavy, dive-bomber version of the Do 217, designated provisionally Do 217R. By January 1942, work had progressed to a stage where the final plans for the Do 217 R-0 series could go into the design phase.

The initial external design of the Do 217R differed from that of its predecessors specifically in that it had a 62 m^2 wing area. In comparison with the later Do 217 M-3 (which was to have a dive-bombing capability also), the dive brake was to be installed in the mid-outer-wing section, for the first time. The brake parachute, in the tail section, was activated by means of mechanical linkages on the top and undersides of the wing. However, this resulted often with the distortion of the rear fuselage by its absorption of the braking force.

As its defensive armament, the designers considered, initially, installing a moveable 20 mm MG 151/20 cannon in the A position. It was proposed also to mount MG 81I-type machine guns in ball mounts in each of the maximum of four side carriage positions. To defend the aft of the aircraft, it was proposed to retain the two MG 131 guns of earlier types. Practical tests of the modified armament were carried out at Tarnewitz Experimental Establishment, where a trial installation of an MG 151/20 in the A position was made in April 1942.

A short while later, on 10 and 13 April, representatives of the Luftwaffenführungsstabes (Luftwaffe General Staff) and the Technisches Amt (which was responsible for the development of military aircraft) all visited the Dornier factory to inspect the Do 217R's fuselage which had been built in the meantime. During the visit, the disadvantages which had manifested themselves on the Do 217K and M (particularly, reflection problems with the all-glass canopy during night operations which had proved to be the cause of several accidents) were discussed actively. As a step towards solving this particular problem, two Do 217Ls, planned provisionally as reconnaissance aircraft, were to be equipped with modified cockpit glazing.

The first R-series prototype, the Do 217RV1 (serial No 0029, TC+ZC), was produced in August 1942 by converting a Do 217E-1. At this stage, the aircraft was fitted with the same canopy as that on the K-1, and was later fitted with larger, 62 m^2 area wings. The powerplant chosen for the R V1 was the BMW 801ML with three-bladed VDM variable-pitch propellers, of 3.8 m in diameter. On 6 August 1942, the R V1 made its first flight at Löwental, piloted by Dornier's test pilot, Hausen. Subsequently, test flights were carried out with different stores configurations, up to and including two SC 1800s, and with take-off weights up to, and slightly more than 16.5 tonnes. Because of its weapon load, however, the Do 217R V1 attained a maximum speed of 395 km/h only, and its maximum rate of climb was 3.8 metres per second, at the most. A climb to 5000 m took 38 min, and its service ceiling was an unsatisfactory 5600 m.

In Friedrichshafen, the first R-series prototype was fitted with dive brakes on both halves of the wing. Providing external stores were not carried (thus reducing the aircraft's all-up weight to 12.1 tonnes) the aircraft could reach a speed of 420 km/h at an altitude of 4600 m. In all other respects, the R V1's performance left a lot to be desired. With a full load, giving an all-up weight of 16.5 to 17 tonnes, the works crew could demonstrate a maximum rate of climb at ground level only of

3.8 m/sec, dropping sometimes to 1.7 m/sec at altitudes of between 4000 and 4500 m.

During the winter of 1942/1943, a number of dive tests were carried out. During the spring of 1943, the emphasis was placed on undercarriage testing. In June, rudder load measurements were made on the Do 217R V1 powered by BMW 801L-2 engines, and the results were found to be too high.

Based on safety considerations, the RLM issued a directive on 21 January 1944, ordering that the aircraft was to be scrapped, but that some of its parts were to be used on other Do 217s.

The Do 217R V2 (serial No 0030, DB+BA) was equipped with DB 603 engines, as its predecessor had been. After having completed a series of dive trials, the new centre tailplane was evaluated with a view to improving performance figures. The R V2 was powered by DB 603As until the end of 1942; it was re-equipped with BMW 801A-2 engines early in 1943. Work on a high-altitude rudder, and in-flight measurements of the aircraft's longitudinal stability were satisfactory for the most part.

On 17 March 1944, the Do 217R V2 was scrapped.

In November 1942, two R-series prototypes were undergoing conversion at Friedrichshafen, although their future was very uncertain. In addition to the Do 217R V3 and R V4 (serial Nos 0031 and 0032), a further two aircraft were scheduled for conversion. A few parts, including an R-series fuselage centre section, were transferred to the production of the Do 217M-1/U1 high-altitude bomber, with TK 9 turbo-supercharger.

Together with the few prototypes which had been completed, two production versions were at an advanced design stage by spring 1942. One of these was the four-seat Do 217R-1, which was powered by DB 603 engines. In this version, the defensive armament had been reduced somewhat by replacing the originally proposed 20 mm canon in the A position with an MG 81Z. To reduce the aircraft's

General arrangement drawings of the Do 217R-1 dive-bomber, dated 6 January 1942, which had DB 603 powerplants and a wing area of 62 m².

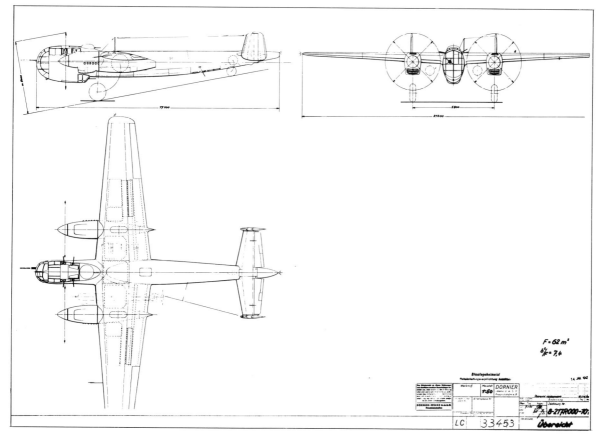

weight, two of the four side-mounted MG 81Is were also discarded. MG 131s, each with 1000 rounds of ammunition, were retained in the B and C positions. Preparations were made for the installation of a type 20/30 camera unit: a small camera was installed as standard equipment. The radio equipment of later production aircraft was to consist of an FuG XP, an FuG 16, an FuB1.2 with APZ 6, and an FuG 101 precision altimeter. The bomb jettisoning equipment could carry a maximum of two SC 1000s, or four SC 500s in the bomb bay.

The second R-series version was designated Do 217 R-2. In contrast with the R-1, the 20 mm MG 151 cannon was to be mounted in a ventral pack. In addition, the DL 131 rotating carriage was to be replaced with a traversable MG 151 gun. A DL 131 rotating carriage was installed in the cabin roof at the B position. The C position was unchanged from that in the Do 217R-1. According to the minutes of a meeting held on 12 May 1942, both of the new versions were to operate as aerial torpedo bombers, carrying two torpedos on inboard underwing pylons, and auxiliary fuel tanks mounted in the fuselage bomb bay. The second role of the Do 217R was to be that of a dive-bomber. However, the Dornier bomber could carry out dive bombing attacks at an angle of 50° only: attacks made at steeper diving angles sometimes resulted with quite significant damage to the fuselage.

Dornier intended to complete the development of the R series, leading up to the Do 217R-2, by December 1942, at the latest. In this context, the realization of the R-2 (which differed from the R-1 specifically by virtue of its having an additional turret in the cabin roof) was especially important. The production of a full-scale cabin mock-up, including increased armament, was given maximum priority and it was hoped that it would be fitted with anti-glare glazing. Following the manufacture of the twentieth Do 217R-1 (described as 'a Do 217 with new, larger area wings'), a lattice-type brake was to be installed in a suitably strengthened tail section, to avoid the risk of damage. The defensive armour had been improved also, especially in the cabin.

These developments became the key subjects discussed at a meeting in September 1942, at which it was decided to equip the Do 217R-1 with the same dive brake as that of the Ju 88A-4, to save both time and money. Finally, those who were present at the meeting discussed the matter further, and considered an improved brake parachute to be a more favourable alternative.

During the winter of 1942/43, Erhard Milch finally drew the line. The Do 217R was considered no longer for the role of a heavy torpedo bomber with a dive-bombing capability.

The already operational Do 217E-4, together with newly-arrived K-1s and M-1s, had to bear the brunt of the heavy losses incurred during operations over the British Isles. The heavy loss of crews and the increasing number of badly damaged aircraft returning to their bases meant that some operational units of Kampfgeschwader in the West required immediate rest, refurbishment, and, in some cases, had to re-group. Britain's fighter defence, together with the increasing accuracy of her sharp-shooting flak artillery were both taking a heavy toll of German bomber crews who operated at night mostly in what were becoming more like intruder raids.

Meanwhile, the Allied air offensive against German targets had so increased both in frequency and in striking power that on 27 November 1943 Adolf Hitler again ordered massive revenge attacks against London. Twenty-four hours after this directive had been issued, Reichsmarschall Göring summoned the Angriffsführer/England and began the preparations for Operation *Steinbock*. Some of the Luftwaffe's chiefs pinned great hopes on the success of massed raids using heavy He 177 bombers, armed with AB 1000 drop cannisters containing 620 kg of incendiaries.

In addition to KG 2, which operated Do 217s and Ju 188s, combat units of Kampfgeschwader 30, 54 and 76 in Luftflotte 2 were also assigned to attack Greater London; as were the Me 410s of I/KG 51 and those Staffeln of II/KG 6 and I/KG 100 which had been resting, or undergoing retraining.

158

In accordance with a directive issued by the Angriffsführer/England, the aircraft's bomb loads were to consist of 70% incendiary bombs and up to 30% high-explosive bombs, such as the SC 1000 with the so-called 'England' explosive mixture, and thin-walled aerial mines. Bombs weighing less than 500 kg were to be used only to bring each aircraft's bomb load up to its full capacity.

The only unit operating Do 217s which took part was the Holzhammer Geschwader which sent three bomber aircraft from the Geschwaderstab (Staff Section), thirty-five Do 217s from I Gruppe and thirty-eight from III Gruppe. KG 2 sent thirty-five Ju 188s of II Gruppe, and all twenty-seven Me 410s of IV Gruppe. In addition to the bomber strength supplied by KG 2, forty-six He 177s, more than 250 Ju 88s, forty-five Ju 188s and twenty-five Fw 190 fighter bombers were assigned to the offensive, which began on the evening of 21 January 1943.

The first wave of the main force, comprising 227 bombers, took off at approximately 19.30 hr. As had the British units operating over Germany, the German crews dropped aluminium strips (Düppel), like 'Window', to jam the Allies' radar defences. Ju 88S and Ju 188 aircraft of 1/KG 66, operated by experienced crews, acted as pathfinder units for the main force. These independently operating units consisted of three (later four) Staffeln, together with a supplementary Staffel which was later assigned to the Pathfinder School in Greifswald. Formed originally from 2/KG 100, this unit became EK 17; in September 1942 it was renumbered 15/KG 6. At the insistence of the Angriffsführer/England, KG 66 was formed from this unit on 1 May 1943.

From the beginning of July 1943, KG 66 was operating Do 217E-4s, K-1s and M-1s from its base in Soesterberg. On 13 July 1943, an attack was carried out against Hull, during which several

The Do 217R-2 (shown here in a drawing dated 29 April 1942) differed from the R-1 variant in that it had a stronger defensive armament.

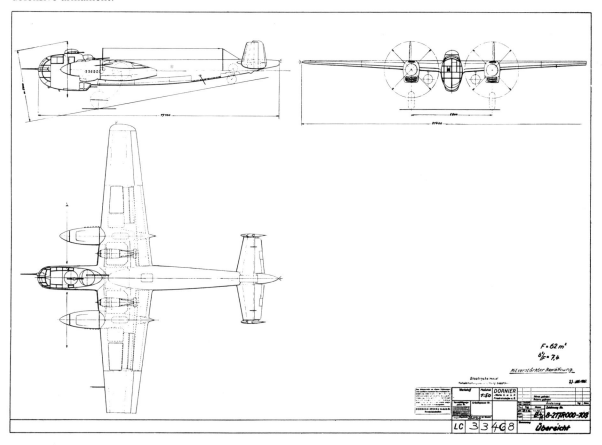

Do 217E-4s were hit by flak. By the end of the month, it had become clear that the Ju 88 S-1 was more suitable for pathfinder operations. The remaining Do 217E-4s and M-1s of I/KG 66 were transferred to either Reims, Montdidier, or Beauvais and were used in tests to evaluate Neptune and Bernhardine equipment.

On 16 December 1943, the first 'Düppel' tests were made, in preparation for Operation Steinbock. Instead of a Do 217, a Ju 188, piloted by Leutnant Altrogge, and including his crew, was used as a pathfinder.

In October 1943, the Ju 88S-1 was a key element in raids against the centre of London. In March 1944, it was used in raids against Bristol and Hull. During the invasion, in which Do 217Ks and Ms played a major role, Ju 88S-1s and S-3s were used to drop visual markers for the main bomber forces from KG 2 and other units.

The scale of the bomber attacks of Operation Steinbock surprised Britain's defences. The first wave of aircraft reached the target and dropped its deadly bomb load over Greater London. As soon as they had returned to their bases, the aircraft of the first wave were refuelled, rearmed and reloaded. A short time later, the second wave, consisting of a strike force of 220 aircraft, took off. According to German sources of information, ten aircraft were lost in the course of these two raids, although British defences reported that a further five aircraft had been shot down, or damaged.

A raid planned to take place on 22 January 1944, had to be postponed day after day because of adverse weather conditions. Not before the night of 30 January 1944 could the last, great Luftwaffe offensive over the Western Front be resumed. Again, the target was to be London. The 285 aircraft which took part in the operation caused extensive damage to the dockland area, and started more than 340 fires to contribute to the pyre of destruction. Of the aircraft which took part in the first series of attacks, 101 (14.5%) were shot down

A Do 217E-2 (3E+HN) of V/KG 6, pictured in northern France at the end of October 1942.

A Do 217E of II/KG 6 which was operating on the Western Front.

For a short period, Do 217s of I/KG 66 were used as pathfinder aircraft. Pictured is a Do 217E-2, Z6+OH.

161

by enemy fighters before they had reached the target (a loss rate that prompted a thorough investigation by the Waffengeneral (Armaments General) (GenTT)). The Waffengeneral's Staff concluded that of the 101 aircraft lost during these raids, seventy-four aircraft were lost as the result of technical problems. The remaining twenty-seven crews had experienced serious problems with their flight instruments, attributable to the fact that many new aircraft were used, and to the inexperience of many of their young pilots and crew. It was concluded also that reports concerning the operational readiness of the British defences had been underestimated greatly.

The German offensive was hampered severely hampered by inadequate ground maintenance organization. Between them, II and III/KG 2 'lost' fifteen aircraft (nine Do 217M-1s, five K-1s and one of KG 2's few Do 217K-2s) not to enemy action, but as the result of a lack of maintenance facilities. Most of the problems were caused by engine faults, damaged navigation equipment, and sometimes to aircraft being turned back by pilots whose flying skills were inadequate. One Do 217 M-1 crew broke off its run-in to the target when a swarm of enemy night-fighters appeared on the scene.

During the first two weeks of February, a further five raids were carried out. On 23 July 1943, Peltz had been awarded the Oak Leaves and Swords to go with his Iron Cross, and was appointed commander of IX Fliegerkorps and General der Kampfflieger (Chief of Staff (Operations)). In spite of his operational skill and the number of very strong bomber units he was able to muster, the damage that the Luftwaffe managed to inflict on Britain remained limited. On 18 February 1944, a force of 200 bombers dropped a combined total of 138.5 tonnes of incendiaries and high explosives on the City of London. Further raids were carried out on 20 and 22 February 1944. Between 22.20 and 22.50 hr on the night of 24 February, Do 217Ks and Ms of I/KG 2 bombed Millwall Docks, from a height of 4000

metres. Crews of II and III Gruppen, flying either Do 217s or Ju 188s, took an active part in the destruction. The bombers of I/KG 2 dropped eleven AB 1000s, twenty-two AB 500s (packed with incendiary bombs), sixteen SC 500 high-explosive bombs, and a dozen BC 50 bombs, directly onto the target area. Some units of KG 54 and KG 100 together with operational units of IV/KG 101 took part in this raid also. The main force was preceded by experienced pathfinder crews of KG 6. Twenty-four hours later, a force of 170 aircraft was directed towards the Westminster area of London. This proved to be a very costly operation: thirteen crews were lost to either enemy fighter aircraft, or flak, six of them over the British Isles.

The 'Steinbock' raids of February 1944 were to cost Luftflotte 2 more than seventy aircraft. Because of the size of the target area, and the number of aircraft that could be deployed against it, these 'vengeance raids' were hardly more than a pinprick, compared with the massive raids being carried out by RAF and USAF bombers, which were beginning to affect the production of the Do 217 in Friedrichshafen. Bombing raids on 16 and 18 March 1944, reduced the centre of Friedrichshafen to ashes, although the Dornier factory survived unscathed. Bombing attacks on 20 July and 3 August resulted with the Manzell factory suffering extensive damage.

Meanwhile, the Dornier and other bomber squadrons of Luftflotte 2 continued the offensive against London. Raids continued against targets in Hull, Bristol and Portsmouth. The 'Small Blitz', as it was called in Britain, but was referred to by the Luftwaffe as the 'Battle of Vengeance' ended with aerial attacks on Weymouth, Torquay and, again, on the dock installations at Portsmouth. Soon, the V-1 (FZG 76) 'wonder weapon', and later the V-2 (Aggregat 4) would be used to continue the fruitless offensive.

German raids carried out in January as part of Operation Steinbock claimed the lives of approximately 100 of London's population, with more than

Do 217E-2s together with an He 111H-3 of I/KG 66, pictured on an airfield in northern France in May 1943.

200 injured. The February raids claimed a further 961 dead and nearly 2,000 injured. However, the Germans suffered heavy losses also: about half of those crews which took part in these raids failed to return, having fallen as victims enemy night fighters, or heavy flak. Nevertheless, the operational activities of the Holzhammer Geschwader were not over yet.

Reconnaissance data gathered in 1943 pointed to the fact that preparations for an Allied invasion in north France were well in hand, and that the invasion would be attempted before the end of 1944, probably. Apart from small intruder raids, attacks on shipping, despite the enemy's air superiority, training continued. Above all, the watchword was 'Wait'.

At the beginning of June 1944, German air reconnaissance reported that shipping and supplies were being amassed in Britain. At this time, the Geschwaderstab (Staff Section) was in Soesterberg, together with the Stabsstaffel (Staff Flight). On 17 June 1944, Oberstleutnant Hallensleben replaced Major Schönberger as Commander of KG 2. At this time, I Gruppe was stationed at Hesepe; II Gruppe was stationed at Münster-Handorf; and

III Gruppe, under the command of Hauptmann Schreiveis, was based at Achmer.

In preparation for the forthcoming invasion, units were deployed, under very difficult conditions, from Orleans for mine-laying operations in the English Channel. On the night of 17/18 June 1944, the aircraft of station commander Major Schreiveis was reported to have been lost. Together with another bomber crew, he parachuted to safety, his aircraft having run out of fuel when flying in adverse weather conditions.

On 11 June, American units launched an offensive from their bridgehead on the east coast of the Cotentin Peninsula which, by 19 June 1944, led to Cherbourg being cut off. As the situation on the ground deteriorated further, KG 2's operations between 18 and 23 June were restricted almost entirely to those of aerial mine laying. On each of these nights, Do 217 and Ju 188 units took off from Soesterberg and Gilze-Rijen, and dropped twenty LMB and more than sixty BM 1000 mines along the invasion coastline. In a few exceptional cases, direct hits were scored by BM 1000s on targets close to the beaches. Several landing craft and armoured landing ships were destroyed.

A Do 217E-2 of 1 Staffel at Montdidier, fitted with 'Y' equipment (FuG 28a and FuG 17E).

The men of I and II Gruppen re-formed to become a purely Ju 188-equipped unit; all of their Do 217s were allocated to III/KG 2.

On the night of 7 June 1944, the first raid against Allied landing craft, situated at Asnelles and in the Seine Estuary, was carried out by a force of twelve Ju 188s and nine Do 217s. On the following night, KG 2 carried out a raid against massed Allied landings, using shrapnel and other bombs. On average, between twelve and eighteen medium-range bombers took off each night. Ju 88s of 2 and 3 Staffeln, KG 66, together with those of I/KG 6 (whose commanding officer, Hauptmann Hans Thurner, failed to return from an operation on 11 June 1944), were flown on bombing operations which were aimed directly at the beaches around St Mère-Église, and at territory which had been overrun in the meantime by the enemy. During these raids, KG 2 lost four of its crews, including those of Leutnant von der Heyde, Unteroffizier Kreisel, and Feldwebel Heiss. Nevertheless, the damage inflicted by the Holzhammer Geschwader on Allied equipment (in spite of heavy flak defences and close fighter cover which assured

Allied air superiority) exceeded all expectations. Units based in the West were soon able to report hits on a 5000-ton freighter, and ships either on fire, or sinking ships as the result of successful attacks.

In accordance with a directive issued on 22 June 1944, KG 2 had to relinquish all of its Ju 188s on 29 June, and crews were to convert to the Do 217. For a time, five Do 217s only, belonging to I/KG 2, remained operational in the West, flying, from Melun and Gilze-Rijen, mine-laying operations, mostly. In all, Kampfgeschwader 2 dropped thirty-nine SC 1000s, 132 DM 1000s, ninety-five LMBs, 165 SC 500s, a miscellany of drop cannisters and light bombs over north France between 7 June and 1 July 1944. As the result of its operations, the Luftwaffe claimed to have sunk fifty-one freighters (totalling 312,000 tons), several destroyers and small naval vessels, and a number of landing craft. On 30 June the operational strength of Kampf-geschwader 2 was reduced to seven Ju 188s and seven Dornier bombers; II and III Gruppen ended the month without any aircraft at all. IV/KG 2, on the other hand, was equipped with a combined total of fourteen Ju 188s and Ju 88s, and eleven Do 17s, 215s and 217s of various marks.

The Stabsstaffel (Staff Flight) of KG 2 was disbanded on 4 July 1944, and re-formed as a forward unit, operating Do 217s. III Gruppe had been used occasionally as a training and conversion unit for the Do 217. A few days later, a directive was issued ordering some units of III Gruppe, including its staff and its technical personnel, together with 9 Staffel to transfer from Achmer to Friedrichshafen, on the Bodensee, for familiarisation with the Do 335, the forthcoming operational bomber.

In the meantime, the remaining personnel of III Gruppe were to continue with their retraining and practical activities. Together with the crews from II Gruppe, crews from III Gruppe were also used for ferrying Do 217s. On 10 July 1944, II/KG 2 was transferred to Münster-Handorf, where they converted to Dornier bombers. A few units only of I Gruppe were operational. Almost every night, aircraft of the Holzhammer Geschwader were sent out to lay mines in the English Channel. These mines were to claim five large warships; at least eleven merchantmen, carrying supplies for the invading troops; and ten landing craft. KG 2 lost approximately ten aircraft, brought down by either enemy night fighters, or heavy concentrations of flak.

At the end of July, I and II Gruppen had a combined total of more than thirty-one Do 217s, and there were a further twenty-two Dorniers available at the Geschwader's training unit. By this time, Ju 188s had been transferred to other units, primarily to Kampfgeschwader 6 and 66, which were glad of this boost to their operational strengths. In August 1944, crews of KG 2 carried out a number of raids (using, on average, fifteen to seventeen Do 217s) on important targets in the Avranches and Falaise areas, and (on the night of 17 August 1944) against targets in west Paris and on the airport at Melun.

On 10 August, KG 2 was forced to withdraw east: first, to Coulommiers, then, five days later, to Tilburg. On 28 August 1944, the aircraft, aircrews and ground personnel of KG 2 were transferred to Schipol, Amsterdam.

By 13 August 1944, the training unit of III/KG 2 had had to cease its operations because of a lack of fuel. Most flying units were assigned ferrying operations.

The production of the Do 217 was halted on 15 August 1944. At the same time, the Luftwaffe High Command issued a directive to the effect that all available aircraft, including those which were almost completed at Dornier's factory, were to be delivered to operational units forthwith. Geschwadern could expected to receive approximately twenty-five only of the 150 new aircraft expected originally, the construction numbers of which had been notified already to the units concerned.

Despite losing more than twenty Do 217s, a review, conducted on 31 August 1944, indicated an effective operational strength of twenty-seven aircraft in I Gruppe, and twenty-three aircraft in II Gruppe. Operational readiness could not be improved upon because of the increasingly frequent enemy bombing of the bases of I and II Gruppen. Attacks against these bases 8, 11 and 15 August, resulted in the destruction of more than fifteen Do 217s.

In addition to the losses incurred during air raids on Gilze-Rijen, Münster-Handorf, Coulommiers and Soesterberg a number of aircraft were lost as the result of accidents. On 4 August, for example, two Dornier bombers of I/KG 2, based at Gilze-Rijen, piloted by Unteroffizier Kaiser, and Unteroffizier Rossel, accompanied by their crews, collided in mid-air on returning from a raid.

When Antwerpen was re-taken by Allied troops on 4 September 1944, the IX Fliegerkorps did not have any option but to order the withdrawal of Kampfgeschwader 2 and other operational units. With thirty-four Do 217s and two Ju 52s, these units withdrew from Tilburg and Schipol to the Münster/Osnabrück area. Shortly thereafter, forward units withdrew from Soesterberg to Münster-Handorf and Münster-Loddenheide.

A Do 217E-2 of Erprobungskommando (Experimental Detachment) XY, which was based at Chartres.

The IX Fliegerkorps, including the Holzhammer Geschwader and its complement of Do 217s, was removed from operational duties on 9 September 1944. Three days later, it was placed under the command of the Luftflotte Reich. Because the supply of new Do 217s had ceased, the armaments and inspection units at Dornier's Heiligenbeil, Wittstock, Wismar and Perleberg factories closed down in mid-September.

On 16 September 1944, the General der Kampfflieger ordered that Kampfgeschwader 2 be disbanded. Some of its units were transferred by the Luftwaffe's Personnel Department to the Waffen SS. The majority of the ground personnel and aircrews were handed over to the General der Jagdflieger. Most of KG 2's operational aircraft were dispersed, for a time, to airfields at Hardenberg and Reppen, near Frankfurt.

On the evening of 19 September, the Commander of the Luftwaffe's combat units was charged with the task of leading the Gefechtverbandes Hallensleben (Hallensleben combat unit), which, at

A Do 217E-2 night bomber of V/KG 66.

166

that time, was comprised of III/KG 51, I/NSG 2, the Detachment Schenck, equipped with Me 262 jet bombers, and III/KG 3.

By 24 October 1944, sixty-two men, including non-commissioned officers, latterly of KG 2, had reported for duty at their new units, Jagdgeschwader 1, 5, 54, or 77. Other personnel, including thirty-six hand-picked ground crews, were assigned to duties with the Luftwaffe's Security Service. At the end of October, the remaining twenty-seven Do 217s of I/KG 2 were re-assigned to the General der Aufklärungsflieger (General of Reconnaissance Units), and thirty-seven aircraft of to II Gruppe were dispersed to Reppen. By the end of November 1944, the Do 217 Geschwader had been disbanded officially. The diary of its operations during the war was at its end. KG 2 had taken delivery of 120 Dornier bombers between June and October 1944, at least forty-three of which were written off either during operations, or as the result of training accidents. The remainder were assigned to other units.

The Wiking Geschwader, KG 100, also operated from airfields in France. III/KG 100 is especially interesting because it was equipped with many versions of the Dornier bomber. Furthermore, in the spring of 1944, III Gruppe was operating Do 217E-5s and K-3s, from its base in Toulouse, against Allied naval shipping and convoys. To avoid early detection during night operations, most Do 217 aircraft had been fitted with flame-retarding tubes by this time.

On 1 April 1944, and again on the night of 12 April 1944, raids were initiated from Toulouse against large shipping convoys. The Do 217 crews of III/KG 26 and Kampfgeschwader 77 together attacked a large American convoy on 20 April. Three merchantmen, totalling 19,800 tons, were sunk, and the destroyer *Landsdale*, together with two other freighters were badly damaged, more or less. 6/KG 100 lost three Do 217E-5s, one of which was badly damaged by the gunfire from a night fighter, and it crashed when trying to land. The other two were shot down over the Mediterranean.

Early on the morning of 29 April 1944, 7 and 9 Staffeln began to move from Toulouse to Orleans. Together with other units of IX Fliegerkorps, their Do 217K-3s were to operate against the harbour installations of, and naval shipping based at Plymouth. After much careful planning, a formation of twelve Do 217K-3s, armed with Fritz-X stand-off bombs, took off on the night of 30 April 1944. The formation was to arrive immediately after aircraft from I/KG 66 had illuminated and marked the target; however, the pathfinders were late. Instead, the formation encountered the Mosquitos of the RAF's No 406 Squadron. With the aid of the Portsmouth searchlight and flak batteries, two Dornier bombers were shot down, including the aircraft piloted by Hauptmann Herbert Pfeffer, the Commander of III/KG 100.

KG 100 regrouped at the end of May 1944. 8 and 6 Staffeln were also reorganized. III Gruppe was equipped with the Do 217, and I and II Gruppen were equipped with He 177s.

As part of the offensive to combat Allied invasion forces on the coast of Normandy, Do 217 aircraft, armed with Fritz-X missiles, operated against British destroyers positioned in the Seine Estuary on 8 June 1944. One destroyer and the frigate *HMS Lawford* were hit. Two Do 217s failed to return, including a Do 217E-5, 6N+MP, and its experienced crew, captained by Oberfeldwebel Obst, which had claimed the sinking of a ship in October 1943. Two days later, 8 and 9 Staffeln each lost two Do 217M-11s and one Do 217K-3. On 16 June 1944, *HMS Boadicea* was hit by a Fritz-X, and sank. In the combats over Cherbourg, three crews of the Fritz-X Staffel were lost. Furthermore, adverse weather conditions resulted with six aircraft crash-landing between 16 and 22 June. 7/KG 100 lost another Do 217K-3 over the Orne Estuary.

A raid carried out on the night of 4 July also took its toll: three Do 217s (K-3/M-11) fell victim to Allied air defenses over the Seine Estuary. Between 17 and 30 July 1944, the III Gruppe's blood-letting continued unabated. In addition to badly shot-up Do 217s returning from the Invasion

The successor to the Do 217; a Ju 88S-1 pictured in northern France in the autumn of 1943.

Front, many K-2, K-3 and M-11 aircraft did not return at all. Operations were concentrated on the waters outside Cherbourg and Brest. The crew of one Do 217M-11 managed to coax its badly shot-up aircraft back to base safely. That crew was luckier than those captained by Unteroffizier Schmidt and Oberfeldwebel Schneckene.

Between 1 and 19 August, numerous guided-bomb raids were made against bridges in north France. On the night of 3 August, for example, the target was the bridge at Pontaubault, which was to be destroyed in a missile attack, thereby hindering an Allied advance. However, because of adverse weather conditions, the target was changed to that of the bridge at Avranches. The bridge at Pontaubault was later destroyed by Oberfeldwebel Kube and his crew. An attack on the road bridge at Pontorsson resulted with further losses for III/KG 100: a Dornier bomber belonging to the Staff Flight and piloted by Leutnant Schlecht was posted as missing. The Do 217M-11s of 7 Staffel were intercepted by Mosquitos of No 406 Squadron before

they had a chance to release their load of Fritz-X missiles. Two crews, at least, did not survive, including that of Oberfeldwebel Doser whose aircraft fell to Mosquito cannon fire over Vannes. On 11 August, one crew succeeded in guiding an Hs 293 glider bomb onto its target, a freighter in the Gironde Estuary which, though damaged, did not sink.

Following the landing of strong Allied forces between Toulon and Cannes on the Mediterranean coast, which broke through the thin line of defence quickly, operations were redirected, in mid-August, towards new targets. KG 100, by then virtually decimated, carried out its last concentrated attacks against thirty-four large and a multitude of small vessels of the marine support group, and against a host of landing craft. The destroyer USS Le Long and two armoured landing craft were sunk. Captain Kube and his crew succeeded in sinking a 7000-ton freighter, and LST 282 shared the same fate. Between the start of the Allied invasion and 16 August 1944, III/KG 100 alone lost thirty-six of its crews. That was the equivalent of an entire Kampfgruppe.

The German retreat from France, via Montpelier and Lyons to Giebelstadt in Franconia, began on 20 August 1944. By mid-September, remnants of ground personnel and aircrew without aircraft were reassembled in Giebelstadt under the command of Hauptmann Schmetz.

On 20 August, the Luftwaffe High Command had ordered the disbanding of Kampfgeschwader 100, excepting its II and III Gruppen, and some other units. This was followed by a directive, which was issued on 7 September, stating that, with the exception of 7/KG 100 (to which the remaining Do 217 aircraft were to be assigned), all of the remaining units of the Geschwader were to be disbanded. Eventually, 7 Staffel was assigned to the Pilot Training Unit B46 and to the Bomber and Pathfinder School. II Gruppe, the

He 177 units of which had sustained a heavy loss of well-trained crews, was disbanded on 2 February 1945.

KG 100 lost more than 110 Do 217E-1s to E-5s, twenty-seven K-2s, twenty-two K-3s, one Do 217 M-1 and ten M-11s, at least, in action and in training exercises. At Kampfgeschwader 40, only 4 and 5 Staffeln of II Gruppe had received the Do 217 between late summer 1941 and June 1943. II/KG 40's initial complement of Do 217 E-1 and E-2s was followed with E-4 aircraft. At that time, it had been intended to deploy 4/KG 40 as an aerial torpedo squadron, the other Staffel being assigned to maritime combat operations. The first low-level attacks carried out by Dornier bombers against Allied shipping took place in July 1941. Following numerous successful operations the unit was assigned to the command of the Angriffsführer England in May 1943.

A Ju 88S-3 of I/KG 66, which crash-landed at the beginning of 1944.

Three months later, on 15 June, a directive was issued stating that II/KG 40 was to be incorporated into KG 2. Accordingly, II Gruppe re-equipped with He 177s at Burg, and undertook its first mission, with a formation of twenty-five aircraft and Hs 293 glider bombs, on 21 November 1943. Based in Cognac, II/KG 40 carried out numerous missile raids throughout the spring of 1943. As were the crews of KG 2 and KG 100, the crews of II/KG 40 (which by April 1944 was equipped with He 177A-5s) were deployed to defend the Allied invasion.

On 27 October 1944, a heavily depleted II Gruppe was relieved of its active duties, disbanded and its personnel were assigned to convert to jet fighter units. However, with units such as JG 7 and KG (J) 54 taking preference, their much-promised Me 262s did not materialize. Small units only of Kampfgeschwader 40 started Me 262 theory classes in Neuburg/Donau, at the beginning of 1945.

CHAPTER NINE
High-Altitude Dornier Aircraft

The maiden flight of the Ju 49 (D-UBAZ) on 2 October 1931, was Junkers' first, tentative step towards developing an aircraft which could operate at very high altitudes.

By 1935, Junkers' test pilots had flown as high as thirteen kilometres, gathering invaluable research data and demonstrating impressive high-altitude performances. Junkers co-operated closely with the DVL to examine the practical aspects of pressure-cabin and aero-engine development. The focal points of these studies were the development of a suitable pressure cabin with an appropriate oxygen supply; and an emergency dive procedure, in the event of a sudden loss of pressure. Of no lesser importance were the data and knowledge gained from the Ju 49, in respect of its performance with high-altitude engines and multi-stage, high-altitude boosters.

Junkers produced two EF 61 development aircraft, which were powered by Daimler-Benz DB 800D engines, specifically to research high-altitude flight. The first of these aircraft, designated EF 61 V1 (serial No 4931), crashed on 19 September 1937, during a speed trial which was conducted at an altitude of 3500 m; the crew managed to escape by parachute. The aircraft was so badly damaged as the result of the crash, that any attempt at repairing it was considered to be worthless. The second aircraft, EF 62 V2 (serial No 4932), which was to have been followed originally by the production of seven 0-series aircraft, was rolled out of the Junkers factory in November 1937. One month later. it crashed and was written-off.

Despite these set-backs, the production of the first series of high-altitude, reconnaissance and bomber aircraft could not be delayed much longer. Accordingly, an order was placed, in September 1939, with Junkers for the production of forty Ju 86P-1 high-altitude reconnaissance aircraft. The first prototype was equipped with a pressure cabin, and was powered by two Jumo 207 diesel engines. It rolled out of the factory in December 1939. High-altitude chamber tests commenced at the beginning of 1940, at approximately the same time as the second and third Ju 86s (P V2 and P V3) had completed their first flights successfully.

On 23 May 1940, the Hs 130A V1, powered by two Daimler-Benz DB 601A engines, completed its first flight successfully. This aircraft was the result of further developments to the Hs 128, which was being used as a research vehicle by the Deutsche Versuchsanstalt fur Luftfahrt — DVL — (German Experimental Institute for Aviation). A second prototype (serial No 3002) was built, after which eight 0-series aircraft were manufactured. From August 1940 until the end of 1941, these aircraft were fitted with DB 601 and DB 605 engines and were used in the research programme which involved Henschel, Daimler-Benz, the DVL and the Commanders of the Experimental Establishments.

In the meantime, by 1 August 1940, Junkers' test pilot had completed forty flights in a Ju 86P successfully, at altitutdes over 10,000 m.

By late summer nothing remained to prevent the Luftwaffe from putting the high-altitude bombers, then at their disposal, into action over the British Isles. Following numerous reconnaissance flights and several intruder raids, the British high-altitude fighters began to get closer. In time, it became virtually impossible for Ju 86P-1s and P-2s to operate unmolested over Britain. Consequently, the Ju 86P-3 ws developed, and this was followed by the Ju 86R-1 in 1941.

A Do 215B-6 research aircraft, fitted with a TK9 turbo-supercharger.

As their predecessors had been, the P-3 and R-1 prototypes were transferred to the Rowehl Command at Oranienburg (later to become the research centre for high-altitude flying). Prior to operational service, both aircraft underwent a series of test flights to determine their performances and useful radii of action. Together with the production of a small number of aircraft at the Junkers factory, the conversion of a number of Ju 86Ps to the higher-performance R version, and various activities at Henschel, the Technische Amt also joined in the development of high-altitude, military aircraft. It was not surprising, therefore, that Dornier, too, had ideas and proposals for a high-altitude aircraft.

As part of the Do 215 development programme, a prototype aircraft had been fitted with a TK 9A turbo-supercharger, developed by the DVL. Code-named 'Umbau Posen' (Posen Rebuild), this work was undertaken in preparation for future Do 217 projects involving TK equipment. As with the He 111H-6, the TK 9 (Umbau Braunschweig), turbo-supercharger increased engine performance at 9000 m by approximately 580 hp to a little less than 900 hp. Additionally, use of the booster resulted with a 23% reduction in specific fuel consumption, according to research reports. The TK 9As were mounted directly on top of the Do 215B's DB 601A engines, in such a way that the air intake was directly above the engine cowling and the exhaust duct was above the top side of the wing.

Following tests with a TK 9A installation in an He 111 and a Do 215, some time elapsed before the German Air Ministry concluded, on 17 November 1942, that both installations were too costly and unsatisfactory for continuous operation. Therefore, the high-altitude, reconnaissance Do 215B-6, powered by DB 601T engines and fitted with a TK 9 booster, was cancelled. The Technische Amt's experience with high-altitude flight was such that its interest in pursuing either development

waned, as they were both proving to be very costly and very demanding in terms of maintenance. Instead, it was decided to concentrate on the developments at Henschel and Junkers.

Dornier's design department in Friedrichshafen first started work on the Do 217A concept (a high-performance, high-altitude bomber, with an enlarged wing area and a pressure cabin which could accommodate a crew of three) at the end of 1940. Together with Do 217A and L project studies, the Do 217 V13, which was flying by the summer of 1943, was a major step forward in the direction of future Dornier, high-altitude Dornier bomber aircraft.

Two Do 217A-0s (serial Nos 2704 and 2705), powered by DB 601R engines giving a greater critical altitude, were used for high-altitude flight tests. A Dornier data sheet No 6 dated May 1941 indicated that the aircraft was fitted with an appropriately equipped pressure chamber also. The three-seat, photo-reconnaissance version referred to in that data sheet could be equipped with two or

General arrangement drawing of the Do 217B-6, dated 2 September 1940, powered by DB 601 engines which were augmented by a TK 9 turbo-supercharger.

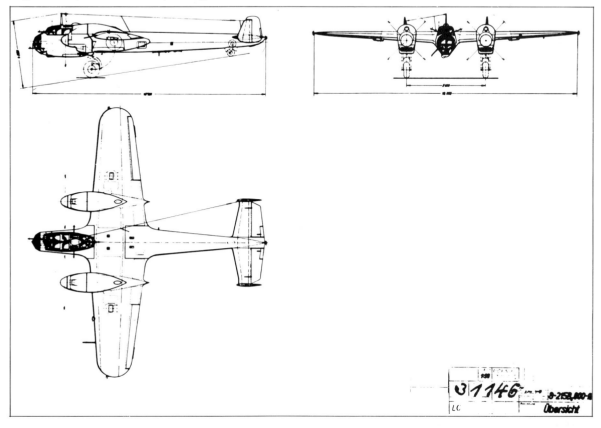

three photo-reconnaissance cameras. Its defensive armament consisted of three MG 81Z machine guns which, in contrast with later high-altitude bomber aircraft developed in Friedrichshafen, were fitted into pressure-tight sleeves and operated by the crew.

The development study, referred to provisionally as Project Do P 183, involved using two DB 601R engines with GM 1 auxiliary fuel injection. The aim was to achieve an operating ceiling of approximately 14,000 m. Calculations made later, however, indicated a maximum service ceiling of approximately 12,000 m. A revised proposal differed from the original in two main respects: first, there were fewer guns in the revised design, to save weight; second, a camera unit was installed immediately aft of the three-seat pressure cabin.

The draft for the Do 217L (a high-altitude reconnaissance aircraft, powered by two DB 603H engines, each developing 2000 hp for take-off) appeared also at this time. With an average all-up weight for the aircraft, the GM 1 auxiliary injection unit was sufficient to maintain a speed of 575 km/h, at an altitude of 15,000 m, over a distance of 600 km. In contrast with the Do 217A which had a high-altitude chamber, the Do 217L had a larger wing area, this having been increased by 5 m^2 to 70 m^2. In 1942, the designers estimated that when maintaining an altitude of 12,000 m, the aircraft's range would be approximately 2850 km and the flight duration would be up to six hours, including one hour using GM-1 auxiliary injection. The glycol-methanol supply was stored in six tanks, giving a total weight of 720 kg. Like the later, high-altitude, reconnaissance conversion of the Do 217 A-0, the Do 217L did not progress beyond the project stage. Therefore, at the beginning of 1942, it looked very much as though the Do 217P, the most important aspects of the design for which had been completed in September 1941, would be the ultimate high-altitude bomber. Instead of short-lived, highly refined, specialized engines with a high critical altitude, Daimler-Benz, Henschel and Dornier used an engine configuration planned in

1941, consisting of two DB 603N propulsion units and a DB 605 booster. It was more than a year before the final configuration of the high-altitude, central booster unit (Höhenladerzentrale, or 'HZ' as it came to be abbreviated) was decided finally. This was to comprise of two DB 603S-0s, and one DB 605T drive unit for the central booster. According to the Daimler-Benz designers, the DB 605T would drive a two-stage, centrifugal fan, the exhaust from which would pass through two intercoolers to feed cooled, precompressed air back to the DB 603s through their booster intakes.

The first test-bed trials were carried out in Stuttgart in October 1941. From May 1942, the Technische Amt assigned a higher priority to the high-altitude central booster for the Do 217P and Hs 130. Prior to Dornier having received an official order from the Technische Amt, a study had been conducted to investigate the feasibility of fitting the forthcoming HZ into the fuselage of a Do 217E-2. Dornier's engineers and designers devoted a great amount of effort to installing the complicated cooling and boost air ducting units into a full-scale mock-up. This having been completed without any obvious difficulties, the Technische Amt inspected the mock-up prior to placing an order for three development aircraft which were to be designated Do 217P V1 to P V3.

As part of the preparations for the flight test programme, vibration and loading tests were carried out on the enlarged wing of the Do 217P. These ground tests were performed at the Dornier factory. The wing was first fitted to a Do 217E-2 (serial No 1221) and test-flown in February 1943. As a second test aircraft, Dornier intended to use another Do 217E-2 (serial No 1270) but, during a quite different test flight, this aircraft crashed near the airfield at Rechlin and was almost completely destroyed. To replace it, Dornier used another Do 217E-2 (serial No 1229), which was modified to become finally Do 217P V1, bearing the markings BK+IR.

The prototype was to have been ready by March 1942, but changes and improvements to the engines had taken longer than expected, with the result that

174

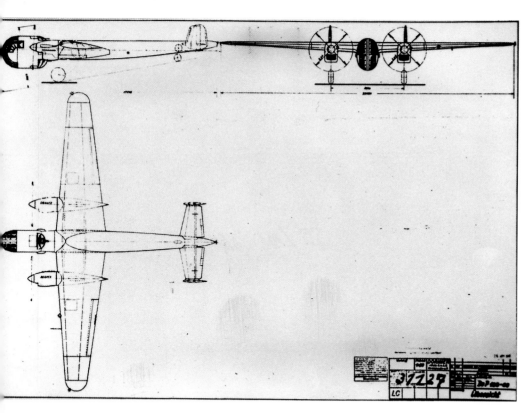

The Do P 183 high-altitude bomber powered by DB 601 special engines, and having a slender fuselage. The aircraft did not advance beyond the project stage.

ground tests began at the beginning of June. Apart from a few minor problems experienced with the DB 603 booster, BK+IR completed its first flight successfully on 6 June 1942 (the central booster was

Test Flights of Do 217P V1, BK+IR —1942

Flight No	Date	Alt. (m)	Comments
1	6 June	—	Trimming flight
2	18 June	—	Faulty oil-pressure gauge
3	22 June	3000	Trouble-free
4	23 June	6200	Faulty central booster reaction jet
5	24 June	10,750	Water temperature unit failure
6	1 July	8000	Trouble-free
7	2 July	10,800	Trouble-free
8	8 July	5000	Trouble-free
9	10 July	11,300	Faulty VDM-gearing
10	17 July	8000	Engine fire
11	23 Aug	—	Trimming flight (new 67 m^2 wings)
12	27 Aug	—	Trimming flight
13	28 Aug	9000	Faulty boost pump

Flight No	Date	Alt. (m)	Comments
14	28 Aug	9000	Faulty central booster engine
15	1 Sept	9000	Faulty central booster engine
16	1 Sept	9000	Faulty central booster engine
17	12 Sept	12,000	Faulty central booster engine
18	12 Sept	12,850	Faulty central booster engine
19	15 Sept	—	Trouble-free
20	16 Sept	—	Faulty fuel pump
21	18 Sept	13,000	Faulty central booster pump
22	19 Sept	12,000	Trouble-free
23	19 Sept	12,000	Trouble-free
24	23 Sept	6000	Starter failure at 6000 m
25	23 Sept	12,000	Trouble-free
26	23 Sept	12,000	Trouble-free
27	25 Sept	—	Trouble-free
28	7 Oct	—	Trouble-free
29	8 Oct	10,000	Trouble-free
30	8 Oct	10,000	Trouble-free
31	10 Oct	12,000	Trouble-free
32	10 Oct	12,000	Trouble-free
33	22 Oct	7,000	Trouble-free

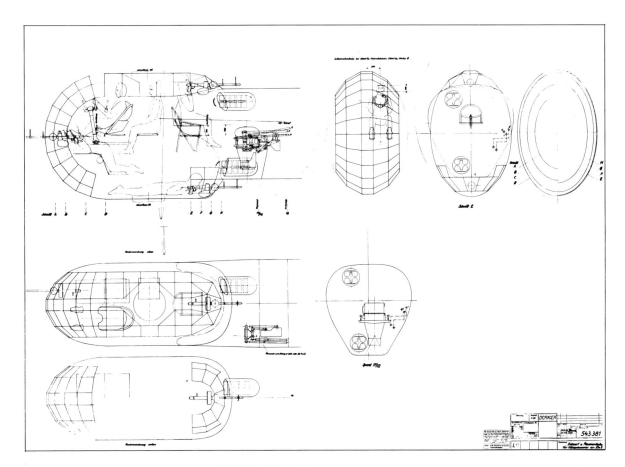

One of Dornier's early designs for a pressure cabin, dating from October 1939.

One of the first pressure-tight gun turrets fitted with an MG 15.

176

not operated on that occasion). The second test flight had to be terminated prematurely because of a faulty oil-pressure gauge. A further three flights were completed without any serious problems arising. However, the first completely satisfactory test flight was the sixth of the series. Twenty-four hours later, Do 217P V1 reached an altitude of 10,800 m, and 11,300 m on 10 July 1942.

During the tenth test flight, Do 217P V1 came close to crashing when one of its DB 603 engines caught fire. The crew succeeded in extinguishing the flames and bringing the aircraft down safely. To avoid a long delay in the test programme, it was decided that the new 67 m^2 wings would be fitted at the same time as the engine was changed (as the result of this incident). Both tasks had been completed by 22 August. Following two test flights (one on 23 August and one on 27 August) to trim the aircraft, and a thorough ground inspection, Do 217P V1 was test-flown on 28 August with the central booster engaged.

Notwithstanding that five of the following six test flights revealed one problem or another with the high-altitude central booster, the aircraft flew to an altitude as high as 12,850 m.

Based on the technical effort and the costs involved, Oberst Rowehl spoke out against the Do 217P. On 28 August 1942, he voted in favour of putting the Hs 130 (fitted with improved, high-altitude engines) into production without delay.

Between 23 September and 22 October 1942, Do 217P V1 made nine test flights (some of them at altitudes of approximately 12,000 m above sea level), with the high-altitude central booster engaged, and these were virtually trouble-free. However, Dornier's crew did report a slight vibration emanating from the booster engine. The metal propellers had been damaged also. Consequently, the test programme was interrupted temporarily, and the aircraft was flown to Löwental. Do 217P V1 made a further two flights before the end of 1942. Up until 31 December, the Dornier crew made a total of twelve flights at altitudes of between 5000 m and 10,000 m. On nine

occasions the aircraft reached altitudes of more than 12,000 m and on three occasions, over 13,000 m.

The unavailability of new propellers caused further interruption to the test programme. When it resumed, the aircraft succeeded in reaching its highest altitude to date — 13,650 m — during test flights on 11 and 30 March 1943. In June 1943, six test flights, totalling four hours' flying were made at Daimler-Benz. The results of these tests demonstrated that the improvements which had been made to the high-altitude central booster to date, resulted with the aircraft being both easier to operate and much more reliable.

The Technical Department of the Air Ministry made a critical appraisal of both aircraft. On 2 April 1943, Department GL/C-E2 circulated a detailed comparison between the developments of the Hs 130E and the Do 217P (with a high-altitude central booster) to the Head of the Technical Department, the KdE, and the High-altitude Flight Research Centre.

By the end of April 1943, Dornier had four airworthy test aircraft. However, at Henschel, the He 130E V2 had become inoperable, after completing a few test flights only. This delayed the test programme until the end of May 1943 because, in the event of an emergency landing, the only means of escape for the crew was through an emergency exit in the floor of the cabin. The Do 217P had been fitted, from the beginning, with an emergency exit in both the roof and the floor of the cabin, providing a means of escape for the crew in the event of a belly landing.

The Technische Amt reported the situation regarding high-altitude flight as follows:

At Henschel, flight testing the prototype and its equipment (defensive armament and release gear) will take until the end of the year (1943), practically. On this basis, development aircraft (V series) cannot be expected before the beginning of 1944, and production aircraft not before spring/summer 1944. The Hs 130E

Front view of Do 217 PV1, BK+IR (serial No 1229).

represents a completely new expense in terms of the money needed to complete the project.

The prototype Do 217P complete with a supercharger intercooler could be produced in two to three months. A further five aircraft could be produced shortly thereafter. Producing an increased number of aircraft would involve little expense . . . . In contrast with the Hs 130E it is anticipated that there will not be any problems with constructing the fuselage, because all of the relevant parts and components have been tested. . .

Equipped with the new supercharger intercooler, the Do 217P attained speeds of between 600 and 650 km/h. at an altitude of 13,000 m, and demonstrated a maximum operating ceiling of 15,000 m.

To summarize the foregoing: it could be said fairly that Dornier's development programme had gone virtually according to plan; while Henschel had been unable to meet the specified schedule.

The proposal of 28 August 1942 for the production of the Henschel high-altitude aircraft tied in with the intention to cease the production of Do 217 series aircraft at the end of 1942. However, in spring 1943, the Air Ministry decided that Do 217M–8 production should continue until 1944/45, and they did not have any fundamental misgivings about the Do 217P at that time. Therefore, the building of a total of six development aircraft could proceed.

Meanwhile, the Hs 130E V3 and Do 217P V1 both underwent numerous measurement and performance tests at the Daimler-Benz factory in Echterdingen. During one of these, on 28 September, the Dornier aircraft was damaged slightly, but the crew were unhurt. The Do 217P V1 was repaired soon, and further high-altitude flight tests were carried out with the Dornier and Henschel aircraft by Flugkapitän Ellenrieder, Daimler-Benz's chief test pilot, who succeeded in taking the Hs 130E up to 15,000 m over Echterdingen. The results from flight tests with the high-altitude central booster engaged showed that it was suitable equally for the Hs 130 and the Do 217. Up to 1 April 1943, the Do 217P V1 completed twenty-three test flights successfully, totalling thirty-four hours' flying.

The first Do 217P to be equipped with a pressure cabin and the costly high-altitude engine, augmented by a supercharger intercooler.

General arrangement drawing
of the Do 217P-1 high-altitude
bomber.

Rear view of the Do 217 PV1
showing the air intake.

180

The Do 217P V1 remained with Daimler-Benz for almost a year before it was returned, in April 1944, to Friedrichshafen, where it was fitted with new 71 m^2 wings. Following the completion of this work, it was to be transferred to the High-Altitude Flight Research Centre, in accordance with a directive issued by the Air Ministry. Meanwhile, the conversion of two Do 217E aircraft (serial Nos 0024 and 0025) had been almost completed.

The second Do 217P which was fitted with the old version of the supercharger intercooler was ready by September 1942 and, after completing its initial works tests, it was intended that it should be transferred to Daimler-Benz. As it did for the Do 217P V1, the aircraft's test schedule overran by almost five months.

In October, the first three P-series development aircraft were flown, while a further three were in production. According to the original schedule, the test-flight programme for the last Do 217P was due to have started in June 1942; obviously, this was impossible. In March 1943 the P V1 and the P V3 were both test-flown to compare the old and new versions of the supercharger intercooler; the results favoured the new version.

The third Do 217P was ready on 2 April 1943. According to an inventory drawn up by the Technische Amt, of the remaining three aircraft in production at Friedrichshafen, one (the V4) was 95% complete, while the V5 and V6 were between 60% and 80% assembled. By the end of the month, the V4 and V6 were both nearly complete in respect of their airframes, at least.

As the result of air raid, the P V2 and P V3 were put out of action temporarily; the P V2 was not repaired until 1 July 1943. This meant that only the P V1 was available for high-altitude flight tests, six of which were made. Having been repaired, the Do 217P was transferred to Cazeaux for drop tests. On 27 March 1944, it crashed at Cazeaux and was written-off. The P V3 had been damaged badly in the air raid, and it was obvious that it was going to take quite some time to repair. Eventually, it was repaired and available for testing by 31 March 1944

(albeit fitted with the old version of the cooling unit and without the high-altitude central booster).

By 24 April 1944, the only P-version aircraft equipped with a high-altitude central booster available for flight testing was the P V1. In the meantime, it had been coaxed to an altitude of 15,200 m. Continuing to climb at the rate of 0.25 m/sec, it had been forced to turn back only because its fuel supply was beginning to run out. The Do 217P V3 and P V4 were both transferred from the Dornier factory to Löwental without their DB 605 engines. Work on the fourth development aircraft had been stopped and an application had been submitted to the Air Ministry for the aircraft to be scrapped. The Air Ministry issued a directive to the effect that all of those high-altitude central booster units which had not yet fitted into aircraft were to be returned to Daimler-Benz. Furthermore, Dornier at Friedrichshafen was instructed to cease the production of V-series aircraft, to destroy the jigs and tools for, and to cease work on P-0- series aircraft.

With the loss of the second development aircraft only the P V1 and the P V3 remained at Dornier. By the summer of 1943, both the P V5 and the P V6 (serial Nos 0027 and 0028) had not been completed. As a result, the Air Ministry's interest in additional

Dornier drawing of the high-altitude central booster unit.

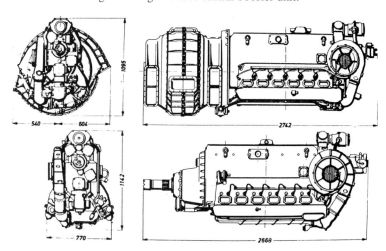

Model of the heavy BMW 803 engine, which was planned for use in the Do 217.

development aircraft waned, and both aircraft, still incomplete, were put into mothballs at Löwental. On 17 March 1944, a directive was issued ordering that both aircraft were to be scrapped and that any usable parts were to be salvaged for use elsewhere.

Following cut-backs in the high-altitude flight test programme in the summer of 1943 and again at the end of the year, both the 0-series (which was then underway) and the proposed production series foundered. In the end, all of this work was cancelled. All that remained were the Do 217P V1 (which, in the meantime, had been fitted presumably with 71 m² wings) and the third Do 217P (without its high-altitude boosters). Together with the Hs 130E-0 (serial No 130054), these aircraft continued the test programme. Then, on 5 September 1944, Allied bombers dealt a crippling blow: during a low-level raid on Stuttgart, all three aircraft were destroyed, together with an Hs 130 A-0 (serial no. 3005) with two DB 605C engines,

and GM 1 equipment. Thus the two remaining Do 217Ps disappeared.

Both the Do 217P-1 and the P-2 never really had a chance.

The Do 217P-1 combined two high-altitude roles, namely those of reconnaissance and bomber. For its wings, the Dornier designers selected the 67 m² type, having a span of 24.5 m. In the reconnaissance role (without bomb load), the P-1 was to have a service ceiling of 12,000 m, and at an altitude of 14,000 m it would be able to achieve a maximum speed of 620 km/h. In the bomber role, its service ceiling was to be 12,700 m. Both versions were usually armed with three MG 81Z twin machine guns. Provision had been made also for the aircraft to carry guided weapons. In addition to Lotfe and BZA 1 stores, the bomber version was fitted with two ETC racks to carry stores totalling a maximum weight of 1000 kg, together with one 500/100/XI, or two 500/XIb, or 500/XII fixed carriages.

From 1943 (or probably earlier) Dornier investigated the possibility of the aircraft carrying either Fritz-X, or Hs 293 guided weapons, on inboard/outboard underwing pylons. However, because of the high cost of in providing the heating equipment necessary for these missiles at high altitudes, the idea of a bomber with a pressurised cabin was soon abandoned.

Together with the Do 217P-1, the P-2 was at an advanced design stage also. Dornier's designers had calculated that, by fitting a new, 100 m² area wing, the P-2's high-altitude performance would be increased significantly. However, the enormous costs involved in its production precluded its approval by the Air Ministry.

In addition to the work on a few P-series development aircraft, and on the P-1/P-2 projects, Dornier's engineers were conducting an in-depth study of the fundamental problems arising from military aircraft operations at very high altitudes. Although they had accumulated the basic research data during the late 1930s, many questions remained and Dornier did not have much time in

The central booster unit which consisted of a DB 605T engine and a fan.

which to find the answers. One of the significant problems was icing which occurred as the result of the extremely low temperatures in the atmosphere at high altitude. Temperatures as low as −60°C could lead easily to icing of the cabin's glazing, or to heavy condensation on the windscreen, at least. Tests were conducted using a high altitude pressurization and cooling system, during which a three-sided cabin was cooled and ventilated by filtered air which was fed from, among other things, the engine booster.

Dornier was working also on heating the inside of the high-altitude pressure cabin, using the same methods as those of their counterparts at Henschel.

Aircraft operating at altitudes of 13,500 m and above had to comply with very strict safety standards which had been set down by the Rechlin Experimental Establishment. Among other things, they covered the so-called emergency dive which would occur automatically in the event of a sudden drop in cabin pressure. The introduction of special rescue equipment, with a separate oxygen supply, was planned, which would enable the crew to escape by parachute, should an emergency occur.

The Engine Department at the Air Ministry collaborated very closely with those companies concerned with making short-term improvements to turbo-superchargers, and developing high performance engines for the He 111, the Ju 88 and the Do 217. As alternatives to the very expensive high-altitude central booster, a series of high-altitude engines was proposed. One of these engines was the DB 627, which was basically a 12-cylinder V-engine with the same C3 fuel system as that of the DB 603G, and a mechanically-driven, two-stage booster and supercharger intercooler. At a critical altitude of 11,500 m, the engine was capable of producing a sustained output of 2,000 hp. Nevertheless, on 24 February 1944, as the result of Air Ministry calculations, developing the DB 627 (which by then was at quite an advanced stage) was cancelled.

A rapid solution was required to the problem of building a lightweight, high-altitude night bomber, without a pressurized cabin, and powered by DB 603 engines. A suggestion from Dornier's engineers at Friedrichshafen proved to be particularly interesting to the Technische Amt at the Air Ministry.

The Do 217M-4 with two TK 9 turbo-superchargers was due to enter production in the winter of 1943. Dornier's proposal concerned the use of GM 1 auxiliary injection. Following a short discussion during a meeting chaired by Generalfeldmarschall Milch on 28 August 1942, the idea was put on file, those present favouring the Ju 88D-6, powered by BMW 801D engines and a GM 1. Later, it was planned to use uprated D-series engines instead of the BMW 801D, to increase the aircraft's service ceiling. Furthermore, the TK 15 turbo-supercharger (an improved version of the TK 11) showed a great deal of promise in the longer term. If the critical operating height was approximately 11,500 m with the normal booster, this could be increased easily to between 14,000 m and 15,000 m using the TK 15.

The Hs 130E-0, which was fitted with a high-altitude central booster, was the Do 217P's most important competitor for some time. Pictured is CF+O2, which was destroyed during an Allied bombing raid on the Daimler-Benz factory at Stuttgart on 5 September 1944.

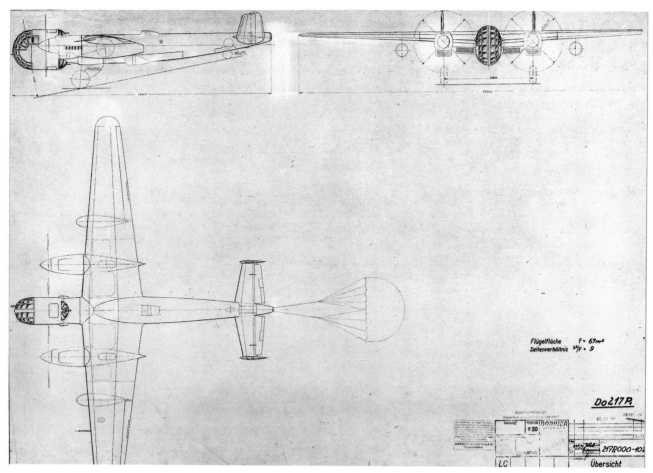

Drawing of the Do 217P-1, dated 25 May 1941, showing the large, emergency brake parachute.

The DB 621 high-altitude engine, augmented by a TK 9 turbo-super-charger, was developed in 1941 from the DB 601T.

185

The plan was to install the TK 15 turbo-super-charger in both the Hs 130 and the Do 217, although, at that time, this was some way ahead in the future. At a meeting convened by the head of the Technische Amt at the Air Ministry on 6 November 1942, emphasis was placed on discussing the various problems arising from the different high-altitude engines and, for the most part, their untenable production schedules. Everybody blamed somebody else! For example, the Hs 130C programme could not get under way because the projected DB 601D power-plant did not go into production on time. As a temporary solution, it was necessary to resort to the use of a DB 601R powerplant, then a DB 605A. However, these powerplants precluded the possibility of the aircraft's having an increased performance. For the Hs 130E (the direct competitor to the Do 217P) it was considered that a DB 603 power-plant, augmented by a TK 15 turbo-supercharger offered the perfect solution to any problems associated with the high-altitude central booster. Furthermore, the turbo-supercharger presented a welcome means of increasing an aircraft's operating ceiling to 16,000 m, and its speed to more than 600 km/h. Fewer than ten Dornier and Henschel development aircraft were built with the high-altitude, central booster installation.

Under the chairmanship of Generalfeldmarschall Milch, a meeting was held on 12 January 1943, during which the Do 217 and Hs 130 high-altitude aircraft were both discussed. The Do 217M-4, armed with a PC 1400 X guided weapon, was expected to be available for high-altitude bombing operations within a few months of the meeting, albeit a few aircraft only.

Operating at altitudes of between 10,000 m and 11,000 m, the crews were expected to be more successful when deploying the Fritz-X than they would be when attacking at more usual altitudes. However, in respect of the TK 9, so crucial to their plans, the representatives of industry and the RLM had deceived themselves constantly.

Meanwhile, successful trials with an He 111 powered by Jumo 211 engines and a TK 11 turbo-supercharger had shown that it was possible to reach targets in central Britain with a payload totalling 1000 kg, at a height of 10,000 m. However, the high failure rate of the TK 11 caused increasing concern.

After Hitler had involved himself surprisingly in the development programme, and had influenced the Air Ministry indirectly 'to pursue the development of high-altitude aircraft at all costs', the Air Ministry's Technical Department apparently stepped up the development of special, high-altitude engines.

From that point, scant attention was paid to the high-altitude central booster, and to various types of turbo-supercharger.

Operations involving the Ju 86 reconnaissance aircraft and dive bombers had to be terminated quite quickly because British development of high-altitude fighter aircraft was proceeding faster than Germany had anticipated, and thereby precluding the viability of high-altitude operations over Britain. For this reason the Do 217 powered by BMW 801D engines was cancelled, in October 1942, in favour of the Ju 88D-6 with BMW powerplants and a GM 1 for added performance. The first of these aircraft was test-flown over Britain in December 1942 by a crew from the Rowehl Kommand. Although the aircraft managed to reach a speed of 585 km/h at 11,500 m, frequent failures of the GM 1 gave a lasting cause for complaint.

Installation of the new, uprated BMW 801TM powerplant, from the summer of 1943, offered a more favourable prospect. To avoid jeopardizing the schedule, Generalfeldmarschall Milch ordered expressedly that production fo the BMW 801J, up till then so strongly approved, the 0-series of which was in production already, was to be cancelled for the most part. Those BMW 801Js which had been manufactured already were to be fitted to the Ju 88 D-6, and the high-speed reconnaissance version of the Ju 88L-0 which was used as a test bed for an auxiliary, high-altitude combat aircraft, until such times as a decision was made finally between the Do 217P-1 and the Hs 130E-1. However, in July 1943 the Technische Amt changed its mind about

Mock-ups of the DB 603 U engine with a TK 15 turbo-supercharger, which were to power the Do 217M-4. The performance figures calculated for this power-plant indicated that it was capable of producing 1810 hp at an altitude of 13,000 m.

the Ju 188L-0 with two BMW 801J engines, and ordered that the BMW engines were to be installed in the more modern Ju 388.

On 6 November 1942 the Ju 186 project (for a high-altitude, four-engined aircraft, which was a development of the Ju 86) was terminated because it used a high-altitude central booster. The decision to terminate the project followed a heated discussion between GFM Milch, Oberstleutnant iG Pasewaldt, Stabsingenieur Friebel, and Oberst Rowehl. Also present at the meeting was Oberst-

leutnant Petersen who was of the opinion that not only the Ju 186 tests, but tests with other aircraft fitted with high-altitude central boosters also should not be interrupted. Friebel claimed, as his opinion, that neither the Henschel nor the Dornier aircraft appeared to be entirely suitable for operational duties. He favoured the more conventional Junkers aircraft.

Oberst Rowehl considered the continuation of long-range reconnaissance operations to be the key issue. He suggested that, together with concentrating wholeheartedly on work concerned with high-altitude operations, a version of the Ju 88 with BMW 801J engines and a pressure cabin should be developed. He reasoned that this would provide an operational stopgap until the aircraft which was chosen finally could be put into operation. Oberstleutnant Pasewaldt's opinion was that, together with the Ju 186, the Do 217 project should be dropped as quickly as possible, also, particularly because the production schedule was such that the aircraft would not be ready in time for the coming battle. At the end of the meeting, Erhard Milch cancelled the entire Ju 186 project, and both versions of the Do 217 JP which were to have been fitted with 67-and 100-m^2 wings. The next step was the cancellation of both the four-engined version of the Ju 188, and the Hs 130 E-1 with high-altitude central boosters.

The next meeting concerning high-altitude aircraft was held on 20 August 1943, at which the final decision was made that three basic versions of the Ju 388 (high-altitude bomber, reconnaissance aircraft, and night fighter) were to be developed. Representatives from the Technische Amt and the Waffengenerale, together with the Commander of Experimental Establishments and Oberst Rowehl all favoured the idea.

However, both the Henschel and the Dornier high-altitude aircraft did not disappear into the Air Ministry's archives. On 7 December 1943, Oberstleutnant Knemeyer brought up the subject of both aircraft for discussion again. Although the number of development aircraft available had been depleted heavily, he urged that those which remained should be used as test-beds for new high-altitude engines and turbo-superchargers.

Future high-altitude bombing and reconnaissance operations were to be performed by both the K and L versions of the Ju 388 which, in addition to the BMW 801J powerplant, were to be equipped with the long-awaited Jumo 222 A/B and its high-altitude version, the Jumo 222 E/F.

Only in the event of there being sufficient extra production capacity available, work would continue on the four-engined Ju 488 heavy bomber and the He 274 (which had been under development for several years).

At Heinkel, the He 177A-7, which was powered by four DB 603 engines, was followed by the B-5 and the B-7. From these, the He 277 evolved, powered by four BMW 801 engines. The final product, the He 274 heavy bomber, could trace its origins to the He 177 which was already on the drawing board in 1942.

From the beginning of 1943, when design work other than that concerned with the cabin, engines and ordnance was transferred to Farman, progress with the He 274 was slow. Its powerplant, consisting of a DB 605 engine and a TK 11B turbo-supercharger, was fitted to a Do 217 (made available for the purpose in March 1943) in order to save development time. Although the He 274 was ready to go into production, a few aircraft only could be expected for operational use. The same applied to the Ju 488 which was due to enter production in May 1945.

With the basic agreement of GFM Milch, Generalmajor Vorwald proclaimed that, in view of the delays that had afflicted thus far the development of all of the aforementioned aircraft, henceforth attention would be confined unconditionally to the Ju 388. In a new attempt to ensure sufficient production capacity, the Technische Amt ordered a review of all of the outstanding contracts and instructions concerning the production of high-altitude aircraft at Henschel and Dornier.

In February 1944, Erhard Milch ordered that all work on the Hs 130 was to be terminated forthwith. The majority of Hs 130C aircraft were to be scrapped. The Hs 130E-1, which was then in production, was dismantled and the materials assigned for re-use. One airworthy Hs 130E-0 only remained parked at a Henschel factory as a precautionary measure. In March, Dornier received a directive, to the effect that its 0-series programme was to be terminated and that all partly-manufactured aircraft were to be scrapped.

The Ju 388 was operational.

CHAPTER TEN
The Search for Bomber B

In July 1939, the Technische Amt of the German Air Ministry invited tenders for a second generation of military aircraft. The Ju 88 V1 had made its first flight on 21 December 1936. I/KG 30 was the first unit to be equipped with the Ju 88 (the A-0 version), taking delivery of their aircraft in the late summer of 1939. Prior to this, from the spring of 1937, the Ju 86 made a short appearance as an interim solution until attention was focussed finally on the Do 17 and the He 111. Most of Germany's Kampfverbände (bomber units), such as KG 4, 26, 27, and 51 to 54, operated the Heinkel He 111, while Kampfgeschwader 2, 3, 76 and 77 were equipped with the Dornier bomber for the time being. Thus armed, the Luftwaffe entered the Second World War.

The He 111 was eminently suited to relatively short-range, 'Blitzkrieg'-type operations; but not to a wide-range of operations over long distances, carrying an effective bombload. An aircraft capable of carrying out the latter type of operations was required urgently. A four-engined heavy bomber had been sacrificed in 1937 in favour of an attack aircraft with a dive bombing capability, which could provide the Army with tactical support. Shortly before the outbreak of the war, war games had indicated the need for a bomber aircraft capable of carrying a 1000 kg bomb load as far as Gibraltar and Iceland, at least. In extreme cases, the aircraft was to be capable of carrying a bomb load of 3000 kg for striking at, and severing (if possible) maritime links with the British Isles. The requirement for a medium-weight bomber, with the performance abilities of a long-range aircraft, was easier to formulate than it was to fulfil.

In June 1940, design office staff at Dornier's headquarters produced plans for a development of the Do 217 (to be designated Do 317), which would have a pressure cabin pressure cabin and improved engines — specifically BMW 801s, or more powerful DB 606s. As they were at Dornier, discussions by other applicants for the 'Bomber B' contract were conducted behind closed doors. To all those who were concerned, it was clear that the success of the entire project depended on the availability of an aero-engine powerful enough to meet the specified performance levels. However, the pace of aero-engine development was slow and could not keep up with airframe developments. It seemed as though the Air Ministry had forgotten that the timetable involved in turning ambitious aero-engine projects into a reality could not be relied upon. (More about that later.)

Initially, four proposals were submitted to the Technische Amt (as requested) for successors to the Do 17, He 111 and the Ju 88. These included the very futuristic Arado E 340, the costly Fw 191, the adaptable Ju 288 and the Do 317.

The Arado proposal, dated July 1939, was for an aircraft having an overall length of 19.15 m, a wingspan of 23 m, and, as requested by the Technische Amt, was fully capable of operating both as a dive bomber and in a conventional role. It had an operating range of 3600 km, and a cruising speed of 600 km/h at an altitude of 7000 m. The engines chosen to power the Arado E 340 were either two BMW 802s, two DB 604s, or two Jumo 222s. A special feature of the Arado design were the separate tail booms, at the ends of which a gun could be mounted. Its defensive armament consisted also of a tail-mounted gun, two powerful twin guns, and a maximum of two 20 mm cannon on the top and underside of the fuselage.

A Ju 288 V2 (D-ABWP) and a Ju 88 V16 (D-ACAR) pictured together at Dessau.

The first Fw 191 prototype for which only BMW 801 engines were available.

In the beginning, at least, the Arado E 340 did not seem to have captured the imagination of the Director of Operational Requirements, or those of Air Ministry Staff, because, when the contracts were placed, in autumn 1940, for the production of the first prototype aircraft the Arado proposal was not included. Subject to the approval of their mock-ups, two prototypes for each of the Fw 191, Ju 288 and Do 317 proposals were to be manufactured as quickly as it was possible to do so, then basic testing could begin.

The Fw 191 was the second competitor to the Dornier project. It was to be powered by either two Jumo 222C/Ds, or two DB 610A/Bs developing 2950 hp. The estimated maximum speed at an altitude of just under 7000 m was between 600 and 620 km/h. Its service ceiling was estimated to be between 10,100 m and 10,300 m. Its maximum all-up weight of 26,650 kg included a bombload totalling 6000 kg. In addition to the then-current calibres of bombs, the Fw 191 could carry four LT 1500-type aerial torpedos. The 19.63 m long aircraft had a wingspan of 26 m and was equipped with an impressive array of defensive weapons: two MG 151 twin-cannon, a ventral MG 151 and another in the tail, together with remote-controlled MG 81Zs on the engine/wing fairing.

Specifications dated 16 May 1940, showed the Fw 191 to be a four-seat bomber/reconnaissance aircraft, equipped with either an Rb 50/30, 20/30, or 75/30 camera. A lack of engines and of electrical equipment to operate many of the systems, which would be operated hydraulically otherwise, resulted in tremendous delays in the production programme.

In September 1940, the stressmen were working on the various loading cases for the first prototype. Because of the situation concerning engine development, proposals to use other versions were not taken up; not even the DB 603, the development of which had not progressed far. The only solution, as

Another B Bomber contender: the Blohm und Voss BV P 163 which was powered by a BMW 803 engine, and fitted with contra-rotating propellers.

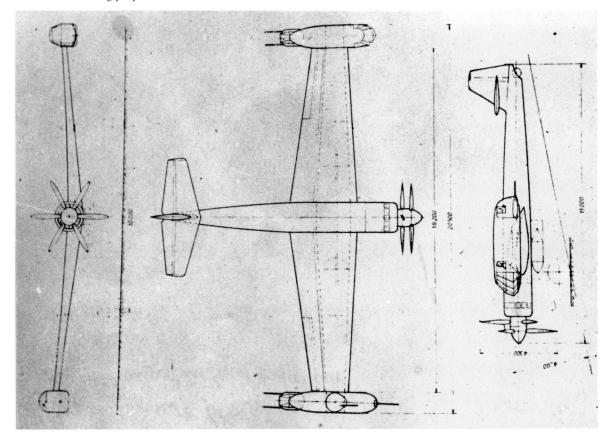

was often the case, was to use a BMW 801 power-plant.

During the winter of 1941, Focke-Wulf's design department laboured with different configurations of multi-barrelled gun for the Fw 191 V13, and worked on the Fw 191 X13 project. The latter was an alternative, in the event of the remote-controlled weapon system not being ready in time — the designers reverting to the installation of manually-operated MG 131s. A proposal dated 20 April 1940 also made provision for a manned turret in the centre fuselage instead of a tail-positioned gun.

The Fw 191 V1 (which had been equipped in the meantime with two BMW 801MA engines) made its first flight in spring 1942 when it was piloted by Dipl-Ing Mehlhorn. It was not possible to power the aircraft with Jumo 222 engines until the sixth prototype was produced. Because of the aircraft's complicated equipment, the Fw 191 programme tended to drag on, with the result that the Ju 288 proved to be a more dangerous competitor to the Do 317.

In common with those of the other applicants, the proposal submitted by Dornier in Dessau also envisaged the use of the high-performance Jumo 222 engine, which was regarded justifiably as highly attractive in view of its unusual air intake, and its well-planned type of exhaust ducting. The small diameter of the Jumo 222 was an added plus offering excellent installation possibilities.

The first prototype Ju 288 was to be ready by October 1940, to be followed by a further two aircraft by December. Junkers' Planning Department Staff envisaged, somewhat optimistically, that production would have started by January 1942. As an alternative to the Jumo 222-powered version, a second version was also proposed, based on the Jumo 223 engine which could develop 2500 hp for take-off, and would give the aircraft a maximum speed of 650 km/h at an altitude of 8000 m. Due to its more favourable field of fire, a twin tail fin configuration was preferred to that of a central fin.

Junkers succeeded in producing a complete cabin and armaments mock-up by May 1940 and this was

General arrangement drawing, dated 9 January 1941, of the Do 317 heavy bomber.

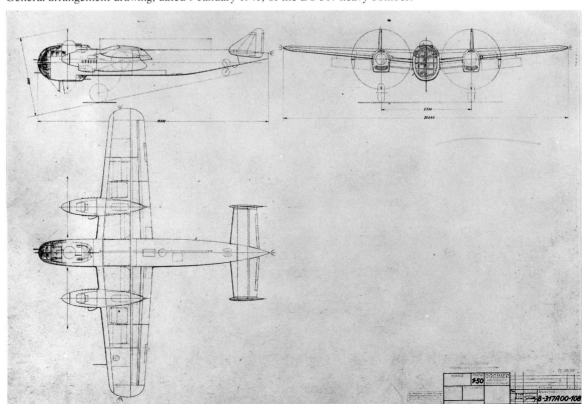

inspected by Air Ministry representatives during the last few days of May, following which the proposal for its temporary installation was approved. This involved the production of the Ju 288A which, in its first development stage, was to be powered by a Jumo 222, generating only 2000 hp for take-off. However, the Jumo engine was not available. Consequently the first Ju 288 prototype had to be fitted with BMW 801 powerplants. The Ju 288 V1 (D-AACS) first flew on 29 November 1940; but on 2 March 1941 it was destroyed by fire. The second and third development aircraft followed in April 1941.

As the first Ju 288 was nearing final assembly, the Do 317A mock-up was undergoing inspection at Dornier. On 17 October 1941, a large group, consisting of personnel from the Air Ministry and the Rechlin and Tarnewitz Experimental Establishments, assembled in Friedrichshafen to assess, in particular, the functionality of the crew cabin.

The Do 317's defensive armament was especially interesting, in that all of its gun emplacements, including the A position, were equipped with the MG 131. Delays at Rheinmetall-Borsig in the development of the HD 131 concealed gun (the first functional mock-up of which was due to be flight-tested in November) resulted in the use of an MG 131 armaments configuration as a temporary measure. As the aircraft's fixed armament, Dornier favoured the MG 151/20 with 250 rounds of ammunition. Proposals to install the Lotfe bomb-aiming system and an emergency release for the stores were both approved by the Technische Amt, without reservation. The Do 317's stores were based essentially on the configuration of the bomb bay, which was the same as that of the Do 217E-2, and was represented on the mock-up by indication only. This prompted a request from the Air Ministry to construct a dummy store. It was agreed generally, however, that it would be possible to carry all of the then-current types of bombs, up to the SC 1000, without any modifications. Two ETC 2000s were fitted for carrying external stores. The idea of carrying aerial torpedos was not favoured because they called for a specially-designed aircraft.

Its radio equipment consisted of an FuG X, FuG 16, FuG 25, an FuBl.1 with autopilot engagement, and a PeilG.6 operated by the radio operator.

Inspection of the mock-up resumed on 22 October 1940, and continued on the 23rd. After the weapons system had been dealt with, and when a few details only remained to be clarified, the specialists concentrated on the cabin layout. Particular importance was attached to the blind flying instrumentation, the oxygen supply, the crew seating, and the auxiliary control. Only minor improvements to the equipment proposed by Dornier were necessary.

As had been the case with the Fw 191 and the Ju 288, the engineers in Friedrichshafen examined the use of second-generation aero-engines, the emphasis being placed on high-performance radial engines. The choice was either the Jumo 222, the DB 604, or the BMW 802. Development of the BMW 18-cylinder, twin radial engine began in 1939. On 28 January 1941, this work was transferred entirely to France where the first engine was produced in spring 1941, with a further two in production. The few engines that were built were used for test-bed trials, which showed that the BMW 802 was capable of developing at least 2450 hp. Nevertheless, the entire project was dropped in the summer of 1942 as the result of technical problems.

Development of the 24-cylinder DB 604 radial engine was also terminated, in September 1942, work on the DB 603 and the DB 605 having taken precedence. The German Air Ministry also expected great things of the Jumo 222. This was a water/glycol-cooled 24-cylinder radial engine, having a dry weight of approximately 1100 kg. From May 1937, when the development contract was placed with Junkers, production and practical tests had seemed to drag on and on. Problems with the crankshaft and connecting rods called for a basic improvement in the design of the engine and the first of the improved Jumo 222 engines was run up on 10 August 1940. The results obtained from this

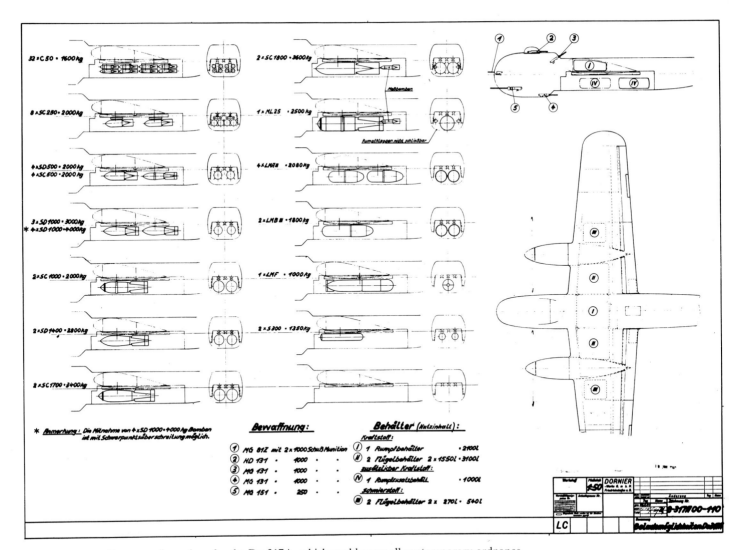

Stores configurations for the Do 317A, which could carry all contemporary ordnance.

test so encouraged Direktor Camweis at Junkers that he envisaged the Jumo 222 being in production by 1943.

In December 1940, Dornier was also working on two other versions (with the DB 603), in addition to that on the Do 317 with Jumo 222 engines, and these were submitted to the Technische Amt in Berlin at the beginning of 1941. These aircraft designs (neither of which incorporated a pressure cabin) were followed by that for the Do 317B, which had a multi-seat, high-altitude chamber, and a larger wing area. A Do 317 with Jumo 222 engines and an improved defensive armament marked the end of this interim stage of development. In this configuration, and in common with the K and M versions of the Do 217, a ventral pack comprising an MG 81Z with 2000 rounds of ammunition was to be incorporated. In addition, an MG 151/20 (for ground attack) was to be built into the nose. Both B positions were equipped with an MG 131, and a 13 mm gun was also placed in the C position, to defend the aircraft's rear.

194

The first Do 317 prototype powered by DB 603 engines and having triangular tail fins.

Do 317 V1 VK+IY pictured during tests with Dornier.

In contrast to the Do 217, the Do 317 incorporated a larger bomb bay in a modified fuselage, which could accommodate either four SC 1000, or eight SC 500 bombs. The bomb bay could carry all of the then-current types of bombs, or four BSB 700 bomb canisters. The Do 317B's defensive armament was heavier. It had an MG 131Z rotating turret in the fuselage centre section, and an MG 151I in the tail. The aircraft could carry four SC 1400 bombs, or two SC 1800s, or one SC 2500, and three LMB airborne mines also. Each of the two ETC underwing pylons could carry a bombload of up to 1800 kg, or an aerial torpedo.

In addition to the three versions of the Do 317 high-altitude bomber with a pressure cabin, a variant with a central tailplane was also on the drawing board. Work was also progressing on a high-altitude aircraft powered by DB 606 engines, and having 4.6 m diameter propellers. To ease the production load, it was decided to fit the Do 217's tail section on the aircraft. Its defensive armament consisted of three rotating gun carriages, each having an MG 131 Z, and an MG 151 in a remote-controlled FLH-151 tail gun: ample protection against the guns of enemy fighters. To improve the aircraft's performance at high altitudes, it was decided to increased the wingspan and the wing area (75 m²).

As an alternative, Dornier designed a version of the Do 317. It was powered by two BMW 801 engines, it had a pressure cabin, and a reduced defensive armament consisting of a rotating turret on the top and undersides of the cabin and a remote-controlled tail gun. In contrast to the ultimate version, this aircraft was to be fitted with the standard Do 217E tailplane. Despite overcoming all of the various design problems, however, this very forward-thinking proposal would remain incomplete as long as the engines remained unavailable.

By the summer of 1941 any real solution was not within sight, at a time when Udet was considering actively the phasing out (even terminating production prematurely) of most medium-range bombers, except the Do 217!

From May onwards, the decision as to which of the new Bomber B aircraft would be put into production was awaited. Although it was not known at the time, the situation would remain thus for several years to come!. The race between the Do 317, the Fw 191 and the Ju 288 did not produce a victor. Instead of having the new bomber in production in 1942, as had been planned originally, it seemed very much as if it would not enter service until 1944.

The dive-bombing capability included in the Air Ministry's specifications for the Bomber B precluded any four-engined aircraft design proposals and restricted the range of possibilities to medium-weight bomber aircraft. More effective solutions, such as the A-7 to B-7 versions of the He 177 and the He 274, were eliminated from the very beginning. The misguided belief that the ensuing few years could be bridged with the use of an uprated Jumo 211 resulted with a half-hearted attempt only to develop the Jumo 213.

Heavy losses which had been sustained in the war against the Soviet Union and on all of the other fronts did not leave room for any experimentation, and resulted with the continued production of the He 111 and the Ju 88 standard bombers. The calls for improved bomber aircraft were becoming increasingly loud, but they did not bring about any visible change in the situation. The General-luftzeugmeister was looking for quality rather than quantity.

Meanwhile, development work on the Fw 191 had slipped more than ten months behind schedule. Aircraft problems and losses had also affected the Ju 288 programme, and the same applied to the Do 317 — the first prototype of which had yet to make its first flight!

Milch decided in favour of the Ju 288 which, according to the information supplied by Junkers, would start coming off the production line in January 1942. However constant changes to the specifications from the Luftwaffenführungsstab (Luftwaffe General Staff), coupled with problems with the Jumo 222 (the endurance performance of

Front and side views of Do 317 VI VK+IY pictured while undergoing tests with Dornier.

which failed to meet the Technische Amt's specifications) precluded any possibilities of keeping such a deadline. At the end of August 1941, Milch called the Director General of Junkers, Dr Coppenberg, and his technical manager, Herr Thiedemann, to obtain binding information on the actual status of the Ju 288. They both reconfirmed that production would commence in 1942, provided that any insurmountable problems with the Jumo 222 did not arise. This information was vague and not very convincing.

A few days later, Milch met Junkers' representatives. Having been subjected to great pressure, Junkers' management had to admit finally that they did not have any immediate solutions to the problems which had arisen with the Jumo 222 cylinders and the connecting-rod bearings. However, Prof Mader and the director, Herr Cambeis, both agreed with Coppenberg and Thiedemann that the Ju 288 could be put into production in June 1942 (powered by another engine instead of the Jumo 222, if necessary). However, this assurance failed to convince those who were in command. In a speech given at the Reichsjägerhof on 6 September 1941, Hermann Goering's message was clear: postpone the Bomber B project and drop the idea of using the Jumo 222.

As far as the mass production of the Jumo 222 was concerned, Goering's decision had its effect — on paper, at least. However, the manufacture of development B Bombers continued unabated. The requirement was modified accordingly. Instead of being cancelled, the production of 0-series aircraft was stepped up to ensure a supply of thirty-six Jumo 222 engines for nine Ju 288s, twenty engines for five Fw 191s, and twelve engines for the first three Do 317s. Because the Dornier aircraft were not ready, it was decided that prototype Jumo engines (including spare and replacement engines) should be made for a Ju 288, as soon as it was possible to do so.

The Fw 191, classified as urgent, would be powered by either DB 603, DB 606, DB 610 or Jumo 211J engines, although the Jumo 222 power-

Drawing of the Do 317 with 68 m² wing area and pressure cabin, dated 20 January 1940.

plant was preferred. Having an all-up weight of 21.5 tonnes (including a bomb load weighing 6000 kg), calculations for the aircraft's performance indicated a range of 1800 km, increasing to 5200 km with only 2000 kg of bombs on board. For maritime operations, carrying four LT 1500 aerial torpedos, its radius of operation would be 800 km approximately. A directive was received by Junkers ordering the production of a further thirty-six Jumo 222 A/B engines. Despite feverish activities and numerous attempts to improve the radial engine, it never went into production. For the time being, a Ju 288 V5 (BG+GU) only was powered by two Jumo 222s, making its first flight on 8 October 1941. All of the other deadlines were impossible to meet.

The prematurely-praised Fw 191 made its first appearance in spring 1942. It was not powered by the Jumo 222, as had been intended originally, instead lower performance BMW 801 engines had been fitted as a temporary solution. Its performance did not live up to the expectations of the Technische Amt. Its complicated equipment resulted later in a number of plans being changed.

By mid-May 1942, the Generalluftzeugmeister had run out of patience also. In a seemingly endless series of discussions and crisis meetings, the sole topic was that of finding ways to make the best of the confused situation which prevailed at that time. It was felt that either an improved version of the Do 217, or the Ju 188 (formerly the Ju 88 E) could offer a feasible, short-term solution. The Technische Amt had already approved the extended wing span of the Dornier aircraft, so it seemed as if this version had been accepted basically. However, in preference to the Ju 188 (which could be completed relatively easy), the RLM revived its interest in the Bomber B.

On 10 December 1942, Junkers' aero-engine division announced that the production of the improved C/D version of the Jumo 222 would not be started until the end of 1944 in all probability. Of the three original Performance Class II engines (the Jumo 222, Jumo 213 and DB 603), each of which should have gone into production in 1943, all that remained was the Daimler-Benz engine which was also plagued by teething troubles. Therefore, it was quite obvious that the production of the DB 609 and BMW 802 Class III engines was out of the question. Consequently, as far as the Do 217 was concerned, the studies had been to no avail, after all. Severe doubts surrounded the BMW 803 also (the sole Performance Class IV engine), as to whether series production could be started before 1947, or not!

Although none of the three Bomber B aircraft had gone into production by the spring of 1943, various aircraft design departments did not lack any new proposals.

The Technische Amt was also involved with the Do 317B, which had had to be redesigned around a DB 610 (as had the Ju 288 and Fw 191). Nevertheless, several months passed by before the Do 317 was rolled out. In June 1943 the first prototype was still in final assembly at the Dornier works in Friedrichshafen. The Do 317 V1, (VK+IY), made its first flight on 8 September 1943. A month earlier, Dornier had had no alternative but to accept an Air Ministry directive ordering the scrapping of the Do 317, of all of those parts held in store for the Do 317 V2, together with all of the 0-series items in production.

At the Air Ministry, a new plan was beginning to emerge. At a meeting held on 9 July 1943, it was decided to step up the production of the Ju 188, and that Luftwaffe Kampfgeschwader would be re-equipped in three phases. Mass production would begin with the A-2, E and F variants of the Ju 188. All three were equipped with a moderately heavy defensive armament. They were to be followed by bomber variants, having a remote-controlled rear turret and a bigger bomb compartment. The Ju 188G-2 and H-2 were followed by high-altitude variants — the J, K and L — which were the forerunners to the Ju 388.

Generalfeldmarschall Milch's immediate response was to express his doubts (and they were justifiable) that the heavily armed Ju 188G and H would be too slow both for day and night operations. Enemy defences over the British Isles and in the West were generally such that a high-speed night bomber, having a remote-controlled rear gun and a rear attack warning indicator, was what was required. Consequently, Milch urged the production of the Ju 188, but without the armament configuration of the B1-Waffenstandes. Oberst iG Peltz also pointed out that with a big bomb compartment and a tail gun, the Ju 188's radius of operation would be reduced too much, and its speed reduced further. Only by reducing the payload to approximately 1000 kg would its range and speed be anywhere near to being acceptable.

Do 217 and Ju 88 production had to continue, in order to provide bomber support on the Eastern Front, until a successor to the outdated Junkers bomber was available.

The Bomber B was the main topic dicussed at a meeting which was held on 23 August 1943, in particular, its powerplant. As they had done more than a year previously, representatives from the Air Ministry, the Erprobungsstellen, and key personnel from those companies involved all brooded over the idea of making one final attempt to get a Bomber B, with a DB 610 powerplant, into production, in autumn 1943. They all agreed that the DB 610 powerplant (consisting of a pair of DB 605 engines, coupled together) was an interim solution, at best, because it could not be developed any further. Even the DB 606 (with which the eleventh development Ju 88 (DF+CQ) flew in July 1942) was not ready by any means.

Seven Ju 288 B-bombers, designated V101 to V107 and equipped with the DB 610, were followed by an additional series of eight development aircraft in October 1943, together with at least five C-1 production aircraft.

Following a demonstration by three Ju 288s to the Reichsmarschall, a development meeting was called, chaired by Erhard Milch, to consider the future of the Ju 288 and, in particular, to decide between the Ju 288 and the He 177. Prof Hertel expressed his belief that the Ju 288 was at least 80 km/h faster than the He 177 B-5 which was

One of a number of drawings produced in 1940 for the further development of the Do 317.

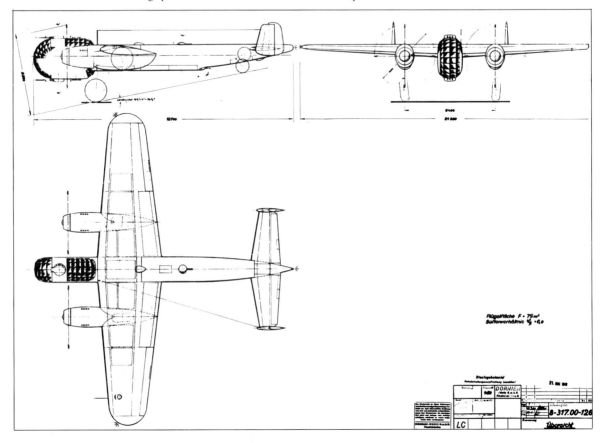

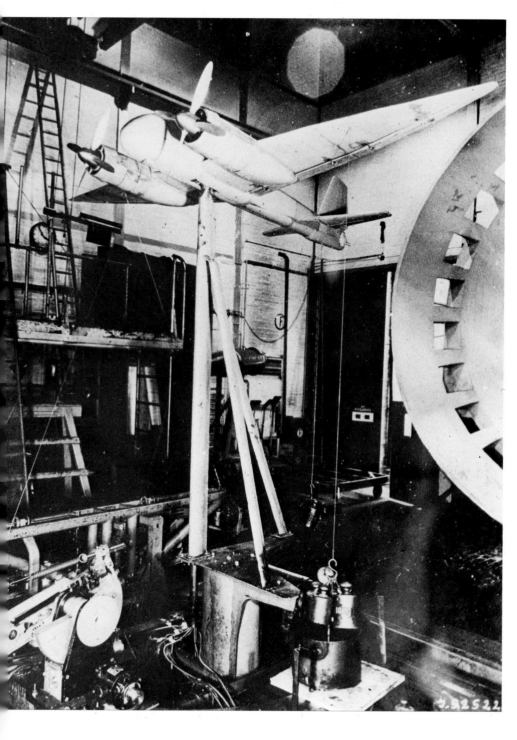

A wind tunnel model of the Ju 388K from which many variants were derived, differing mainly in respect of their powerplant and armament configurations.

powered by four single engines, and which had a new cabin configuration. The KdE (Commander of Experimental Establishments), Oberstleutnant Knemeyer, estimated a speed difference of 30 km/h approximately, under operational conditions, although this was treated with more than a little scepticism by the Generalluftzeugmeister. The only way in which a decision could be made would be to hold a fly-off between the two aircraft.

However, the matter did not get that far. Oberstleutnant Knemeyer had a clear idea already as to how the problem could be resolved. The He 177 and the Ju 388 would both be followed by the Do 335 high-speed bomber which, in turn and in the next stage of development, would be replaced by the Av 234 'Blitz' bomber. By the end of the discussion, Generalfeldmarschall Milch left no doubt in anybody's mind as to how he viewed the position. Two years previously, the intention had been to drop the entire Bomber B programme and thus both the Ju 288 and the Do 317, but this had been hindered by Heinkel's sticking stubbornly to the unreliable coupled engine, persistent over-optimistic deadlines, and the inflexible attitude of the Luftwaffenführungsstab. The shortage of materials which had occurred in the meantime led, finally, to a significant cut-back in the production of heavy aircraft: no more than 100 four-engined aircraft per month could be produced. Further attempts to bring the Jumo 222 to fruition failed in the first half of 1944. From 30 June 1944, the motto became 'fighters, not bombers'.

With the setting up of the 'Jägerstab', by Reichsminister Speer on 1 March 1944, the era of the 'blue pencil' began on 25 March. Heading the Air Ministry's list were the Ju 288C-1 and the Heinkel He 177. The first development aircraft not having made any further test flights, the chapter on the Do 317 also ended.

CHAPTER ELEVEN
Do 417 — The Workhorse

The Do 217 had not gone into production, and the night-fighter variant with DB 603 engines was in its infancy when, on 23 July 1942, the official technical specifications for a new, multi-role aircraft were sent to all of the large aircraft manufacturers. The aircraft resulting from the project (known as the Arbeitsflugzeug (workhorse)) was intended to replace all of the mid-range bombers by the winter of 1944/45 at the latest.

The Technische Amt required a conventional aircraft in which all of the experience gained from the previous bombers could be utilised. Not only was the aircraft's design to be simple and easy to manufacture, it should make use of steel scrap and other spares also, thereby saving valuable raw materials. Furthermore, the new aircraft was to be easy to maintain and service, even under combat conditions, because its ability to be in a permanent state of readiness was given high importance.

The concept behind the new aircraft was that it should function as both a general bomber and a dive-bomber. The new, robust aircraft was to be also used as a reconnaissance aircraft, a torpedo-carrying bomber, and a carrier for guided missiles. The crew was to be limited to three men, although one extra crew member could be added, if necessary. In normal circumstances, the pilot was to be accompanied by a navigator, who would act as a radio operator and also a missile controller. The third crew member would be in the rear of the aircraft, to ensure its safety. Its defensive armament was to be installed in such a way that there would not be any blind spots which would make the aircraft susceptible to enemy fighters. The Air Ministry was no longer interested in an aircraft having a gun in the usual C, or in a second B position. The navigator was to be able to operate the guns in the aircraft's nose, because it was not possible then to rely on remote control. A manually aimed MG 151/20 in the A position and an HD 151 swivel gun in the rear of the fuselage were therefore obligatory.

The cockpit was designed to give all-round vision to the pilot and his navigator. Also, the aircraft was to be equipped with a double set of controls so that the navigator/radio operator could take over, if anything happened to the pilot. Tried and tested engines only (such as the powerful BMW 801D, Jumo 213 or DB 603) were to be considered. Thus equipped, it was calculated that the bomber would have a range which would enable it to reach targets up to 2500 km distant, while carrying a 2000 kg bomb. (The OKL laid great store in the fact that it should make a gliding run close in to the target itself.) All larger fuselage stores were to be carried externally. Plans for a large, lavish bomb bay were dropped, leaving more space to carry fuel tanks.

With a take-off weight of up to 17,000 kg, the aircraft was expected to reach easily a speed of 600 km/h and an altitude of 7000 m. The twin-engined aircraft was to be designed with the thought in mind that, during battle, one engine could be put out of action by either enemy flak or fighters. The aircraft was to be equipped with a powerful de-icing system, and a Kutonase (cable-cutting equipment), similar to that on the Ju 88 A-4 and several Do 217Es. With the installation of dive brakes, a dive from 7000 m, at an angle of 60°, and an airspeed not exceeding 600 km/h, should be quite feasible. These specifications (especially that for a manually, later remote-controlled tailgun) gave rise to endless debates and were brought up constantly by the Reichsmarshall. Following meetings and talks with night fighter crews, who were concerned

Munich-Riem in the summer of 1944. Nearly all of Germany's combat aircraft types are pictured: the He 177, the Ju 188, and several Do 217 bombers and night-fighters.

about the fire-power of RAF aircrafts' quadruple tailguns, it was impossible to ignore constantly the wishes of German airmen for an effective defensive armament. A major re-think concerning the improvement of the new aircraft's performance was vital, if it was to have the opportunity to carry out offensive actions with any degree of success.

With this in mind, Generalfeldmarschall Milch declared, on 3 November 1942, that the performance and proposed design of the Do 217 was unsatisfactory. Oberst Vorwald demanded more BMW 801s to equip the Ju 188, dropping this demand only in order to equip the many, engineless, Dornier bombers. Anyway, the end of Do 217

production was in sight. However, the General Staff and that of the Air Ministry were unable to agree as to how to finalise production. At that time 213 engineless Do 217s were distributed around various airfields in Germany — more than enough to equip an entire Geschwader! A ministerial meeting decided that some of the aircraft, at least, should be fitted with DB 603A engines as soon as it was possible to do so, even though these engines had a number of faults remaining which were being rectified only slowly.

In early December 1942, two plans concerning the policies of equipping the Luftwaffe began to crystallise. Either all of the existing Do 217s were to be fitted with DB 603 engines, or all those Do 217s without Kehl apparatus (mainly those belonging to Kampfgeschwader 2) were to be taken out of commission and have their BMW 801 engines removed to equip Fw 190 fighters. Following this, the Do 217s would be fitted gradually with BD 603 engines and returned into commission. The General der Kampflieger was prepared to try the latter; however, the fact was that KG 2 was occupied mainly with the battle over Britain and the English Channel, even a short-term release of its aircraft was impossible.

At that point, Hauptmann Hermann stepped in and presented the points of view of the of the Luftwaffe airmen. Thanks to its greater manoevrability, the Ju 88 was the best choice for airborne battles in the West. The Dornier bomber would be deployed best mainly over the Mediterranean, where, by reason of its more effective defensive armament, it could be used in a broader spectrum of operations. However, a firm decision could not be made. In any event, it was certain that the Ju 88 would be replaced soon by the Ju 188, which was a better fighting aircraft. Whether or not the Junkers bomber and the Do 217 would both remain in service, whether or not both be replaced by a 'workhorse' aircraft remained to be decided.

The 'workhorse' project's specifications had long been in the hands of Heinkel, Junkers, Focke-Wulf and Blohm & Voss by the time they arrived at Dornier's design department. The invitation for official tenders (inasmuch as the mere sending of project data can be called as such) was received just before the official closing date.

A visit by Erhard Milch to Heinkel led to a confidential discussion on the development of a general-purpose aircraft, having a penetration of 1000 km at least, and a total range of 3000 km while carrying 1000 kg of stores. The new aircraft was to be able to take off from a runway of 1200 m only, and be ready for production within two years. On 27 and 28 June 1942, a meeting took place between Prof Heinkel, Major Storp and the Hauptleute Dithfurth and Fischer. Together with the concept and construction of a new heavy fighter which was due to replace the Bf 110, the subject of the general-purpose aircraft was discussed in detail. Follownig this, great interest was expressed in the preparation of a mock-up of a tailgun having a 90° field of vision.

A memorandum was produced on 13 June, 1942, when further details for the eventual production of the Heinkel design were discussed. Major Storp presented Erhard Milch's view that he wanted an all-purpose aircraft which could not only function as

A Do 217K-1 of I/KG 2 pictured together with a BMW-engined Do 217N-2 night-fighter at Munich-Riem.

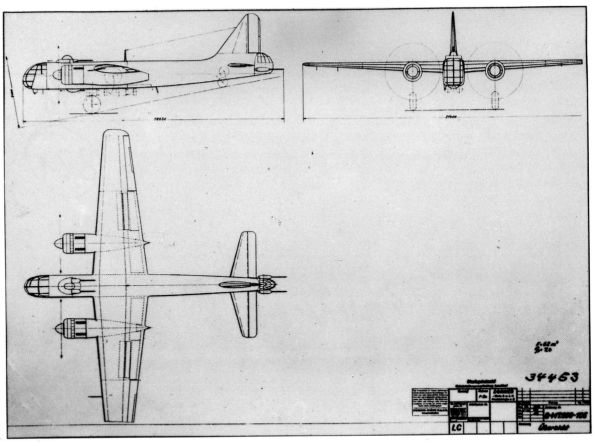

The Do 417 was to have a completely new appearance, as shown here by the drawings for the A variant.

a heavy fighter but also as a heavy fighter-bomber. The need for a new heavy fighter was more urgent than that for a general-purpose aircraft, because a replacement for the Bf 110 was required. However, Storp was aware that GFM Milch's demand that the general-prupose aircraft have a speed of 700 km/h could not be met using those engines which were available at that time. Nevertheless, he felt that a cruising speed of 600 km/h was not unrealistic, if the aircraft was not handicapped by very heavy equipment, and if the crew was limited to three members. Finally, Major Storp put forward the Luftwaffenführungsstat's point of view that the development of an all-purpose, workhorse aircraft was to receive a greater priority than anything else, given the fact that the Bomber B was apparently not to be counted upon. The situation was compli-

cated further by the immovable attitude of the Führungsstab (General Staff), who were more inclined to vote for the existing Bomber B project, than for a completely new one.

Having had the advantage of prior, privileged information, Heinkel's director was certain that any one of the three designs for a general-purpose bomber submitted by his company would make all the running.

When compared with the Bomber B's mean weight of twenty-five tons, the general-purpose aircraft was a real lightweight. According to almost all of the RLM's designs, the new aircraft was to have a take-off weight of between fifteen and seventeen tons. The resulting need for fewer raw materials would give the aircraft added importance. In June 1942, Göring calculated that, by the time

206

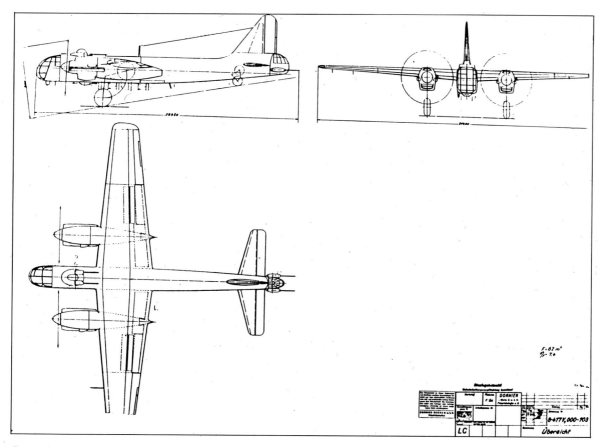

General arrangement drawing of the Do 417 V1, dated April 1942, the first prototype of which was equipped with DB 603 engines.

that its production was completed, the general-purpose aircraft would have replaced 75% of the Ju 88 and Ju 188 bombers, while the Bomber B would have replaced only 25%. Later, when the Junkers bombers became redundant, the general-purpose bomber would total three-quarters of all those bombers in Kampfgeschwader service. The remaining aircraft would all be special, high-altitude bombers. Furthermore, the Luftwaffen-führungsstab placed particular importance on the general-purpose aircraft having simple, uncomplicated handling characteristics, and tolerant flight characteristics, so much so that an average crew would not have any difficulties in flying either at night or in adverse weather conditions.

Having heeded all of these requirements, on 22 June Ernst Heinkel submitted a thick folder containing a range of designs for the Heinkel P 1065 general-purpose bomber; a whole month before the official tender date. Three main designs were presented: a conventional aircraft, an aircraft with a double engine fitted in the nose, and an asymmetrical, crew nacelle, incorporated in the wing. Finally, the designers presented a variant powered by DB 619 engines, strongly reminiscent of the earlier He 119. Although it had not been awarded the contract as yet, Heinkel declared himself to be prepared to build the mock-ups of the three variants at its own expense.

Officially, all of the recognised manufacturers were to be given the chance to tender for the project, therefore they all received the project's specifications in July 1942. For the sake of appearance, Prof Heinkel was presented with a copy.

Junkers' design work regarding this project is unkown at the time of writing this book, as is that of Focke-Wulf.

Blohm & Voss, however, replied quickly with two variants of their P 163 project, powered by either DB 803A or DB 613 engines. According to the plans, the crew would be placed in two nacelles incorporated in the wingtips, and the aircraft bore a certain resemblance to the BV 141. Both variants weighed 15,000 kg, and had wing areas of 55 m^2. Their defensive armaments consisted of two MG 151s installed at the ends of both nacelles, and, for protection against enemy fighters, an MG 151 in the nose. However, because they had had more than enough problems with the BV 141, the Technisches Amt regarded such forward-looking projects with scepticism.

In the end, apart from the He P 1065, there was only one other choice: the general-purpose Dornier Do 417, the plans for which were first presented on 22 January 1943. They showed the aircraft to be useful in both the bomber and the reconnaissance roles. Unlike the other projects, the Do 417 was to have a crew of four, three of which would be situated in a glass cockpit at the front of the aircraft. To defend the aircraft against barrage balloons, the entire cockpit was covered with Kuto strips, which continued along the leading edges of the wings. As they had in the Do 217, the designers had positioned the dive brakes over and under the wings, between the engine nacelles and the outer wing joints.

In addition to armour-plating the pilot's seat and the tail guns, the designers partly armour-plated the water and oil cooling systems. As an extra safety precaution, high-altitude breathing apparatus was installed, together with fifteen bottles of oxygen. Should the aircraft crash into the sea, the crew could hopefully save themselves in the one-man rubber dinghies provided. As did those for all of the other general-purpose aircraft, the plans included a hot-air de-icing system for the cockpit glazing, and a de-icer for the propellers. A camera unit could also be taken on board; a small, hand-held camera

was considered to be obligatory, as it was in all other bombers.

As its defensive armament, the weapons' specialists wanted an MG 151 in the nose, an HD 151 with a 500-round magazine in the B position, and an HL 151 with a 500-round magazine in the tail. All this was to be the standard armament of the production model. As its bomb aiming system they fitted the tried and tested Lotfe 7D, in addition to an improved BZA system. The design included only three fuselage bomb racks, for carrying fifteen 50 kg bombs. However, an allowance was made for a maximum of two 2000 kg bombs to be suspended under the aircraft's belly.

Initially the Dornier bomber was to be powered by two DB 603A engines, to be replaced later by DB 603 Gs. These were expected to give the aircraft a low-altitude maximum speed of 460 km/h, and a speed of 600 km/h at 8000 m. An operational altitude of 4000 m could be reached in fourteen minutes; 5000 m in eighteen minutes; 6000 m in twenty-three minutes. The aircraft's operational ceiling was calculated to be 11,000 m. With a take-off weight of 17,000 kg, carrying a 2000 kg bomb load and 2400 kg of fuel, the Do 417's range was calculated as 2050 km. Its average speed at altitudes of 7500 m would then be 565 km/h.

Several important improvements, not found in the original specifications and data sheets of January 1943, were made to the Do 217 which was in production by the spring of 1943. For example, the manually operated MG 151 was replaced with a small rotating turrent, with an MG 131Z under the front of the fuselage. All of the remaining armament was unchanged. The first prototypes were to be powered by DB 603A-2 engines. Use of the more powerful Jumo 222 was dropped, as was the case with the Do 317 and the Ju 288, because of the problems with this powerplant.

By October 1942, it became obvious that internal opinion favoured the Do 417 general-purpose aircraft. In all, the Do 417 seemed to be a perfectly adequate design, although it faced a strong competitor in the Ju 188. Would its production ever by approved by the RLM? Because the Ju 188 had such an undeniable head start, by reason of the experiences already gained with the development of the Ju 88, this was not an easy question to answer.

On 15 December 1942, a representative of Dornier's management stated emphatically that, as far as could be seen, the Do 417 V1 could be flying as early as August 1943. Dornier estimated that the first ten prototypes would be ready by the spring of 1944. Series production was expected to begin in April 1944 (immediately following the completion of the Do 217 V10) with a total of three aircraft per month. The rate of production would be increased gradually so that, by late summer 1945, there would be enough aircraft to equip the first Einsatzstaffel (operational squadron).

However, initially the Generalluftzeugmeister had compared the performance figures for the Ju 188 with those for the Do 417, without considering these rather vague targets. Because the calculations for the Do 417's performance seemed poorer on all fronts than those for the Junkers aircraft, scepticism was rife at a meeting in Berlin of all of the significant members of the RLM and the Technische Amt. Despite the fact that the Do 417's armour weighed 50 kg less than that of the Ju 188, which had more or less the same armament, the former aircraft had a horizontal speed which was 15 km/h greater than that of the latter. The Ju 188 had the best performance as a dive bomber, and would be ready, according to Junkers' calculations, for action a year earlier than the Dornier aircraft (ie in the summer of 1944). Furthermore, the difference between the qualities of both aircraft was not great enough to make it worthwhile to produce both.

Nevertheless, Oberstleutnant von Lossberg continued to refer to the advantages of a central fuel supply, the problems arising from which Dornier's engineers had solved far better than their counterparts working on the Ju 188. Furthermore, the Do 417's fuel tanks were far better protected from enemy fire, and its MG 151/20 tail guns were far superior to those of the Ju 188 prototype. In fact,

The HL 131/1 which was installed in the Ju 188 was a possible candidate for the tail gun of the general-purpose aircraft.

tests with the Ju 188's MG 131Z were not due to commence until summer 1943, by which time the Ju 188 V27 would be undergoing its practical tests in Tarnewitz. However, because von Lossberg had reckoned with the Ju 288C (which had a four-barrelled tail gun) he could not see the Do 417 having any chance.

209

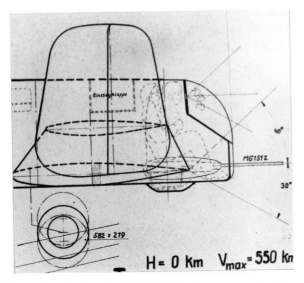

Drawing showing the MG 151/20 twin gun mounted in the Heinkel general-purpose aircraft.

Oberst iG Kleinrath also rejected the Do 417 as a bomber, because he was certain that the anticipated shortage of raw materials precluded production of middle-range bombers. Neither Oberstleutnant Petersen nor Oberst iG Vorwald could see any advantage in producing the Dornier aircraft. Therefore, Generalfeldmarschal Milch decided against all further development of the Do 417. He emphasised that if a rapid re-equipping of bomber squadrons was to be possible, all three Dornier factories would have to be engaged in the production of the Do 417. In turn, this would endanger the production of the Me 410, which was on the Dornier production line, in which the Generalfeldmarschal saw all the advantages of a fast, well-armed bomber having a performance which could be improved easily with the addition of more powerful engines. As it was, the project remained as just a few plans at the Friedrichshafen factory, unable to affect developments.

At a meeting held on 15 December 1944, it was decided which bombers would be completed during the following year: 410 Ju 88s and Ju 188s per month, seventy Do 217s, and a small number of He 111s. Furthermore, the Technische Amt voted for the Do 217 to be cancelled in favour of the manufacture of more of the Me 410s. Three plans were drawn up for consideration: Dornier's factory in north Germany would produce Ju 188s only. Its south Germany factory would continue to manufacture a large number of Do 317s. The final plan was for all Do 217s and Ju 188s to be replaced by Me 410s with Jumo 213 engines.

The KdE and the General der Jagdflieger both came down heavily on the side of retaining the DB 603 powerplant in the Me 410, while confirming that Fw 190 fighters with Jumo 213 engines were supremely effective. Study 1015, discussed on 22 December 1942, also predicted the end of Do 217 production by 1944, leading to the con-

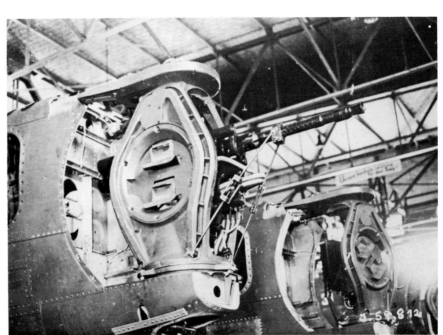

The HL 131/1 tail gun which was operated by an FA 14/15 remote-control system in many Ju 388s.

210

The Do 217M-1 was used as a stop-gap instead of the Do 317 and 417. Pictured in the centre of the photograph is U5+CS of 8/KG 2.

sideration of a reduction in Do 217 production between November 1943 and October 1944. The Ju 88 and the Ju 188, however, were both to continue in production, at a rate of 300 aircraft per month, until the end of 1945.

Meanwhile, Dornier's Wismar and Oberpfaffenhofen factories continued to produce Do 217s fitted with DB 603 engines; minor production delays were unavoidable because of hindrances in engine supplies. Maintaining the supply of Do 217s was of supreme importance to those units engaged in the Western Offensive, because supplies of the Me 410 had been affected by considerable production problems. There were not enough skilled workers available, and the concentration camp prisoners put to work in their stead were not sufficiently qualified.

In April 1943, a new directive was issued by the RLM: an extra 100 bomber aircraft were to be produced each month to keep pace with the

The Ju 188A-3 (this one was operated by III/KG 26) was also to have been replaced by the Do 417.

211

number of aircraft lost in action. However, supplies of the Do 217 foundered because of the existing problems concerning engine supply. Then, a new crisis arose.

Because the Do 217M, the night fighter Do 217N, and the Me 410 all needed DB 603 engines, a decision had to made in order to solve the supply problem. Milch favoured the Me 410, and consequently, within a short space of time only, 110 'completed' Do 217s were without engines. The Wismar factory had to give absolute priority to the Me 410, and provided the Munich factory only with the minimum amount of assistance in its Do 217 production shortfalls. This situation was not resolved until the end of May 1943, when a number of BMW 801 engines were delivered.

However, the units operating in the West were not satisfied. In addition to a failure in the supply of necessary DB 603 spares and replacements, there was a lack of special tools needed for the maintenance of both the Me 110 and the Do 217. The situation eased slightly in the summer of 1943 with an improved supply of both the BMW 801 and the DB 603. This was partly the result of a cut-back in

Me 410 production, and a higher priority being given again to the Ju 188 bomber. Also, Erhard Milch had stated categorically that the Ju 88 and the Do 217 should continue in production because they were needed on the Eastern Front both as reconnaissance aircraft and in the battle against enemy tanks.

In this period, 107 sub-standard DB 603 engines alone were produced in June. In addition, a further forty-three engines did not have crankshafts and were also useless.

During the autumn of 1943 and the ensuing months, hopes for a significant change in the situation seemed unrealistic. The same was true for regarding improvements to the Do 217's cabin, and the fitting of 67 m^2 wings. Both of these difficulties led to the cancellation of the promising Do 217M, and the rapid winding-up of the Do 217N-2 project. Many versions were cancelled at the construction stage, while others did not get any further than the prototype stage.

In the end, a few tried and tested models only remained in production, to be put into the fray against a vastly superior enemy.

Towards the end of the war the standard bomber was replaced by the Ju 388. A Ju 388L-1 reconnaissance aircraft is pictured.

212

The end for the Luftwaffe squadrons in northern Germany. Bomber units were by then equipped mostly with either Ju 88, or the Ju 188.

CHAPTER TWELVE
The Last Do 217

Following the almost complete disintegration of Kampfgeschwaders 40 and 100, nobody really believed in continuing the use of the Hs 293 and the Fritz-X. In early November 1944, KG 40 re-equipped, as a maximum readiness unit, with the Me 262A-2 bomber. In accordance with the wishes of the Luftwaffe General Staff, only 8/KG 40 and 4 (Kehl)/Ergänzungsstaffel (Replacement Training Squadron) of the Ergänzungskampgruppe (Replacement Training Combat Group) would remain for missile attack operations.

On 6 November, the Luftwaffe High Command re-grouped its forces again. By taking strength from the Ergänzungskamfgruppe's IV(Erg)/KG(J) 40, 8/KG 40 became Transportfliegerstaffel 'Condor', and the 4 Kehl-Staffel became the Ergänzungs-und Erprobungsstaffel FK (Replacement Training and Experimental Squadron). Lehr-und Erprobungs-kammando (Instruction and Experimental Detachment) EK 36 which, together with a few He 111s, had several variants of the Do 217K and M, capable of carrying the glider bomb and the remote controlled FX-missile.

EK 36 was charged often with the task of testing the many new Henschel glider weapons, when such tests could not be carried out at the Karlshagen Experimental Establishment. Tests of the Hs 293 and 394, which were fitted with a 'Fernsehkopf' (TV head), were especially pressing. By this time, the Hs 293 tests were particularly well advanced, twelve test launches against target ships having been made by 10 October 1944. No fewer than eight of these missiles had either hit the target, or were only near misses, their paths having been transmitted, via their heads, to a TV screen inside the aircraft which was used to correct their courses. With the re-naming of EK 36 to Versuchsverband

(Trials Unit) KG 200 on 31 November 1944, a new and eventful chapter was expected to begin in 1945.

By January 1945 the situation on the Eastern Front had deteriorated severely. Hitler and the OKW (Oberkommando der Wehrmacht — High Command of the Armed Forces) wished to use all of the means at their disposal to halt the Soviet advance. This included the destruction of all of the bridges over the River Oder and the River Neisse. Hitler charged the Kommodore of KG 200, Oberstleutnant Baumbach, with the destruction of all of the means of crossing the rivers. In addition to KG 200, all suitable Luftwaffe units and all the necessary equipment of both the Army and the Navy were placed at his disposal.

On 1 March 1945, KG 200, together with six Mistel I and eight Mistel III units, was ready to attack and destroy the railway bridges at Warsaw, Deblin and Sandomierz. It was decided that a mountain in the vicinity of Magdeburg would be used as a launch pad for fourteen 'Beethoven'-equipped aircraft and nine pathfinders. However, the mission was prevented by bad weather, although high water levels did destroy a pontoon bridge erected by the Russians. Baumbach's second-in-command, Oberst Helbig, was of the opinion that, even if it were possible to destroy all the bridges, it could be done only by using all of the resources available. This meant a combination of Mistel units, ground-attack units (SG 1 and 2), explosives units, frogmen and paratroopers. The most vital elements, however, would be the projectiles carried to their target by aircraft of Versuchsverband 200. The plan for III/KG 53 to drop mines from its He 111s was hardly expected to meet with success. Finally, the already limited activities of the remaining bombers of Lehrgeschwader (LG) 1, and those

A Do 217M-1 (K7+CH) of Fernaufklärungsgruppe Nacht (Night Long-Range Reconnaissance Group), carrying a defensive armament consisting of MG 17s and MG 131s.

of the Ergänzungsstaffel of KG 1 were paralysed further by a shortage of aviation fuel.

The main delaying factor in the early days of March was constant bad weather. Operations involving Fw 190s and crews from Versuchsverband 200, flying Do 217s and He 111s, had to be postponed. On 5 March, four He 111s were able to attack the north Göritz bridge; however, this did not affect the general movement of vehicles. Only one Hs 293 had scored a direct hit; a further three hit the east bank of the River Oder and could hardly be said to have caused any damage. As if that was not enough, one He 111 was shot out of the sky by a Soviet fighter.

Aircraft of 4(F)/14 which was equipped with the Ju 188F-1 and the Do 217M-1, both types being fitted with a camera for reconnaissance operations.

Several, futile 'waterbomb' drops (ie, containers of Glam C 250 incendiaries) to set fire to the temporary, wooden bridges were followed on 8 March by the first missile attack. Four teams were sent to attack the bridge at Göritz. One of the flying bombs scored a hit and caused the central arch to collapse totally. Meanwhile, two Ju 88s and four Ju 188s attacked Soviet anti-aircraft units deployed around the bridge, causing them to cease their firing temporarily. One Ju 188 was lost to Soviet flak.

Twenty-four hours later, the Luftwaffe was on its way to the Eastern Front on a night raid. As the result of constant rain, the main missile attack fell into the drink, literally.

On 20 March, the Versuchskommando formulated a new plan. The crews of three He 111s and three Do 217s were to attack the bridges to the centre and the north of Göritz with six Hs 293A-1s. The crews of both a Dornier and a Heinkel were able to report a direct hit each. One Henschel bomb destroyed twelve metres of road. There was also one near-miss, which caused little real damage. Apart from one direct hit, the Dorniers did not have any luck, both bombs missed their targets as the result of equipment failure.

The following day, the Versuchskommando again despatched three He 111s and three Do 217s. In very little cloud (visibility being a good 20 km), and as expected by the Soviets, the six special bombers arrived at the target between 18.23 and 18.29 hr. Two Henschel bombs swallowed up the north Göritz bridge, while a further three missed the target narrowly. For some unknown reason, one Hs 293 plunged into the water, out of control.

By 21 March, having sustained only a few losses, the Versuchsverband had nineteen He 111Hs and six Do 217s at its disposal. However, only eleven of the Heinkels and four of the Dorniers were operational. A lack of aviation fuel, resulting from the virtual breakdown of the supply and reinforcement organisations, precluded any further attacks. The following day, one of the special bombers was shot down by an enemy aircraft over the Oder. Of a total of six projectiles fired, only two found their targets; the remainder fell alongside the Göritz and Rathstock bridges.

On 23 March, fifty-eight Fw 190s from I and II/SG 1 attacked anti-aircraft units in addition to transport routes and a number of bridges used by the Soviets (one of the bridges was hit by two SC 500s).

The FK unit went into action again with its Do 217s and He 111s. Six special bombers took off between 10.46 and 10.54 hr, reaching Göritz and Rathstock by 11.36 hr. A thick mist over east Germany, bringing visibility down to approximately 1500 m, made this operation very difficult. Suddenly, out of the mist, Soviet fighters appeared, accompanied by anti-aircraft fire from the ground. Two German aircraft were damaged severely and had to turn back through the thick clouds. Meanwhile, a Dornier 217 had returned to its base already, with its Hs 293 intact. At approximately 12.36 hr, the last aircraft landed at Burg. The crews were unable to report any successes.

Seven attacks made by II/LG did little to change the situation. Between 11 and 23 March, Ju 88A-4 bombers made constant forays over the target bridges but, apart from one direct hit on the north Göritz bridge on 21 March and a number of near misses, all their efforts came to nothing. For the following attack, the Versuchsverband had five He 111s serviceable.

The target on 25 March was a river crossing south of Göritz, which was hidden rapidly by smokescreens put up by the defending Soviets. The resulting fog was thicker than the natural mist which lay often over the Oder. The only direct hit was on the north Göritz bridge.

The greatest action thus far using projectiles on the Eastern Front began on the night of 26 March 1945. Four He 111s and four Do 217s took part. At 23.55 hr, five Hs 293s were fired. Two direct hits and one near miss had been noted when a small Soviet Airacobra unit began to attack. The overwhelming number of enemy aircraft caused the pilot of the last Do 217 to release its glider bomber

This Do 217E-4 was operated by a Verbingdungstaffel (Liaison Squadron) on the Eastern Front.

and return to base, undamaged, as did all of the German aircraft.

The limited success in destroying bridges led Oberst Helbig to make a critical appraisal of the contributions made by his Ju 88s, the ground-attack units, and the FK carriers, paying particular attention to the amount of fuel they consumed. An attack carried out by sixteen Fw 190s, each carrying an SC 500 bomb, used 7 m³ of fuel on average. In comparison, eight Ju 88A-4s, each carrying a 2000 kg bomb load, used 8 m³ of what was at that time, extremely valuable fuel.

The Versuchsverband's glider bomb carriers fared little better. Five FK raids, between 6 and 23 March 1945, resulted in nine direct hits and several near misses on the target bridges. Twenty-eight aircraft took part in these raids (sixteen He 111s and twelve Do 217s), all of which were able to drop their Hs 293s without any significant loss. Because the number of glider bomb-carrying aircraft was limited, the damage caused by their missiles could hardly be spectacular. Following the appraisal, everything remained the same as it was before.

On 27 March, to everybody's surprise, the number of bomb-carrying Do 217s at the Versuchs-verband's disposal rose from two to eight (albeit only four of them were capable of operating that morning). In addition, nine He 111Hs arrived, having an operational range which was perfectly adequate for raids in the local vicinity.

A Do 217E-2 of KG 100, which was used for training purposes.

A Do 217E-1 (serial No 1094) of the Pilot Training School in Neubrandenburg.

Twenty-four hours later, the effectiveness of the Hs 293 against the bridges was reviewed again. Oberstleutnant Baumbach felt that the success rate was far too low. An explosive head of 500 kg was not powerful enough usually, unless it succeeded in taking out one of the bearing elements of the bridge, thereby causing an entire segment to collapse. Also, attacks against pontoon and other temporary bridges did not bring any lasting success because, by reason of their narrow width, these targets were almost impossible to hit. However, given the situation which prevailed at that time, Baumbach not could see any alternative course of action because other methods were not at his disposal.

The efforts of the Mistel units were still the exception. At the end of March, Hitler could not make up his mind as to which target could be attacked with the greatest chance of success: the bridges on the Eastern Front, or raids on power stations (Operation Eisenhammer) for which more than eighty Mistel teams were available. The Luftwaffe High Command argued for a drastic reduction in 'Eisenhammer' operations, in favour of a forced campaign against the many river crossing on the Eastern Front. Finally, Gen Koller was able to win the fight for more Mistels to be sent against the bridges over the Oder.

Glider-bomb attacks would carry the destruction further. If necessary, fifteen fully operational special bombers (four of which were Do 217s) could be put on standby. Up until 1 April, the Versuchsverband received a further 200 aircraft, although its complement of Do 217s remained at eight, and that of He 111s rose to eighteen. Two days later, a group of four Do 217s and two He 111s made a glider-bomb attack on the bridges at north Göritz and Rathstock. The by then experienced crews managed one direct hit, and two near misses to one side of the centre of the bridge.

Following an air raid on Parchim air base where, together with a few Mistel teams, Versuchsverband 200 was based, the future looked dim for further raids using 'Beethoven' equipment. In particular, the cessation of Ju 88 'Mistel' production at Merseburg began to be felt. Reinforcements could no longer be relied upon. The FK Unit was also experiencing trouble. A lack of spare parts and engines, further reductions in fuel allocations, and the damage done to its Do 217s and He 111s during the Parchim raids resulted with planned future operations having to be cut back.

On 7 April 1945, only three Do 217s were operational. During the night of 11 April, these three,

218

This Do 217E-2 (6N+CU) was stationed at Schwäbisch Hall as one of KG 100's training aircraft.

together with a few He 111s carrying Kehl equipment, bombed the bridges at south and north Göritz. The attack was a failure: not one bomb hit its target. The same lack of success plagued Mistel operations during the course of the ensuing few days. The target area, Warsaw, was reached by only one Mistel aircraft, of the twenty-four Ju 88s despatched. Further attempts to destroy the railway bridges at Küstrin also failed.

In mid-April, Versuchsverband 200 of Einsatzkommando 200 (FK) was renamed. On 17 April 1945, it possessed only nine He 111s and one Do 217 with Kehl equipment. On 20 April, the Red Army advanced again towards the capital of the Third Reich. Artillery fire rained down over the exhausted city of Berlin. On 26 April, the final chapter of the German offensive was played out in a desperate Mistel attack. Any further missile raids are not recorded.

Other Do 217 units took part in the defensive actions on the Eastern Front. These were 2 and 4(F)/Aufklärungsstaffel Nacht (Long-Range Reconnaissance Squadrons) of Fernaufklärungsgruppe Nacht.

Having presented the Rowehl detachment with a mock-up of the Do 217A-O with DB 601 engines, Dornier produced a small number of Do 217 reconnaissance aircraft. (The production of greater numbers was not possible.) Although there were a number of high-altitude reconnaissance aircraft (a photo-reconnaissance camera having been installed in the Do 217 E, K and M as standard), apart from some intensive work on the high-altitude reconnaissance Do 217P, there seemed to be little interest in using the Do 217 as a reconnaissance aircraft only. Up until December 1943, at least, the Rüstungsführung (Armaments Directorate) did not commission any more of them. The production level for Do 217 bombers was sufficient to cover the losses sustained by the Kampfgeschwader (Bomber Wings). The chronic bottleneck in the delivery of more powerful engines (which had led, at one time to the cancellation of more than 200 Do 217s) was responsible for the rest.

Since their formation on 1 June 1941, the four Staffeln of Fernaufklärungsgruppe Nacht operated mostly Do 17Ps and Ms.

However, the fourth Staffel existed on paper only. It was not equipped with aircraft until 27 August 1942 when, instead of the Dornier reconnaissance aircraft, it was allocated the slower He 111. While 1(F)/Nacht patrolled the south area of the Eastern Front, 2 and 4 Staffeln took care of the centre. At this time 3(F)/Nacht was operating within the Heeresgruppe Nord (Army Group North). From 1942, the first Staffel was part of Fernaufklärungsgruppe 4, the second became part of FAGr 2, the third became part of FAGr 1, and 4(F)/Nacht became part of the Luftwaffenkommando Don, prior to being grouped into FAGr 3.

In autumn 1943, 1 Nachtaufklärungsstaffel was equipped with Do 217M-1s which had been fitted with photo-reconnaissance cameras. One of the first losses was that of aircraft K7+DH, which was completely destroyed on 14 November 1943. The Do 217's performance prompted the General of Reconnaissance Command to order further aircraft of that type. On 21 December 1943, Oberst Peltz advocated the conversion of ten Dornier 217s to reconnaissance aircraft. Although the General of Reconnaissance Command expressed repeatedly his preference towards the Do 217, and Erhard Milch did not spare any opportunity to intone his agreement, the RLM rejected the request at the end of the year.

In addition to units of the Nachtaufklärungsgruppe, 4(F)/14 also flew Do 217s, together with its Ju 88D-1 to D-5s. Taking both types together, the unit had fifteen aircraft stationed at Baranovitchi. 3 Nachtstaffel was able to use fifteen Do 217s, stationed mostly at Riga-Spilve, for reconnaissance duties. At that time, 1 Nachtstaffel was stationed at Focsani, and it operated a few Do 217s together with its He 111s. A total of fourteen aircraft were available, plus a few at Budapest-Frehegy.

With the disbanding of Kampfgeschwader 2 and the formation of the Gefechtsverband Hallensleben (Hallensleben Combat Units), the Nachtaufklärungs-gruppe was allocated sufficient Do 217K-1s and M-1s. The conversion of twenty-seven aircraft began on 24 October 1944, with their transfer to the auspices of the General der Aufklärungsflieger (GdA). The majority of these aircraft came directly from the factory, more or less, as they had not been delivered to the Holzhammer Geschwader before July 1944.

Many aircraft were transferred as the result of the Soviet advance in the East where, in the worst places, many Do 217s were inoperable because of damaged engines. By January 1945, 2 (F)/Nacht was stationed at Kolberg, from where it later transferred to Oranienberg with twelve Do 217s, leaving only a small task force behind. In addition to this unit, 1(F)/14 with seven Ju 188 D/Fs, and 2(F)/122 with three Me 410s and one Ju 88 T-3 were grouped within Fernaufklärungsgruppe 2 at that time. A further Ju 188F and a Ju 88 C-7 were also operated as staff aircraft.

Fernaufklärungsgruppe 3 (consisting of three Ju 188 Staffeln: 2(F)/100, 4(F)/121 and 4(F)/11) was not far behind in terms of operational strength. Its lost Ju 188s were replaced with a mixture of twelve Do 217Ks and Ms, almost half of which had to be laid up in spring 1945 due to the lack of spares. On 1 February 1945, 2 Nachtaufklärungsstaffel despatched four of its eight Do 217Ms, together with four Do 217Ks and Ms from 4/Nachtaufklärungs-gruppe to the Eastern Front with more than photo-reconnaissance operations in mind. On 3 February 1945, faced with a seemingly unstoppable Russian advance, 2(F)/Nacht transferred to Neuruppin. Three days later it was decided that, if Upper Schleswig fell, 4(F)/121 and 5(F)/Nacht would both be pulled back to transpor equipment from Breslau to Königgrätz.

As they had done during the preceding months, reconnaissance and bombing operations went hand in hand. Fernaufklärungsgruppen 2 and 3 carried out numerous raids at both dusk and night, using Do 217s, Ju 88/188s and Me 410s against enemy units and railway installations behind the lines. The objective was to try to relieve the front by bringing to bear the combined strengths of Nachtschlacht-gruppen (Night Ground Attack Group) 5, 8 and 10, the Fw 190Fs of the Schlachtgeschwader (Ground Attack Wing) with a drafted complement of fighter pilots. Long-range reconnaissance aircraft were deployed mainly in dropping canisters filled with SD-1 onto Soviet transport columns which were heading west. During one such operation on 9 March 1945, a Do 217M-1 (K7+GK) of 2(F)/Nacht failed to return, almost certainly having fallen victim to enemy fighters. A further aircraft (serial No 326221), carrying Feldwebel Brenners and his crew, was also lost in action.

On 23 March 1945, Fernaufklärungsgruppe 3 consisted of 2(F)/100, 4(F)/121, and 4 Nacht-aufklärungsstaffel. In addition to the two staff Me 410s, the Group's strength amounted to a further five Me 410s, a mixture of eighteen Ju 188Ds and Fs, and nine Do 217s (although only four only of the Dornier aircraft were operational). Five Do 217s were unserviceable as the result of either faulty VDM propellers, or Daimler-Benz engines, or combat damage.

The general situation in Fernaufklärungsgruppe 2 was somewhat better, the Group being able to put up twenty-eight Ju 188s, eleven Me 410s, six Ju 88s and ten Do 217s, it could when its low fuel supplies permitted this. These aircraft served with 4(F)/11,

1(F)/14, 3(F)/22, 1(F)/122, 2(F)/122, and 2(F)/Nacht. In addition to the Do 217, the Nachtstaffel also operated variants of the Ju 88 and Ju 188, which particularly aggravated problems with maintenance which had to take place often under the poorest of battle conditions. In addition to being hampered by the weather, flight operations were restricted by disruptions to fuel supplies, due either to fuel tankers falling victims to marauding Soviet combat aircraft, or to a lack of fuel in the dumps.

On the night of 21 March 1945, the crews of two Do 217s of 4 Nachtaufklärungsstaffel dropped twenty-three AB 70s on the Fourth Armoured Division's positions, and on the 17th Army. 66,000 leaflets were also dropped over the enemy troops. Meanwhile, four Do 217s and a Ju 188 from 2(F)/Nacht dropped sixteen canisters containing a total of 170,000 leaflets over enemy occupied positions on the Eastern Front. The following night, three Dorniers of Fernaufklärungsgruppe 3 raided the area around Glogau-Bunzlau-Gleitwitz. Twelve AB 70s were dropped on a transport convoy and a further dozen were dropped on the airfield at Brockendorf, which was occupied by Soviet aircraft. Another dozen were dropped on railway installations close to the front line.

Meanwhile, three Do 217s of FAGr 2 flew reconnaissance missions in the Oder bridge area

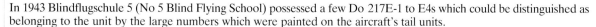

In 1943 Blindflugschule 5 (No 5 Blind Flying School) possessed a few Do 217E-1 to E4s which could be distinguished as belonging to the unit by the large numbers which were painted on the aircraft's tail units.

and dropped 64,000 leaflets. One of the aircraft was forced to withdraw because of a malfunction of its bomb jettisoning equipment. The two remaining aircraft concentrated their efforts on railway junctions and supply columns, dropping eight AB 70s. These raids were supported by five Si 204 staff aircraft of Nachtschlachtgruppe 4.

Throughout the days that followed, the crews of both reconnaissance groups reported a seemingly never-ending stream of horse-drawn and mechanized columns, in addition to the movements of heavy armoured units. At the end of March, the situation was such that the last long-range reconnaissance aircraft had to be pulled out of east Prussia, with the result that 5(F)/122 became a welcome reinforcement to the strength at Wittstock. Incessant fuel shortages meant that increasingly few night reconnaissance operations were flown. Those that were flown (such as that of 26 March) were carried out mostly by a few Do 217s of 2 and 4 Nachtstaffeln, operating from Neuruppin and Alt-Lönnewitz. Two days later, Dornier reconnaissance aircraft dropped leaflets and a few AB 70s in the centre of the Army Group's position.

During the last days of March, attention was focussed on reconnaissance operations in the Oder and Vistula areas was the main focus of attention. On 1 April 1945, 4(F)/Nacht lost another experienced crew. Also, 2(F)/100 and 4(F)/121 were each forced to write off a Ju 188.

Many of the Do 217 crashes during February and March could not be attributed to either the Do 217's landing gear, or its engines. According to a report issued by FAGr 2 issued at the beginning of April 1945, many were the result of the poor and inadequate training of young crews assigned to operational units.

On 1 April, both night reconnaissance Staffeln could muster a total of eighteen Do 217s and four Ju 188s between them. Three days later, the number of Dornier aircraft which were operational had been reduced to fourteen. On 6 and 7 April 1945, FAGr 3 moved all of its airworthy Ju 188s to Königgrätz. The few Me 410s and elements of 4(F)/

Nacht which remained were transferred to Prag-Rusin. On the night of 7 April, three Do 217s of 2 Nachtstaffel raided positions ahead of the German 2nd and 3rd Armies and the weakened 9th Armoured Division. Twelve SC 70 bombs were dropped on a transport column, and the railway station at Landsberg was bombed. The crews also dropped 122,000 leaflets.

During the days which followed, Me 410s and Ju 188s from both reconnaissance groups flew photo-reconnaissance missions over the entire Russian advance towards the Heeresgruppe Mitte (Army Group Centre) and especially around the Vistula. On the night of 9 April, an Ar 66 of Nachtschlachtgruppe 5, three Si 204s of Nahaufklärungsgruppe (Short-Range Reconnaissance Group) 3 and a total of six Fw 189s from Nahaufklärungsgruppen 6 and 15 were in operation. In addition, a Do 217 and a Ju 188 each raided positions ahead of the 9th Army and the 3rd Panzer Army, dropping twenty-two SD-70 fragmentation bombs on Soviet vehicles, and a further 40,000 leaflets. Hardly a major cause of concern for the enemy on the Eastern Front!

The next morning, as usual, photo-reconnaissance flights were made with the faster Ju 188. The Oberbefehlhaber of Luftflotte 6, von Greim, was full of praise for the efforts of his reconnaissance groups:

'During the last few days of enforced reconnaissance missions, often in poor weather conditions, the crews of Fernaufklärungsgruppe 2, and especially those of 2 Nachtstaffel, have surpassed the limits of what is possible for any airman. During their reconnaissance operations over Pommerania, and in particular through their constant observations of enemy movements, they have provided our leaders with vital information.

I would like to express my particular regards to the crews for their excellent performance and, in particular, for their supreme flying ability. I am convinced that FAGr 2 will

A Do 217E-1 pictured in Neubrandenburg where it served with the Blind Flying and Bad Weather Flying Training Unit.

continue to do its utmost to provide Heeres-gruppe Vistula with a clear picture of enemy movements which is so vital to them.

They continued to fly, even when their squadrons had ceased to exist, to all intents and purposes.

Following the disbanding of 1(F)/12 at Neu-brandenburg on 8 April 1945, its staff were assigned to Fernaufklärungsgruppe 3. The remaining members of 1(F)/122 joined 5(F)/122 and relocated to Prague immediately. Those members of the operational units of FAGr 3's 4 Nachtstaffel who had not departed already took the remaining Do 217Ks and Ms to Prague.

The orders for operations on the night of 11 April included a continuation of the attacks on the Göritz bridges, and actions against the bottleneck of traffic which trailed back over the approaches to the river crossings. At the same time, the order was given to fly reconnaissance missions along the Reichs-autobahn to Breslau. Intelligence brought during

the night by a Do 217 and a Ju 188 contained depressing forecasts only. These fitted into the mosaic of information which had been gathered during the preceding weeks: new unit after new unit, and endless columns of tanks and vehicles heading towards the capital.

By 14 April, 4(F)/Nacht was reduced to six Do 217 M-1s only, of which three were operational. Forty-eight hours previously, a Do 217 M-1 (serial no. 6331, K7+IM) and its crew, led by Leutnant Fritz Weigt, failed to return from enemy territory.

During the night of 15 May, 1(F)/122 and 4 Nachtstaffel, both based in Prague, flew into action with a greatly reduced aircraft strength, together with 3/NSG 4. The Nachtschlachtgruppe's thirty Ju 87s and Nahaufklärungsgruppen 2, 4 and 15's nine Fw 189s all flew deep into enemy territory. Two Do 217 M-1s dropped twenty-seven SD 70s on the military column which was backed up along the Reichsautobahn at Forst Haynau, while a bombing raid was also carried out over Steinau an der

Three Do 217M-1s of Fernaufklärungsgruppe Nacht, pictured in May 1945 in Beldringe, Denmark.

Neisse. Reports dated that night illustrate how, with a greatly reduced strength, the Germans tried desperately to halt the Russian advance, until the bitter end. Their ability to halt the advance had been an illusion only, because the armoured divisions, units and companies resembled one long train along the way. Three Do 217s managed to destroy two transport vehicles belonging to the main army group, and rained more than thirty SD 70 bombs down onto a collection of other vehicles.

On 18 April, practically all of the Fernaufklärungsstaffeln could see the end in sight. 4 Nachtstaffel had one Ju 188 and two Do 217 M-1s left. Even then, only two of the aircraft were airworthy and ready for the final effort; one Do 217 remaining unserviceable on the ground. The situation was as bad for 2(F)/100 and 4(F)/121. The combined maintenance crews managed to bring most of the fifteen Ju 188 D-2s to a state of readiness. However, there was something missing

— aviation fuel! One Ju 188 only of 3(F)/Nacht took part in the night operations of 17/18 April. The crew flew over the Küstrin-Posen-Goerlitz area and made a run over an enemy column.

On 20 April, the Fernaufklärungsgruppe was disbanded. The lack of aviation fuel did not leave any other choice. During the last days of April, the men parted from their aircraft with heavy hearts; 2(F)/11 at Kirchbaum, and 2(F)/33 at Hörsching. The remnants of 2(F)/121 and 1(F)/Nacht were gathered together at Linz. Six days later, on 26 April 1945, reports showed that, together with ten Ju 188s of 3(F)/121, 1 Nachtaufklärungsstaffel had a combined total of eleven Do 217s and He 111s in an airworthy condition. In addition to those aircraft which remained in Hörsching, there were those of the Luftflottenkommando (which had been placed under the command of 1(F)/Nacht); other aircraft were no longer available to those remaining which remained inside the tiny centre of German power.

CHAPTER THIRTEEN
Summary

On 3 September 1939, the German Coastal Aviation Groups, on the order of the Commander-in-Chief of the Luftwaffe, received the following message:

> *Aggressive actions against British Naval units, both in harbours and at sea . . . are now permitted, when warranted by similar British aggressive actions.*

With this memorandum, the invasion of Poland escalated officially, causing Germany's confrontation with France and Britain. The enemy at sea was Britain, the battle areas were the seas around the British Isles, the English Channel and the Bay of Biscay.

The first offensive action was relatively long in coming. This was the first attack by He 115s (the standard naval aircraft), when heavy losses were incurred. Göring and his Chiefs of Staff rejected the idea of direct offensive operations by these aircraft, because they were of the opinion that their main purpose was that of armed reconnaissance. The Luftwaffe General Staff considered the He 115 to be totally unsuitable for operations against targets at sea. Other naval squadrons were not offered this aircraft. The general-purpose squadrons, then being formed, were to be equipped with more powerful aircraft and, under the direct command of the Luftwaffe, not the Navy, prepared for action over the sea.

The He 115's inferior performance could not be hidden from Grossadmiral Raeder: he ordered that his Staffeln be re-equipped with the Do 217, and this was to be done as soon as it was possible. However, the first Do 217s which came off the production line on 21–31 December 1940, went to Kampfgeschwader 2 and II/KG 40 in early 1941, not to the Naval Aviation, as Raeder had hoped. The Navy's request for the formation of twenty-four Seefliegerstaffeln (Naval Aviation Squadrons) could not be granted. Göring had the greater backing and, therefore, had no need to compromise.

It was intended that the Do 217 and the BV 138 would bear the brunt of the operations over water, together with, to a lesser extent, the Do 18, He 59 and He 115 seaplanes. This decision meant that, in addition to the Ju 88 and the He 111, a third bomber aircraft had joined the ranks of large-scale production bombers: the Do 217, first conceived as a naval bomber and which later carried out most of the Luftwaffe's operations over Britain.

By the end of May 1942, KG 2 had seventy-eight Do 217s; II/KG 40 had twenty-eight Dornier bombers, of which 83% were operational. By the end of 1943, more than 190 Do 217s were available for both the Western Offensive and operations in the Mediterranean Theatre. For a short while, they were joined by Do 217s of II and III/KG 100 and the Zielfinderverband (Pathfinder Unit) I/KG 66. However, most of the Dorniers were engaged in actions over land when the airborne torpedo had proved to be as useful as it was thought it would be. This picture did not change until 1941. Up until 17 October, the naval pilots were able to sink 82,000 tons of enemy shipping, scoring a hit rate of 29%. Despite this success, the aerial torpedo was, and remained, a maintenance-intensive and unreliable weapon, for which personnel had to undergo a long training programme. It was not possible to increase production because of the need to manufacture German U-boat weapons. Notwithstanding the fact that Hitler gave the task of aerial torpedo development to the Luftwaffe, there

225

A Do 217E-2 pictured in flight.

was not a significant increase in the number available.

The potential of the Do 217, which was ideally suited as a torpedo-carrying aircraft, remained unrealised when it became clear that the air offensive over Britain had failed and that the enemy was by no means on its knees; therefore, Operation 'Seelöwe' (Sealion) had to be cancelled. The constant bombardment of civilian and military targets in Britain was given top priority in the Western Offensive. Furthermore, it had become obvious that the, until then more utilised, Ju 88 and He 111 were both unable to fill any other roles than that of tactical aircraft in the aerial battle (apart from their involvement in the Blitzkrieg).

At the beginning of the war, the idea of a strategic bomber had not been given a chance. Now, when the idea was being aired again, it was too late. Lack of resources precluded any chance of

there being more than a limited number of heavy fighter bombers. Consequently, in the summer of 1942, the Do 217 was put into the affray over Britain. The aircraft were part of a plan to cause as much damage as it was possible to do, using a limited amount of resources, and, at the same time, to keep British aircraft manufacturers in such a permanent state of alarm that production would be affected severely. However, constant raids, and the superior number of enemy forces (specifically, night-fighters and British anti-aircraft units) caused a high rate of loss of German men and machines.

During a visit to Luftflotte 3 in March 1943, General Koller and Oberst von Lossberg both had a chance to speak to Major Bradel of KG 2. It was apparent that, apart from operations near to the coast, and having taken into consideration the German strength available, any other operations would lead only to catastrophe. Even though nearly

226

all of the nightly operations by KG 2 were carried out at low altitude (an attack occurring every five minutes approximatley) and, very often, one out of every ten Do 217s and their crews which took over never returned, Bradel believed firmly that the Dornier bomber was more suited to the task than the Ju 88 which had been suggested also. The Major had said:

> *If the Ju 88 Geschwader were put into the battle against Britain, they would be slaughtered within fourteen days.*

The superior armour of the Do 217 was the deciding factor in relegating the Ju 88 to second place. The 'Y' navigation system, which could be used only in direct, unswerving flight, was inoperable as the result of concentrated enemy defences. Precise aiming could not be carried out and unaimed bombing became the rule. The radio operator doubled up as a gunner and there wasn't any time spare to operate the FT navigation equipment. Consequently, operations were limited to major bombing runs and the mining of British harbours by

Kampfgeschwader 2 and units of the Luftflotte. A break in the raids over London did not occur until 17 January 1943, but this was to prove an exception. Up until April 1943, approximately fifteen fighter bombers flew over the Channel every night. Nevertheless, the combined forces of Luftflotte 3 could not cause any permanent damage; large operations were split up into a number of small actions over various targets. Attempts to mine all British coastal waters to block the passage of sea transport did not have any overwhelming success. All these actions were no more than pinpricks.

On 18 June 1943, Oberst Peltz, who was in charge of the operations against Britain, was invited to a meeting with the Generalluftzeugsmeister (Director of Operational Requirements) to update Erhard Milch's report on the Luftwaffe's activites on the Western Front. It was his opinion that the Kampfgeschwader had had some success in their raids over the English Channel. The marking and illuminating of targets made it possible to locate and bomb them successfully. As an example, he cited the bombing of Sunderland on the night of 24 May 1943.

Do 217E-4s pictured flying over the French Alps (BA).

However, Peltz made no secret of the fact that he thought that *the Do 217 is an unsuitable aircraft in this field of battle.* He expressed his opinion that the heavily armed aircraft was more suitable for daylight raids over the Eastern Front, than night raids over the British Isles. Furthermore, the Battle Commander added that Do 217 crews had to accumulate approximately 30% more flying time before they could fly operationally. Not only that, the losses of Do 217 groups were 30% greater than those of the enemy. Presumably, Peltz ignored the fact that KG 2 Staffeln had been equipped with the new Dornier bombers for a short time only, therefore, there were bound to be some teething troubles.

Nobody could argue with the fact that by usng DB 603 engines, the already limited operational range of the Do 217K-1 was shortened further. Additional fuel tanks had also reduced the aircraft's operational altitude, and the installation of further tanks in the bomb bays utilised the space in which 2000 kg of bombs could have been carried.

Given all of these poor figures, it was impossible to agree to the Dornier aircraft continuing in its then-current operational role. Basically, Oberst Peltz wished to equip the units of his command with the Ju 88 — or, better still, the Ju 188 — for their operations over Britain. In addition to operating over the Eastern Front, the Do 217 would be configured as a torpedo bomber, as had been planned already, and, together with a reserve of 200 torpedo-carrying Ju 87s, would spearhead the attack against the expected Allied landings.

Meanwhile, RAF raids against targets in the Third Reich had not been without effect. On 27 November 1943, Hitler declared a war of destruction on London. All the resources available were to be directed towards the attack. The He 177 particularly, loaded with incendiaries, was expected to have every chance of being successful. The idea was that the Do 217 and the Ju 88 would both complete the destruction. However, that was not the case. Operation 'Steinbock', which began on 21 January 1944, led to the loss of a large number of Germany night bombers in the West, and a subsequent weakening of Germany's defence in the face of the coming Allied invasion. The final bombing raid of March 1944 revealed the paralyzed state of the Kampfgeschwader.

On 1 June 1944, I and II Gruppen of Kampfgeschwader 2 could only muster seven Do 217s. Replacement aircraft, expected during the summer, never came. That was not the result of the Do 217's performance, it was the result of the war situation. The airmen did not fail. Accusations of failure could not be directed towards the performance of the medium-weight Heinkel, Junkers and Dornier bombers. The failure was the result of bad war policies which led to the lack of a much-needed strategic bomber and of more powerful aeroengines. Statistically, Do 217 units fared no worse than those units which were equipped with other aircraft types.

At the beginning of its development, the Dornier bomber was fitted with engines which were not very powerful. The most-flown E-4, K-1 and M-1 variants could not achieve a higher altitude performance, or carry heavy loads of ordnance. A reduction in its fuel consumption, or the use of extra fuel tanks, would not solve these problems. External bomb loads, the installation of flame retarders (vital for night operations) and of additional armaments and equipment — all took their toll, resulting in the aircraft having an increased weight, increased drag, and reduced flying capabilities.

More successful (if not leading to fewer losses, or having any decisive effect on the success of the war) and spectacular were those operations with Hs 293 and PC 1400X special weapons. Remote-controlled weapons were to revolutionize the war at sea.

A detailed report by Henschel, dated 29 July 1943, illustrated the cleft stick in which Germany's leaders and its troops found themselves. For example, there was total confusion concerning the deployment of glider bombs, although the Staffeln (which had undergone re-training) were somewhat more positive about the Hs 293 because of the low

Aircraft of II/KG 2 being rolled at Soesterberg for operations.

A ground maintenance crew of III/KG 2, pictured in front of a Do 217E-4 (serial No 4305).

Aircraft of V/KG 40 during a raid over Britain in the spring of 1940.

altitude required for its launch, compared with the Fritz-X, which could be deployed only at higher altitudes. As it was, the first deployment of a glider bomb did not take place until the end of August 1943, and then only as a result of the crews' insistence! (This could have happened only under the then deteriorating conditions.)

The Do 217 fitted with underwing Hs 293 racks and launchers had a reduced range of only 900 km. Its BMW engines could not withstand the high Mediterranean temperatures, its tyres could not tolerate the heavy loads, and its electric systems failed as the result of salt-water contamination. In addition to all that, the special truss required for the

A bomber of 7/KG 2 equipped for operations over the sea and fitted with cable-cutting equipment, pictured in late summer 1943.

guided bomb did not do anything to improve the aircraft's manoeuvrability. The inevitable result was that, of the maximum number of nineteen Do 217s which could carry the He 293, usually between five and ten actually took part in the attacks.

However, there wasn't any alternative to the Do 217 E-5; the preferred long-range bomber, the He 177, would not be ready for some time. Another factor was that, in many cases, the crews of those aircraft carrying glider bombs came face to face with the enemy for the very first time and often did not have any experience of action. Added to this, often Do 217s had to be made operational at very short notice and many faults were not rectified, with the inevitable results.

Given the number of bombs launched in relation to the success they achieved, the result is that only one battleship, two cruisers, approximately ten destroyers and ten freighters, three large landing craft, and a few small vessels fell victim to this weapon.

The course of the war and the gigantic Allied landing operation could not be influenced by the small number of Dornier bombers, or the alter arrival of the Fw 200 and the He 177. Following a number of raids with heavy losses, the use of guided bombs against a numerically far superior enemy had to come to a rapid end, regardless of the aircraft type which carried them.

A similar fate was shared by a number of Dornier night fighters. Without adequate engines, and having an all-up weight that was too high, the Do 217J and N had both to make way for more manoeuvrable and less complicated night fighters such as the Ju 88, Bf 110 or He 219. For a while, the Do 217 had a role to play within the Fernaufklärungsgruppe Nacht, 4(F)/14 and, to a lesser extent, with I/KG 200. The sturdy night reconnaissance aircraft remained with these units until the final weeks of the war on the Eastern Front.

In the beginning, the Do 217 trainers at the Blind-Flying School in Terespol were beset by a number of problems which included handling, and frequent engine failures, among other matters. However,

most of the losses incurred could be attributed to the poor airfield conditions and the almost total lack of flying ability of the training staff and their pupils. Dornier works pilot, Dieterle, had failed to demonstrate that the Do 217 was perfectly easy to fly, that it was even possible to do low-altitude stunt-flying, and that landings with only one engine operable could be done without any problems.

From 1943 onwards, the increase in the number of losses was confined to long-range reconnaissance aircraft. The bomber formations were affected particularly, regardless of the aircraft type they operated. The greatly reduced training periods and the lack of experience of the often very young crews must have contributed greatly to the number of losses incurred. This opinion was spelled out by the General der Truppentechnik (GenTT) in his report of 9 February 1944:

> Following the evaluation of extensive investigative reports, it was clear that the breakdown of the battle in the West could be attributed mainly to the lack of engines and equipment, and the training level of the crews.

When comparing Do 217 losses with those for other, more frequently used aircraft, such as the He 177, Ju 88/188 and Me 410 in the raids over Britain, it is noticeable that many Dornier bomber crews had problems achieving full control of the aircraft, the result of first successful re-training being completed as late as 1943. From a tactical viewpoint, it is true to say of the operations over Britain in 1944 that Germany's inferior strength could not match the enemy's superior defences.

Finally, the vast loss of life among the crews can lead us only to question the concept of Operation 'Steinbock'. Following the destruction of the Dornier-equipped Kampfgeschwader 2, and that of KG 100 with its glider-bomb carriers over France, the end of the middle-range bomber was only a matter of time.

Jet-propelled aircraft enabled the protagonists to enter a new era in aerial combat.

The eighth Do 217 prototype which was equipped with the FuG 202 and powered by DB 603A engines.

A Do 217N-04 (GG+YD) pictured in 1943 at Friedrichshafen-Löwental.

APPENDICES

Do 217 Types and Numbers Produced

Type	Number	Manufacturer
V1-V12, V1E	13*	DWF
A-0	6	DWF
C-0	10	DWF
E-1	94	DWF, DWM
E-2	185	DWF, DWM, NDW
E-4	258	DWF
E-5	70*	DWM
HV1-HV3	3*	DWF
J-1	130	DWF
KV1	1*	DWF
K-0	10	DWF
K-1	ca. 300	DWM, NDW
K-2	50*	DWF
K-3	40	NDR
MV1	1*	DWF
M-0 & M-0/U1	5	DWF
M-1 & M-1/U5	ca. 440	DWM, NDW
M-2	1*	DWF
M-4	1*	DWF
M-8	1*	DWF
M-11	37*	DWF
NV1-NV2 (N-O)	2	DWF
N-1	CA. 240	DWF, DWM
N-2	95*	DWF, DWM
PV1-PV3	3*	DWF
RV1-RV2	2*	DWF

* These aircraft were taken from earlier production models and either converted or re-fitted.

DWF: Dornier Werk Friedrichshafen
DWM: Dornier Werk München (Munich)
NDW: Norddeutsche Dornier Werke (Wismar)

Do 217 Serial Numbers

Type	Serial No	Remarks
A-0	2701–2706	
C-0	2710–2719	
E-1	1001–1150	
	5051–5100	
E-2	1101–1200	
	1201–1380	
	4201–4300	
	5301–5400	
E-4	4201–4600	Partial conversion from E-2 variant
	5301–5600	
	24301–24400	
	52401–52500	
E-5	5601–5667	
H	80021–80023	
J-1	1151–1380	Partial conversion from E-2 variant
K-0	4401–4410	
K-1	4411–4690	
K-2	4501–4600	Partial conversion from K-1 variant
K-3	4701–4750	Partial conversion from M-1 variant
M-0	1241–1245	
M-1	2801–2900	
	6001–6400	
	56001–56200	
	322701–326300	
	722701–722800	
M-11	2901–3000	Conversion from M-1 variant
	3001–3100	
	6401–6500	
	336401–336500	
	722701–723100	
	723001–723100	
N-0	1401–1402	
N-1	1403–1500	
N-2	1501–1700	
P	80024–80028	
R	80029–80030	

Do 217 serial numbers are incomplete and cannot be considered to be accurate.

A Do 217K-1 (U5+AD) of the Staff Flight of III/KG 2, flying over France in 1943 (BA).

A Do 217K-1 (F8+GS) of II/KG 40, after taking off from an airfield in northern France.

An aircraft of 7/KG 2, pictured during early summer 1944 at a Dutch air base.

This Do 217M-1 (serial No 722753- U5+LR) was shot down by a Mosquito night fighter on 15 August 1943.

One of the last Do 217Es, pictured in 1945.

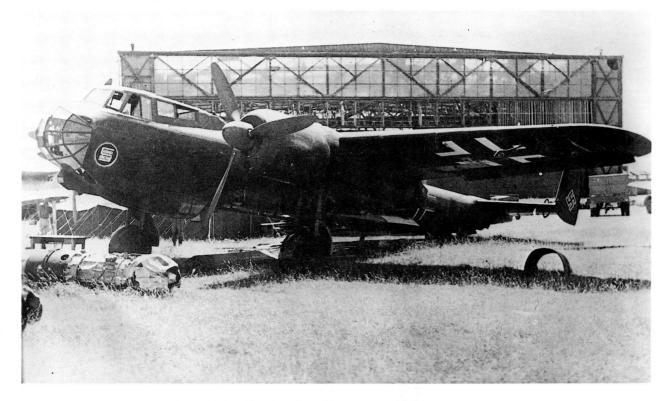

DORNIER Do 217
Production Chronology

Type	Role	Engines	Remarks
Do 217A-0	Long-range reconnaissance	DB 601 B-1	Long ventral pannier with automatic cameras. 3 x MG 15
Do 217B-0	Bomber/reconnaissance	Jumo 211B	Equipment as Do 217V-1E. Project
Do 217C-0	Bomber	Jumo 211B	Development of the Do 217A-0 with small pannier
Do 217E-1	Bomber	BMW 801A-1	New ventral pannier, otherwise similar to Do 217C-0
Do 217E-2	Bomber	BMW 801ML	Similar to Do 217E-1, but with rotating MG 131 cupola
Do 217E-3	Combat aircraft for Atlantic operations	BMW 801ML	Similar to Do 217E-1, but with MG FF gun position
Do-217E-4	Combat aircraft for Atlantic operations	BMW 801ML	Similar to Do 217E-3
Do 217E-5	Special duties combat aircraft	BMW 801ML	Similar to Do 217E-4. Fitted with missile racks and used in glider bomb trials
Do 217G	Floatplane	DB 603G	Development of the Do P 85 project. Airframe and equipment as Do 217E-1. Project only
Do 217H	Glider-bomb carrier	DB 603A-1	Similar to Do 217E-1 except for powerplant
Do 217I	High-level bomber	DB 603A-1	Similar to Do 217E-1, except for powerplant. Exhaust-driven turbo-superchargers in engine nacelles. Project
Do 217J-1	Night-fighter	BMW 801ML	Similar to Do 217E-2 but with nose armament. FuG 202 search radar
Do 217J-2	Night-fighter	BMW 801ML	Development of the Do 217J-1 with FuG 212 AI radar
Do 217K-0	Bomber	BMW 801A-1/ML	Similar to Do 217E-2, but with redesigned cockpit
Do 217K-1	Bomber	BMW 801ML	Similar to Do 217K-0. Series aircraft armed with MG 81Z and MG 131
Do 217K-2	Special duties combat aircraft	BMW 801ML	Similar to Do 217K-1, but with wing area increased to 67 square metres
Do 217K-3	Special duties combat aircraft	BMW 801ML	Similar to Do 217K-2
Do 217L	Long-range, high-level reconnaissance	DB 603H	Project with pressure cabin and clear-vision cockpit
Do 217M-0	Bomber	DB 603A-1	Mainly similar to the Do 217K-1, except for the engines
Do 217M-1	Bomber	DB 603A-1	Series production version of the Do 217M-0 with 57 square metre wing area

Type	Role	Engines	Remarks
Do 217M-2	Torpedo bomber	DB 603A-1	Development of the Do 217M-1 with aerial torpedo installation. Wing area 57 square metres
Do 217M-3	Dive bomber	DB 603A-1	Comparable to the Do 217M-1, but with 59 square metre wing area and triangular tail fins
Do 217M-4	High-level bomber for special operations	DB 603A-1	Comparable to the Do 217M-3, but with TK 9 exhaust-driven turbo-supercharger and R15 equipment conversion pack
Do 217M-5	Glider-bomb carrier	DB 603A-1	Similar to the Do 217M-4 but minus the TK 9 turbo-supercharger
Dp 218 M-8	High-level bomber	DB 603E	Similar to the Do 217M-3, with TK 9
Do 217M-9	Bomber for special operations	DB 603A-1	Similar to the Do 217M-3 but with altered cockpit glazing. DL 151 armament
Do 217M-10	Bomber for special operations	DB 603A-1/2	Do 217M-1 conversion
Do 217M-11	Bomber for special operations	DB 603A-2	Similar to Do 217M-3, but with FX missile attachment under the fuselage. Tail armament
Do 217N-0	Night-fighter	DB 603A-1	Similar to the Do 217J-1 but with nose armament of four MG 151/20 guns and FuG 202 radar
Do 217N-1	Night-fighter	DB 603A-1/ BMW 801ML	Similar to the Do 217N-0, converted in part from the Do 217M-1
Do 217N-2	Night-fighter	DB 603A-1/ BMW 801ML	Similar to the Do 217N-1. No defensive armament, modified fuselage. Some fitted with brake parachutes
Do 217P-0	High-altitude combat aircraft	DB 603/605	Do 217E-2 conversion with pressurized cockpit and high-altitude superchargers
Do 217P-1	High-altitude combat aircraft	DB 603/605	Similar to the Do 217P-1, with 67 square metre wing area
Do 217P-2	High-altitude bomber/ reconnaissance	DB 603/605	Similar to the Do 217P-2, with either 71 or 100 square metre wing area
Do 217R-0	Dive bomber	DB 603A-1/ BMW 801ML	Similar to the Do 217M-3, but with 62 square metre wing area, dive brakes and heavier defensive armament
Do 217R-1	Dive bomber and torpedo-bomber	DB 603A	Similar to the Do 217R-0 but fitted with dive brakes
Do 217R-2	Dive bomber	DB 603A	Similar to the do 217R-1, with heavier armament
Do 217T	Bomber	BMW 802	Bomber project with two BMW 802 engines
Do 217W	Floatplane	BMW 801A-1	Project, similar to the Do 217E-1 but float-equipped
Do 217Z	Destroyer	BMW 801A-1	Provision designation for the Do 217J-1 and J-2
Do 317A	Heavy bomber	DB 603/Jumo 222	Bomber project with enlarged fuselage and 68 square metre wing area
Do 317B	Heavy bomber	DB 606/ DB 610	Bomber project, similar to the Do 317A but with a wing area of 75 square metres
Do 417	Heavy bomber	DB 603G/ Jumo 222	Bomber project with 62 square metre wing area